AND TOMORROW THE STARS

AND TOMORROW THE STARS

The Story of John Cabot

KAY HILL

Illustrations by Laszlo Kubinyi

DODD, MEAD & COMPANY

NEW YORK

Library of Congress Catalog Card Number: 68-27819

Printed in the United States of America
by The Cornwall Press, Inc., Cornwall, N. Y.

for
Shirley and Donnie

Introduction

This was supposed to have been a straight biography of the fifteenth-century explorer, John Cabot, and to assist in the necessary research a grant was generously provided by the Canada Council. However, when I set out to do this research, I found that on John Cabot, his early life, and even on his Voyages, there was about enough properly documented and indisputably accurate material to fill out a single chapter. What to do?

Pad with exploration material? Conscientiously reproduce all the old speculation and argument about John and Sebastian Cabot? Add one more general account to the already voluminous literature of the Age of Discovery, leaving Cabot what he had been for five hundred years—a dim featureless figure overshadowed by his better publicized son? No, I thought not. But what if I took the meagre bones of his story, fleshed them out with imagination, and told the story dramatically, as though it were actually happening? I would still have plenty of research to do in order to set the story firmly inside the period, but I could invent suitable action and dialogue to match the essential character of the discoverer as he emerged from authentic record and so make him seem a living person. Then, so as to leave no doubt in a reader's mind as to what was fact and what was not, I could insert at the end the actual documentary material, or excerpts from it. From these Historical Notes the reader would then be able to decide for himself on the evidence whether or not the invention was consistent. That is what I have done. This, in other words, is how it all *might* have been.

My main source was *The Cabot Voyages and Bristol Discoveries under Henry VII*, edited by the late Dr. J. A. Williamson and published by Cambridge University Press on behalf of The Hakluyt Society. Permission has been given to reprint the excerpts from the source material which appear in the Historical Notes.

I acknowledge with gratitude the help I received from the staff of the Map Department of the British Museum, the Office of Public Records in London, and from many museums, libraries, and printed books. I acknowledge with particular thanks the help given to me by the late Captain W. Barclay Armit and my brother-in-law, B. A. Marshall, on ships and navigation of the fifteenth century.

And, of course, the book might not have been written at all without the help of three kind referees—Miss Phyllis Blakeley, Dr. Helen Creighton, and Dr. Thomas Raddall.

Kay Hill

Contents

Part Two: CABOT THE MAN

Illustrations

AND TOMORROW THE STARS

Part One

THE BOY CABOT

I

Genoa, 1459

The boy chose the highest rock on the beach and climbed to the top, and, with his back to the walled city of Genoa, sat gazing over the Gulf. No sign of Emilio, but it was early yet, the sun hardly a hand's breadth above the horizon. He settled to wait.

It was warm and quiet, and smelled of wet sand.

With half-closed eyes, he dreamed, building his dreams on stories he had heard from early childhood. In the beginning, he was Jason setting sail with the Argonauts in search of the Golden Fleece. Later he was Hercules, slaying the serpent and plucking the golden apples of the Hesperides. Later still, he was Odysseus superintending the construction of the wooden horse, plottting the ruin of Troy. In all these familiar stories the boy Giovanni Caboto played the hero, supremely confident that one day he too would win a name in history. When one is eight years old and steeped in stories of the ancient Greeks, all things are possible.

When he was tired of dreams, he came down to earth and considered his immediate prospects. If Emilio happened to be in a good mood, he might let Vanni help gut his catch.

The men drove him away from the fishing boats, generally, saying he was too small to handle the knife. An excuse. He knew the real reason. They had heard so often his father's reproachful cry—

"Come away from the beach, Vanni! Leave the boats! Why do you waste time watching the fishermen? Watch the men in the warehouse, if you hope some day to be a spice-seller."

It was just about certain that some day he would have to adopt his father's trade, but he did not view the prospect with pleasure. What glory or adventure lay in the business of packing, weighing, measuring, buying, and selling spices? Instinct and inclination drew him to the beach, and he stubbornly resisted the efforts of the fishermen to dislodge him. Emilio was his one hope. When the catch was good, Emilio was apt to be indulgent. Once, when his boy Gino wasn't there, he had let the Caboto boy come into the cockpit and cut bait, and when the old man's back was turned, Vanni had laid his palm on the silky wood of the tiller. Brief rapture! It had fitted his hand to perfection.

To work on a fishing boat was his one ambition now. He could handle a rowboat with ease and dexterity. He must learn the secrets of rudder and sail. It was important to be able to handle a boat as well as the fishermen's sons, as it was important for him to excel in anything he tried. But there was no one to teach him, unless Emilio— But common sense told him the old man had a better use for his spare time. Vanni would simply have to learn by watching.

Basta, it was hot. He untied his Sunday hose from his doublet, discarded the doublet too. Now in his blue shirt he looked like any of the fisher boys. Mamma would be cross about his running off after Mass without breakfast, but at least she wouldn't have to grumble about soiled clothing.

He stretched and stood. The dead fish under the rocks

were starting to stink in the heat of the sun. His eyes roamed
to the harbor full of foreign ships, galleons from Spain, *cogs*
from Bruges, one of the new three-masted *nefs* from Brittany. He studied the latter, noting how full she was in the
stern, and wondered why she carried a sail under her bowsprit. Such great ships, however, were beyond his comprehension and he sat down once more to watch for a humbler
craft. Just then he saw her, saw the tip of her dingy sail bob
along the top of the mole. His toes curled with expectancy.
Please, San Giorgio, let Emilio have a good catch! Let him
be cheerful!

He watched the fishing boat come 'round the end of the
mole, a small *barca* gray with age, with a flat stern and a
patched sail. Once in the shelter of the cove, she would have
to fall back on her oars. Yes, there, the sail began to flutter,
and when the fisherman left the tiller to stand and gather
the canvas in against the mast Vanni saw that Emilio was
alone. The old man was waving to someone on shore and the
boy looked back, expecting to see Gino on the beach, but
there was no one.

"Vanni!"

Incredulous, he waited.

"You! Vanni Caboto!" The fisherman beckoned and
pointed to the small boats pulled up on shore. Then at last
the boy flew into action, scrambling back over the rocks,
racing across the sand. He shoved Emilio's skiff down to the
water, tumbled in, grabbed an oar and sculled in figure-
eights, standing, like the fishermen. In minutes he was alongside the larger craft.

"I am off to the salt store, boy—no, not the one in town,
they rob a fisherman blind. Alongshore to Dini's, my wife's
cousin. You want to come?"

A nod. No breath for words.

"Make the skiff fast then." The old man paused, gave him a sharp look. "Your people will not be looking for you?"

"No, no! Of course not." Oh please, San Giorgio, don't let him worry about Papa *now*! The fisherman shrugged. He may even have winked.

"Ah well. We won't be all day."

"Where's Gino?"

"Business in the town." The boy saw the catch was small and knew that Emilio had been out alone since before dawn. Perhaps the fisherman was tired and wanted an extra hand at the oars. That was all right with Vanni—he would row his arms out of their sockets if necessary!

The sail flapped and the boy felt a puff of wind on his cheek. Emilio moved to untangle a shroud, spoke casually over his shoulder.

"Take the tiller, boy."

Had he heard properly? Had Emilio really said—?

He leaped to the steersman's place.

"Put your helm to starboard."

"Yes, sir!" Starboard right, larboard left. He must make no mistake! The boat heeled as the wind took the sail, and he felt rather than heard the soft brush of water under the keel. She had obeyed him!

"Back. Not too much! Watch the sail."

He learned quickly, learned to watch the back edge off the canvas, to feel the tiller respond to his least touch, to steady her as she slid over the bow wave of a passing boat.

"Steer for the second house on the point."

"Yes, sir."

They were out beyond the mole now, the stubby mast swaying through a small arc of the sky. The sun beat on his arms, burning the tender skin, and his heart spilled over with ecstasy. Now in truth he was Jason steering the *Argo* across the wine-dark sea—no, he corrected himself at once. He was

Emilio's fishing boat

Giovanni Caboto steering a real boat on the real Gulf of
Genoa, and it was better than anything he had ever imagined.

To the last day of his life he remembered every detail of
that sail to Dini's, every breath of wind, every rock and
shallow, every fishing cove they passed on the way. He
wished the day would never end. In sight of Dini's, the
breeze fell off and they drifted.

"It is possible this will take longer than I thought." The
fisherman pulled gently at the oars, shaking his head at the
boy's offer to help, pointing to a basket under the seat. There
was a swallow of wine left from breakfast, some bread and
cheese. The boy hadn't known how hungry he was until his
teeth sank into the dry loaf. Drops fell from the oar blades,
the sails flapped, the wavelets whispered against the bow.
On the blue Gulf there was utter peace and contentment . . .

"What's out there, Emilio?"

"Water." The Mediterranean. That much the boy knew.
His father had told him.

"I mean, if you went straight, what land would you come
to?"

"Corsica. Sardinia, maybe. Tunis in Africa, supposing you
sailed long enough. Ten or twelve days."

"Have you ever been to Africa?"

"No. To Corsica once."

"How big is the Mediterranean?"

The fisherman pondered this for a bit.

"Must be a fair size. It takes near two months for the grain
ships to sail from Barcelona to Alexandria."

These names sounded familiar, but Vanni had no idea at
all where these cities were in relation to Genoa. He had
never seen a map. He tried to picture ships sailing for weeks
in the limitless blue of sea and sky.

"How do they know where they are? How can they tell

which way to go?" This was a mystery that must be explained.

Emilio wiped his lips and threw the wine bottle over the side.

"They've got written-down directions," he said. "And charts—what they call *portolani*. These *portolani* show all the capes and shallows and that all over the sea." His voice grew somber. "They've got that devil's tool, the compass, too."

"Compass?"

"A kind of needle, Vanni. Floated in a dish of water, she keeps swinging north and that is not a thing in nature. Mariners say they can reckon their course and position by it though, and it's true enough that when you know where North is, you can find South behind you. Then East is right and West is left. All the same, I will have nothing to do with a piece of magic brought out of the heathen lands of the East!"

"How do you do it then, Emilio? How do you find the North?"

"Like my father and my father's father, boy—by the sun in the daytime, by Polaris at night. Have you not heard of the North Star?"

"Oh yes! Papa showed me how to find it. It is the star that does not move." He watched the sea for a while, all shot with sun-daggers. "Is the Mediterranean the biggest sea in the world?"

"I believe it is, boy, though seamen off the alum ships tell me the Ocean Sea is bigger. But on that sea, it is well known that if you sail too far, you will fall off!"

The boy's eyes rounded.

"Off the edge of the ocean?"

"Off the edge of the *world!*"

Vanni tried to picture it, felt himself falling and falling—

"And then," said the fisherman, "there are terrible sea monsters out there." The boy looked quickly to see if Emilio was teasing, but the slitted eyes were serious. "They lurk in sea meadows of weed, waiting to swallow whole ships, crews and all. Out there, too, a ship's liable to be blown south to the place where the sun burns a man to cinders—or carried north to the Frozen Sea where no human being can live."

Delicious shudders played up and down the boy's spine. Sea monsters! Burning suns and frozen seas! What a lot of interesting things they left out of the schoolbooks!

"Me," said Emilio emphatically, "I stay within the Pillars of Hercules where it is safe."

The boy, however, wanted to go and see it all for himself— see the land behind him go away and the land on the other side of the horizon come to meet him. He wanted to sail over *all* the seas, like Jason and Odysseus, and meet with adventures. He lusted for at least a glimpse of a sea monster!

The sail gave a warning rustle.

"She will carry us the rest of the way now. We will tie up by Dini's boat."

At Dini's there was the labor of lifting the salt on board and no lingering when the job was done, for the wind was blowing strong now and the fish must be cleaned and salted before dinnertime. All the way back, they were blown by a following wind and the boy was filled with a boisterous gaiety. He tasted the salt spray on his lips, laughed aloud when a sea came aboard and drenched him. He was careful to meet each wave at the proper angle.

"You're doing fine, boy."

No praise had ever sounded so sweet.

Passionately he envied Gino having a father like Emilio. He looked at the old man, memorizing in detail the leather-brown face with its white bristle of beard, the horny hands, idle for once, clasped loosely, the bare brown feet crossed on the boards. Something rose from his uttermost deeps—a welling warmth. He loved Emilio, loved him with passion and gratitude, and wanted to be like him. He loved his father, but he didn't want to be like Papa, fussy and worried all the time about business. He wanted—

What did he want? He was conscious of conflict.

The boy Vanni was pulled in two directions—to be like Jason and the Trojan heroes, excelling, achieving, making his name a legend, and at the same time to be like Emilio, calm, unhurried, unambitious, his life tuned to wind and weather, bound in sweet partnership with the old gray boat. Then close on the wave of uncertainty came inspiration. A fisherman's way of life would surely be a natural training ground for a sea hero! If he was to travel the path of Odysseus, Vanni must learn all there was to learn of boats and the sea. So let Papa put Piero to merchant's work and apprentice him, Vanni, to a fisherman! The whole thing seemed so eminently reasonable he could not imagine Papa raising any serious objections. He would put it to him plainly this very day, so no time would be wasted. Then it would be simply a matter of finding some fisherman who needed a helper.

"Easy there! You'll have the mast out."

Hastily, the boy eased the tiller.

"Emilio, I've decided! I'm not going to be a spice merchant! I'm going to be a fisherman like you!"

Emilio chuckled indulgently.

"That so? Then you'd better come out with me on Sunday and learn something about fishing. Gino's off to ship on a grain vessel this summer, so I'll need a mate."

Vanni's spirits soared. To sail every day with Emilio! The miracle of Gino vacating his place just at this time seemed to him a sign that it was all meant to be.

"There is Gino on the beach." The old man was unaware

of the fact that he had taken the boy's breath away. "He will help me unload. You had better run home, Vanni. They may be anxious about you. Eh—*guardi*! You see that boy?" Emilio directed Vanni's eyes to a rowboat passing across their bows at a brisk clip. The oarsman was a boy his own age, freckled, with hair red in the sun. He was pulling hard, frowning with concentration, looking neither to left nor right.

"He is another like you," said Emilio. "Yes, you two are as like as two peas." But that's not so, thought the boy indignantly. Nobody was like him. He was the one and only Giovanni Caboto!

"His hair is red! Mine is yellow!"

"All right, but he is as bad as you for boats—always after the men to take him fishing." That was different. What boy wouldn't love boats! "Cristoforo his name is—son of Colombo the Weaver."

Cristoforo Colombo was dismissed impatiently. He, Giovanni Caboto, had more interesting matters to think about.

On shore, hopping about on one foot while he replaced his hose and doublet, Vanni was anxious to get home and have the business settled.

"*Addio,* Emilio!"

Then he was off, running up the beach, flashing through the town gates with a wave to the guard, plunging into a tangle of streets and stairways which climbed steeply up the slopes of the Ligurian Alps. Just short of the north exit, he stopped for breath and a hand clutched his sleeve.

"Vanni! Where have you been?" It was Piero, his younger brother. "We looked everywhere. You'll catch it now!"

"It's not that late."

"A letter's come and Mamma's crying and you'd better hurry."

"All right. Come on—"

Out of the city again, between the towers of San Andrea,

past the house of Colombo the Weaver and down the open road, coming at last to the modest villa at the end. There stood Mamma at the door, excited, tearful.

"*Caro diavolo!* At last! Quickly! Papa is waiting." He heard her murmur between a sob and a laugh, "My first-born! How can I bear to lose him?"

Bewildered, he let himself be hurried into his father's study. Papa rose to his feet at sight of him, waving a letter.

"Where have you been? Never mind—look! A letter from Uncle Luigi!"

Vanni knew Uncle Luigi only as Mamma's brother who lived in Venice, the rich man of the family, but unconsciously he braced himself for trouble. "He is going to help you, my son. He will give you a home—"

"I have a home!" he shouted, startled.

"Let me finish, Vanni. You remember your cousin and his Mamma died last year of the plague? Well, ever since, Uncle Luigi has been lonely and now he has made up his mind— you are to take his son's place. Not immediately, of course. Say in six or eight months—"

"But I don't want—"

"It is what I have prayed for," beamed Signore Caboto. "My business can never support two sons and their families —not properly. Also, Vanni, your Uncle will see that you receive a better education than I can afford for you. If you behave well and don't go running off to play with boats, which incidentally you won't be able to do so easily in Venice, then some day you will be taken into his warehouse and—who knows—" His father's face warmed with generous hope. "He may even make you his heir."

The boy's head jerked to the right and to the left, seeking some escape, but there was none. His brother and his sisters looked merely envious. His father's whole attitude told him that this time it would do no good to beg or cry or throw tantrums. Even Mamma could no nothing to help him.

All his wonderful plans tumbled down. The bright day fell in ruins . . .

II

Venice

His clothes were new, and richer than any he had ever owned. He enjoyed the feel of the good velvet hugging his skin, was pleasantly aware of the green jewel in his cap and the ornamental dagger at his belt. He felt the envious glances of humbler folk sweltering amidships, denied the shade of the awnings in the after section and the privilege of dining with the ship's officers. It all helped a little to ease the remembered pain of parting—but he must not think of Mamma and the children, not if he wished to preserve the illusion of nine-year-old sophistication.

Vanni turned his thoughts instead to the future—to Venice. What was she like, this Queen of the Adriatic, richest and most powerful of all Italy's city states? He knew she was a Republic whose warships commanded the Eastern Mediterranean, whose merchants were lords of the trade routes from England to the Levant, whose streets were made of water and whose Grand Canal was said to be the most beautiful street in Europe—and that was all he knew. He'd looked at water for eighteen days now. Water would be no novelty, anyway.

The voyage had been a disappointment. Though he had seen the land go away as they left Genoa, the course had not been a straight one to Africa, but a cautious skirting of the Italian coast, with now and then a stop in port for supplies. They had hardly ever been out of sight of land. They hadn't even met any pirates. He had hoped for something in the narrow seas between Sicily and Africa, but nothing had happened.

Now he was bored with the ship, tired of the tasteless diet of black biscuit and hard meat, weary of the heat and the crowd, the stink of bilge water and ballast. A poor thing in his opinion, the *Golgotha*, with her heavy sails and old-fashioned side-rudders. She was an elderly pilgrim vessel, which for countless years had carried the faithful to Jaffa, the nearest port to Jerusalem, and she was sluggish in calm weather, but rolled like a ball in the least wind. With a familiar ache in the back of his throat, Vanni remembered a certain fishing boat on the Gulf of Genoa, a miracle of lightness and balance by comparison. During the last six months, as a final paternal indulgence, he had been allowed to go fishing with Emilio every Sunday. He had satisfied one ambition anyway, that of handling a small sailing craft with ease and confidence, but he missed Emilio as much as ever . . .

"Land to port!"

At the lookout's hail, Vanni raced to his favorite perch on the starboard bulwark, homesickness forgotten, eager for his first sight of Venice. What he saw was a group of flat islands dotted about with poor-looking structures, a glimpse of mainland blue in the distance beyond. On all sides the watery waste of the Adriatic still encompassed them. There was nothing here to see that was half as fine as the approach to Genoa, where the tall stone houses seemed to stride up the pine-clad mountain. Then the *Golgotha* nosed through

The Golgotha

the San Nicolo passage into the Lagoon and the city proper, hidden until then by the long stretch of the Lido, burst on his astonished eyes.

San Giorgio!

It was like—what *was* it like? Yes, it was like a ship! A large and beautiful ship anchored on the gleaming green water. White marble porticoes and rose-red campaniles rose behind the pink walls of the Doge's Palace and all was surrounded by rank on rank of shipping. This was Venice—"fairest and pleasantest city in the world" and the most proud!

An offshore breeze brought the smell of flowers.

Cursed by the sailors hurrying to brail up the sail, Vanni dropped to the deck. Signore Caboto had to shout above the noise of flapping canvas—

"What do you think of Venice?"

"Wonderful!" The boy added with awe, "All those ships!"

The anchor fell with a splash.

"It is part of Venetian policy," said Signore Caboto rather sourly, "to make all other states jealous of her magnificence. A very practical people, the Venetians! Come now, it is time to go."

The tender carried them to the Customs and on the way Papa pointed out a winged lion rampant on a tall column in the Piazzetta, which led into the great Piazza of San Marco and to the Cathedral with its five golden domes.

"San Marco," said the father, "is the patron saint of Venice and the lion their emblem. The Cathedral is a 'robber's cave' full of treasures stolen from Genoa and Constantinople in the old days!" Signore Caboto recalled with mild bitterness how his own business had been reduced in the long struggle between the two cities for commercial mastery. Still, the Genoese were practical too. "You can make your fortune here, my son, if you play your cards well."

The tender discharged them on the quay and Signore

Venice, circa 1450

Caboto went off to deal with the *dogana* men, leaving Vanni to ponder his words. The boy did not know exactly what was meant by "playing his cards" but he pictured fortune as a key to unlock his future. According to Papa, fishing in the Gulf of Genoa was not the way to become a successful sea rover.

"Selling spices," his father had told him, "is a much better way. To be a successful merchant in Venice means to be a rich man, and riches procure freedom of action, Vanni. If, when you are rich, you still wish to emulate your Greek heroes, you will have the means and the power to do it."

So for the first time the boy learned the meaning of the word "compromise." One sometimes had to give up certain things in order to acquire something else one valued more.

"Please your Uncle, my son, and the rest will follow."

Vanni stared across the water, picturing himself a citizen some day of that fabulous city, with all the money he needed to do as he pleased. Very well, if that was all he had to do— please Uncle Luigi—he would charm that relative of his to the top of his bent! He would comfort his Uncle for the loss of wife and son and always do exactly as he was told—

"*Sia stalia!* Keep to the right, *idiota!*"

The cry drew his attention to a swarm of waspish craft darting about on the Lagoon. They were easy to recognize from Mamma's description—"gondolas, Vanni, very long and narrow with an iron peak like a halberd, the prettiest little boats in the world! There are thousands of them in Venice!" Vanni watched a black one come bobbing over the waves. The gondolier, very smart in a green doublet and parti-colored hose, with a blue feather in his cap, propelled the craft from a standing position in the stern. At that moment Caboto Senior returned with the luggage.

"Ready now, Vanni." Papa saw the gondola and directed a shout towards it. "*Servizio!*"

At once the black boat fairly leaped over the waves, her gondolier crying out to another contender—

"*A oel!* Look out!"

Boy and man watched as the gondola slid between a row-boat and landing stake with barely an inch to spare on either side, and without reducing speed. How the boy's hands itched to hold the oar!

"Take us to the *palazzo* of Signore Luigi Romano on the Canale Rossi."

While the gondolier stowed the luggage, the two Genoese stepped aboard. Last in, the boy in an excess of zeal and to show his familiarity with boats, shoved off vigorously from the dock. The boatman, reaching for the oar, was taken by surprise. Thrown off balance, he staggered, recovered himself and turned on the boy passenger.

"*Idiota! Stupido!* What are you? Crazy? Do not interfere with the boat!"

The boy felt the blood rise to his cheeks with surprise and embarrassment. He did not know that these boatmen were a skilled and privileged class in Venice, with a strong guild, their arrogance humored even by the State. Had he known, he still would not at that moment have cared.

"*Idiota* yourself! Don't speak to me like that!"

"If you knew anything about gondolas—"

"I know about boats! I've handled an oar before!"

"And you think you can handle this one, eh?"

"Certainly! Give it to me. I'll show you!"

"Vanni—" Too late, his father stretched out a restraining hand. Vanni scrambled to the stern cover, ready if necessary to do battle, but the gondolier merely grinned and proffered the oar with a mocking bow.

"Go on, little simpleton, try!"

Vanni had no doubts. Hadn't he rowed the fishermen's boats? Standing up, too. Of course the shaft of this oar was

longer than the ones he was used to. He was a little uncertain where to grasp it, but would not on any account ask for
instruction. He fitted it into its odd-looking oarlock, grasped
it near the middle, braced, and gave a hard push.

The gondola slid lightly over the water. And so did
Vanni! Utterly amazed to find himself suddenly stranded,
embracing the oar with both arms, he scrabbled frantically
with his feet to keep out of the water.

"*Dio mio!*" groaned his father, his voice mounting to a
shout as boy and oar began to topple. "Save him! Save my
son!" But the gondolier was laughing too hard.

Gathering speed, Vanni plunged into the water and his
head struck the mooring stake as he fell. The oily waves
closed over him, but almost at once his feet touched bottom
and he came to the surface again, dazed and gasping, unable
to take the single stroke necessary to reach the boat. He felt
himself grabbed by the back of his doublet and hauled
bodily into the gondola and dropped like a wet sack.

"Now see!" growled the gondolier. "You've soaked my upholstery. I hope you're satisfied!"

Vanni was not by any means that. Regaining his breath,
he scrambled to his feet—but this time his father caught him
in time.

"I can do it," Vanni pleaded, struggling, reaching toward
the oar. "I know I can!"

It was no use. He was hauled back, sobbing with rage
and frustration.

"Foolish boy!" cried his father. "What shall I do with you?
Look! You've cut yourself!" His voice rose. "My son is hurt!"

"The Franciscans, Signore, have a hospital on the Guidecca—"

"Take us there! Ah, what am I doing, leaving such a vain
and heedless boy in this watery city, to drown perhaps before the year is out! If your Mamma could see you now!"

Suddenly aware of his condition, dripping wet and blood-ied, a ridiculous figure, all the fight went out of Vanni. He had lost his cap with its green jewel and his wet hair dripped uncomfortably down his neck. His velvet suit would never look smart again. What a way to arrive in Venice!

A fine show he'd make before his Uncle and these super-cilious Venetians. Passionately he wished himself at home, with Mamma to cosset and comfort him. It was hard to be shamed and hurting, but still nine years old, too old to cry.

"Here we are, Signore." The gondola slid alongside the water-gate of the monastery.

"Quickly, Vanni!"

The boy stepped out with all the dignity he could muster, carefully avoiding the boatman's eye, but a hand touched his sleeve and he had to turn. The gondolier held out the wet green cap with its jewel intact.

"Don't forget this. And don't feel too badly." The youth's face was friendly. "Nobody learns to be a gondolier over-night. I'll give you a lesson some day if you like."

Taken aback, the boy could only stammer.

"Just ask for Danieli on the Riva degli Schiavoni."

Vanni pulled himself together.

"I'll remember," he said.

With an easier heart, he followed his father into the Mon-astery. In the hospital, a large whitewashed room with a pharmacy at one end, his clothes were removed and taken away to be dried and cleaned. His head was attended to by a boy even younger than himself under the supervision of a brown-robed friar. Vanni suffered these ministrations along with his father's explanations and scoldings, his eyes roam-ing over the shelf of queer-looking jars, his nose identifying the herbal ointments. *Basta!* That one stung! He turned his grimace into a grin for the benefit of the boy whose face was so near his own.

"It didn't hurt, not really."

The other boy looked relieved. The pharmacist's helper was a small lad with a round, naive face and quick, neat hands. He looked shyly into Vanni's eyes and the other looked back and liked what he saw. Friendship was given and accepted between the two without words—as is the way it sometimes happens.

"Very good, Michiele," said the Brother. "Now the bandage. What actually happened, Signore?"

The would-be gondolier blushed to hear his father tell the story. How had he managed to make such a fool of himself?

"And then, Fra Andrea, after falling into the water and cutting his head, that wasn't enough! He must try to do it all over again!"

The Franciscan looked at the boy with interest.

"So you want to be a gondolier."

"Not exactly."

"What then?"

"I just—like boats."

"What do you want to be when you grow up?"

Vanni glanced at his father.

"He is to be a merchant, when he finishes his studies," Signore Caboto answered for his son. "Signore Luigi Romano is my brother-in-law. Perhaps you know him?"

"There are many merchants in Venice," said Fra Andrea absently. "What education has the boy had so far?"

"He has learned his catechism, writing and spelling, some mathematics, and he can read Latin fairly well. I myself have taught him a little astronomy. He could do better, but he wastes his time playing around the beach. He thinks of nothing but boats!"

"How will he be taught in Venice?"

"By tutor, I imagine."

"H'mmm."

Not by the quiver of an eyebrow did Fra Andrea show what he thought of tutors, but it was implicit in the suggestion which followed. "If the boy needs additional instruction, send him to us. We teach other subjects besides medicine. I myself instruct in the humanities."

The boy groaned silently and looked at Michiele, who smiled sympathetically.

"Excellent!" cried Signore Caboto. "I shall tell my brother-in-law."

Vanni was to pay heavily for the morning's scrape. As if a cut head and ruined clothing were not enough, all his time in Venice would be spent in the schoolroom! He caught the Franciscan's wise and kindly eye at this point and was surprised to hear him add—

"However, I never force a boy to be educated against his will." Here was something new! Who would study if he were not obliged to? "I do not need to beg for students. Only those who are willing, as well as intelligent—like Michiele here—are accepted."

Vanni was not to be caught by flattery.

"I'd sooner learn to row a gondola," he said flatly.

His father looked scandalized but the friar smiled.

"Gondolas don't go far, Giovanni. Just in and about the canals of Venice. And Venice is not the world. If you like boats, it is probable you also like to travel and see things. Learning, you know, is another way of traveling and seeing. Learning can carry you to far places, very far places indeed!" The Little Brother's eyes gleamed with apostolic fervor. "Even to places where no man has been before!"

The friar spoke in metaphor, naturally, but how was the boy to know that? Vanni was startled and took the Little Brother's words for literal truth. Go where no man had been before? Ah! That's what he'd like! He thought of Prince Pelops in the days when very little was known of the Mediterranean world, sailing westward through the Dardanelles not knowing what lay beyond the next headland. If the Franciscan's learning included the necessary knowledge of seamanship and navigation, then—

"I'll come," he said simply.

"Say thank you!" exhorted his father.

"Thank you, Fra Andrea." The boy's mind ran far ahead to the day when he could put such learning to work, when he was a man with gold in his pocket and able to go where he pleased. If Fra Andrea would teach him to follow charts and figure courses and if Uncle Luigi would provide unlimited wealth in exchange for an obedient smile and agreeable manners, then—by San Giorgio—life was not going to be so bad in Venice after all!

Over-optimism, his failing. He was wrong on both scores.

III

Uncle Luigi

Far from being charmed with Vanni, Uncle Luigi, having seen him, appeared to regret his impulse to adopt a Genoese nephew.

"The boy understands, I trust, that he is not here to enjoy himself." The voice was soft and clipped at the end of each phrase, producing a most chilling effect. "He must earn his way from the start, first by completing his education, then— five or six years hence—by working in my warehouse. I shall expect him to work as hard, or harder than, my ordinary employees."

"Naturally, Vanni understands—"

"There is a galley leaving for Genoa this evening, Julio. I would advise you to take passage on her."

"But so soon?" Caboto stammered. "I had thought to spend some time with—"

"It would be wiser to go at once, believe me." Signore Romano endeavored unsuccessfully to inject sympathy into his tone. "Partings are difficult at the best of times. The shorter, the better, in my opinion." It was hard for Vanni to believe that this was the brother of his soft-hearted Mamma. And to think he had planned to comfort this man!

"You will be kind to Vanni?" urged Papa. "His mother was against sending him so soon. He is barely nine and he has been brought up in a large and affectionate—"

"Second thoughts, Julio?" the merchant of Venice cut in coldly. "At this late date?"

"No! No, of course not. Only—"

"I employ eight servants, a private physician—"

"I'm sure he will have the best of care." Signore Caboto looked unhappily at his son.

"He shall be called Zuan hereafter, of course," pronounced the Uncle. "That is the Venetian variant of Giovanni. We must remember that he may some day become a citizen of Venice."

"As you wish, of course, Luigi, but try to give him some warmth, some affection!"

"I am not a sentimental man." The Venetian's mouth primmed, as if he had mentioned something a little indecent. "I shall certainly not make a baby of him as you and Simonetta—"

"He is no baby!" Caboto Senior rose at last in his son's defense. "Vanni has plenty of spirit and very good understanding for his age." He turned to his son with urgency. "You know I do this for your good, Vanni?"

"Yes, Papa." The words had to be forced past a constriction of the throat. He felt his father's arms close about him.

"Be a good boy and do as your Uncle tells you." A last hard squeeze. "*Addio, carissimo!*"

Caboto shook his brother-in-law's hand and strode hastily from the room. The boy felt a terrible urge to spring after him, beg to be taken home, but something else—some hopelessness or pride—kept him silent, rooted to the spot, ears straining after his father's departing footsteps.

"I trust you will not disgrace us both by crying."

Anger flared, a welcome bulwark against tears.

"I am not crying!" The boy glared at Signore Romano, and found that, curiously, the merchant was avoiding his eyes. How like Mamma he was. Brown hair, fair skin, blue eyes like hers and his own—yet not like Mamma at all! Every feature in Luigi Romano looked colder and sharper, and dignity was wrapped around him like a mantle of ice. Restless under his nephew's stare, Signore Romano walked to the head of the table, pointing to a chair at the far end.

"Sit down, Zuan. Eat your food."

A servant held the chair. Waiting for his meal to appear, Vanni took note of his surroundings for the first time. He had never seen so much wealth and magnificence before at such close quarters. The Venetian was certainly a far richer man than his father. The room seemed to swim in crimson upholstery and window hangings. The floors were creamy marble and the walls paneled in leather. Vases of amber and blown glass twinkled in the light from the tall windows, golden now with the setting of the sun. And what was this thing beside his plate—a long thin piece of metal with two prongs—

"That is called a *forchetta*. Use it as I do."

The boy, after watching a moment, lifted his meat on the utensil and conveyed it successfully to his mouth. The food was dry, dull and tasteless, not like Mamma's cooking. He swallowed with an effort.

"Tell me," said his Uncle out of a heavy silence, "do you understand how fortunate you are?"

Fortunate! For a moment the boy could only see what he had lost—the loving ministrations of his mother, the companionship of Piero and his sisters, happy days on the water with Emilio. In place of these delights, he must live with this cold fish of an uncle, study for another four or five years, then apprentice to a trade he despised. On the other hand, as Papa had said, this was Vanni's opportunity, his guarantee of the future. Through Uncle Luigi he could hope one day to become a respected merchant of Venice. After that, it was up to himself.

"I suppose," he said at last, morosely, "on the whole, it will be good for me."

Uncle Luigi, not unnaturally, was displeased with the answer.

"Let us hope," he said severely, "it will be good for me as well. Your single concern, Zuan, for the moment will be your studies. After that you will go to work in my warehouse. Success in one's profession is all that matters, even if one must trample one's own feelings and the feelings of others underfoot." Clearly, he was imparting his own philosophy. "You may think me hard, but you will one day thank me."

The boy made no reply. It was all so different from his easy hopes and expectations.

"We will see a good deal of each other," went on Signore Romano in an even tone. "That will be unavoidable. Do not presume on our relationship, speak respectfully, obey my orders, follow my example in all things." There was a little pause, and Uncle Luigi's control snapped momentarily. "And answer when I speak to you!"

"Yes, sir." The lips barely moved. The half-eaten melon was pushed aside.

"You have finished, I see." The merchant regained his composure. "You may go. The servant will take you to your room. If you need anything of a personal nature, speak to Signorina Baretti, the housekeeper. In the morning, I shall send my own servant to dress you and put on a fresh bandage."

Uncle Luigi could be considerate of the body if not of the spirit. His nephew, after all, was an investment and Signore

Romano was not a man to be careless of his investments.

The boy's bedroom was on the second floor. It was small but luxuriously appointed, with a balcony overlooking the canal. Vanni flung off his wrinkled clothes and plunged into the bed. After ten nights on shipboard, the bed was softer than anything he had ever experienced, only he had never felt less like sleeping. The long-faced Signorina came in, took away his clothing and the candle with a mournful goodnight.

Vanni lay very still in the dark, knowing he must not cry. Wasn't he practically grown up now? He turned on his side, threw his arms outside the covers. It was too warm in Venice, too quiet. At home now there would be the sound of children squabbling, laughing, crying.

No movement anywhere. Only a kind of stealthy silence. Maybe everyone in the house had died!

At the sound of the midnight bell, Vanni could stand it no longer. He slid out of the rumpled covers and tiptoed to the balcony. Though his flesh was hot, he was shivering. Dimly, he perceived the shine of water in the light cast from a lower window. A laugh far down the canal echoed up through the watery canyon, went chattering by between the houses— someone ignoring the curfew. Even whispers could be heard out here, greatly magnified, the words indistinguishable.

Somewhere a door opened and music poured out, a song his mother had often sung. It was cut off almost at once by a closing door. Then, as if it were a signal, the damned-up emotion in the boy burst through its gates. The relief of tears was enormous. He wept self-pityingly, mourning over a poor creature cast up on an alien shore, abandoned by all those whom he loved, separated from his only real friend. At thought of Emilio, his sobs grew wilder. What if he never saw Emilio again? The fisherman was old. In seven years anything could happen. Anger mixed now with his sorrow.

He hated Uncle Luigi, he hated the servants and Signorina Baretti. He even for that moment hated Papa for abandoning him and Mamma for not being there when he needed her.

Finally empty, washed out, he rubbed his stinging eyes, looked up at a sky blazing with stars. There were the familiar constellations—Arcturus and the rainy Hyades, and the two Bears, the same familiar stars he had known in Genoa. A few familiar companions were left to him after all. Soothed to a degree, he crept back to bed and this time fell asleep.

He awoke next morning, feeling both ashamed and defiant, making sure before he went downstairs that last night's grief did not show. He went to meet the new day, however, with a pain somewhere deep inside, as if new skin had grown too quickly over an unhealed wound. On the staircase, he heard his name called in a loud whisper.

"Vanni—Vanni!"

There in the window embrasure leaned Michiele, red in the face, breathless.

"I ran out! No one was looking and—and I took the boat—"

Michiele waited while Vanni scrambled out through the window, then blurted—

"I wanted to say I know how it is. I felt awful too at first, but it wears off." The pain in Vanni's breast eased a little. Michiele's eyes questioned him, a little timidly. "It helps, I think, if you have a friend."

Vanni knew the tears would come again if he spoke, so he simply nodded and smiled and the two walked together down to the canal.

"Oh, and I brought you this," cried the pharmacist's boy in a lighter tone. He held out his hand. In it was one gold earring, heavy and smooth from use. "My father left it to me. It belonged to his brother who was a sailor."

Vanni took it, held it, grateful.

"I shall keep it always."

IV

Fra Andrea

In the days and weeks that followed, the boy settled down. It could not be said that he was happy. He was resigned. He grew accustomed to the queer dialect of Venice, to being addressed as Zuan instead of Giovanni, to eating his food with a fork. He tried not to think too often of home.

The tutor, a shabby little man concerned to impress the Uncle rather than excite the student, drilled Vanni in grammar, history, rhetoric and psalmody according to a strict timetable. The boy was introduced to the new arithmetic which involved the use of Hindu-Arabic instead of the old Roman numerals, and had to memorize the trader's textbook with its weights and measures, multiplication and conversion tables, insurance and cargo data, and all the arithmetic of the merchant.

"Two merchants buy a ship and Merchant A has three times the cargo Merchant B has. If the cargo space is fifty ells by ninety—" and so on.

The tutor also supervised the boy at Gymnasium in courses of fencing, dancing, riding, and shooting the crossbow. Here, in accordance with his Uncle's careful plan, he

met youthful members of the patrician class and was often
severely snubbed by them. Genoese were ridiculed in Venice. Vanni made no real friends among these boys. The
teaching of advanced Latin and Greek was left to the Franciscan, Fra Andrea, in the daylight hours that were left.

"You must learn Latin and Greek well enough to unearth
the great treasures of the past," said Fra Andrea, and the boy
said uncomplimentary things under his breath about treasures of the past. He knew now that the friar had spoken
fancifully about discovering new worlds. Fra Andrea's new
worlds were those of the mind. He was one of the new breed
of churchmen, allowed by tolerant superiors to propagate
the New Learning even though it began with the study of
man rather than with the mysteries of God. Fra Andrea, like
many of his calling, had somehow managed to come to terms
with it in a way which satisfied his religious conscience as
well as his natural intelligence. Now as a teacher his fervent
ambition was to arouse in his pupils an interest in the ancients as great as his own. But the boy Vanni felt cheated.

"I thought you meant you'd teach me how to sail a ship,"
he said reproachfully, "and how to find my way across the
seas."

"Dear me!" The Little Brother looked apologetic. "I'm
sorry I gave you that impression. I know nothing of seamanship or navigation, I fear. However," he added brightly,
"one of our order, Fra Roberto, has been making a study of
the new Euclid which I understand is used in astronomy and
so is closely related to—"

"Oh no!" cried the sorely pressed student, "no more lessons, *please*, Padre!"

So the subject was dropped. If it were not for Michiele
who shared the study hours, Vanni might have been tempted
to find a way of dodging Homer and Virgil, but Michiele's

friendship was all that made life bearable in those first months. In his small way, Michiele too was a rebel.

"I don't care in the least about studying medicine. I intend to be a barber if I can manage it." The barber's profession was a sociable one. Friends congregated in a barber's shop to talk and drink wine and play music. Michiele, a Genoese orphan of the plague, could never have enough of friendship! However, since a barber's trade was considered frivolous by the Franciscans, Michiele was obliged to temper his independence. As a charity student, his shelter, his food, and his education all came through the generosity of the friars.

"As for me," said Vanni, throwing out his arm in a grand gesture, "I shall have a great ship with sails and go off to kill tyrants and rescue Ionian maidens! I shall sail all over the world, from—" He hesitated, wondering what places were most widely separated. Geography was not a subject taught to boys in the fifteenth century, not at least until university, but one of Emilio's remarks came back to him. "—from Barcelona to Alexandria. And back again! And when I stop in Venice between voyages, I shall come to your shop, Michiele, and have my hair cut and my beard trimmed!"

"Good. That's settled then."

"Unless of course you'd care to come with me?"

Michiele brightened.

"Yes, of course! I could do both—go back to my shop between voyages."

They were daydreaming, of course, and knew it—but what better way to spend a half-holiday than to loll in the sun on the Riva degli Schiavoni with Danieli the gondolier, and arrange their futures to suit themselves. There were many holidays in Venice, fortunately, enlivened by elaborate and colorful parades. It was one way for the Senate to keep the populace happy and unaware of their essential lack of political freedom. Danieli had been hired by the Little Brothers to take the boys to the festivities in the Piazza. Now the spectacle was over, the procession had disappeared inside the Cathedral, and Danieli, glancing up at the sky, decided it was time to go.

"You promised to take us to the Arsenal!"

The Arsenal of Venice was the largest shipyard in the western world. Employing two thousand workmen, it could turn out a galley every hundred days.

"Too late today. Some other time," said Danieli. "There's nothing to see there on a holiday anyway."

Another promise broken. To show he didn't care, the Caboto boy began to declaim the *Aeneid* in ringing tones, first in Latin, then in the vernacular for the benefit of the comparatively uneducated gondolier.

> *"Arma virumque cano, Troiae qui primus ab oris*
> *Italiam fato profugus Lavinaque venit litora—*

" 'I sing of arms and the man who first from the shores of Troy, driven forth by fate, came to Italy and the Lavinian coast—' " The sonorous words echoed over the canals. Presently Vanni switched to a favorite line of the *Odyssey—* " 'Now, sailing well in order, smite the sounding billows! For I mean to sail beyond the sunset till I die!' " How splendid that sounded. It expressed his feelings precisely.

Danieli let him go on until he thought the boy had showed off long enough. Then— "Poetry is all very well, but real things are better. You may know Latin and Greek, Zuan, but I know the world."

"Venice isn't the world," shot back Vanni, wondering where he had heard that statement before.

"It's all of it that matters." This, Danieli firmly believed. He was calmly sure that to be a citizen of Venice was the greatest good which could befall any man, and in this opinion he was joined by most of his fellow-citizens. Michiele could not let the statement pass, rising to the defense of the native city he barely remembered.

"Genoa is just as rich and just as important!"

"Not since the Battle of Chioggia, my lad. There is no city in the world like *La Serenissima!*"

This was a sweeping statement, certainly! Was there in truth no city to compare with Venice? What about Florence?

Danieli made a face.

"Down there they're fighting all the time."

"Rome, then. The city of the Pope!"

"What has Rome got besides St. Peter's?"

"What about Barcelona?"

"Just one more Mediterranean port."

Vanni sought in vain for the names of other cities, but of even the ones he had mentioned he knew only their names. If only he could speak with authority and put this Venetian boaster in his place! Did Danieli really know so much about the world?

"How big is the world?" he asked at random.

"Pretty big."

"That's no answer." Michiele sensed the game and joined in. "Is it as much as a thousand miles wide?"

"About that," said Danieli carelessly. The two boys tried, but failed, to visualize a world so large.

"How do you know?"

"Because I do."

"What shape is it?"

"Does it hang in the air or float on the water?"

"What holds it up?"

"Where does the sun go when it sets?"

"What are the stars? Tell us, Danieli!" The young voices mocked. "You know all about the world. Tell us!"

Danieli laughed good-naturedly.

"You want a lot! Think I don't know, is that it?"

"Tell us!"

The gondolier frowned, partly because another craft was crossing his bow in the crowded Grand Canal, partly through having to remember the lessons he had learned some years before.

"A oel!" he shouted: "Who told you, you could row! Watch where you're going!" Having thus relieved his feelings, he thought for a moment and began slowly. "The world is one big island, flat like a plate, and it lies in the Ocean Sea, which is a river flowing around it. Let me see now. Paradise is in the East and Europe and Africa lie north and south of the Mediterranean which is the exact middle of the earth." He went on more confidently as the lessons came back to him. "The sun goes down into the Ocean beyond the Pillars of Hercules every night to cool off. The sky is the floor of Heaven and the stars are bits cut out, so God's light can shine through." He skimmed triumphantly past the lovely Ca d'Oro and into a smaller canal leading to the Guidecca. "Anything else you want to know?"

The boys looked at each other, silenced for the moment. Danieli sounded so sure. Yet how, thought Vanni, could anyone know all these things without stepping outside the world to look at it from a distance, which was plainly impossible. Moreover, Danieli was wrong about the sky. The stars weren't bits cut out of anything. Papa had told him they were heavenly bodies which revolved about the sky, changing position a little each night. Skepticism was born in him at that moment.

"How do you know all that?" he challenged.

"I learned it from the Fathers at the Church School."

Gently, the boat kissed the monastery steps.

"Out with you, Michiele. Better run or you'll be late for

dinner. I suppose, Zuan, your Uncle's sending Bartolomeo for you?"

"Yes."

"*Addio* then."

From the top of the steps, left alone, the boy Vanni watched Danieli bob away down the canal and, seeing him so from the back, he was reminded of his last morning in Genoa watching his friend Emilio row off from shore alone. Dispair fastened her cold hand on him, as it did every so often even now, and once again he felt a small lost boy, desolate among strangers.

"What is troubling you, Vanni?"

Fra Andrea was the only one besides Michiele who called him Vanni. The good friar had come up unnoticed, hands clasped behind him as usual, in a way that hitched up his brown robe, revealing scrawny ankles and battered sandals. He was a thin, handsome man with brown eyes and brown skin—brown all over. The boy did not want pity. He sought hurriedly for any reason but the real one.

"I—was wondering—since one cannot very well look at the earth from outside, how can we know what it is like? Danieli says the earth is a flat island in the sea with Paradise—"

"Nothing of the kind!" The brown eyes sparkled with contempt.

"Not flat?"

"Certainly not! No educated man today believes in a flat earth. Not even the Church—apart from a few ignorant diehards. The world, Vanni, is round! Round like a ball, round like an orange. And the sea is a part of it."

The boy stared.

"How do you know?" He did not ask it rudely. He really wanted to know, and Fra Andrea seemed to understand this.

"You do well to ask," he said approvingly. "It is a question which ought to be asked more often! Very well. Use your eyes, my son. Watch a ship coming in from the sea. What do you notice first?"

"The mast?"

"Precisely. And only later the hull appears, which suggests—" He waited, bright-eyed, for comprehension to dawn. "Of course! It suggests that the ship is sailing up over a curved surface! Have you ever seen an eclipse of the moon?"

The boy shook his head.

"You will, some day. Note then that the shadow on the moon's face is curved. It will be obvious to you at once," said the good friar confidently, "that only a sphere could throw such a shadow."

"So if the earth is round—" the boy tried to relate this roundness to something Emilio had once said— "and if you go too far out on the Ocean Sea, you will fall off!"

"No, no! Try to visualize how large the world is, Vanni. Think of an orange, enlarged a hundred times, or a hundred thousand times. Then think of a tiny fly walking on it, down the side, even underneath. Does the fly fall off?"

"No, but why doesn't it?"

"According to Aristotle and his fellow-philosophers, all matter tends to fall together toward a common center in any object that is round, thus preventing any part of it from falling or flying off into space!"

This was too much for him.

"Danieli says the world is only a thousand miles wide," he offered. Fra Andrea gave a disgusted snort.

"Why do you go to a gondolier, a youth whose horizon is the outermost islands of the Lagoon, for important information?" Fra Andrea waved his arms excitedly. "You should go to Strabo—to Aristotle—to Hipparchus! Don't listen to Danieli—listen to Ptolemy! Go back to the ancients, Vanni, back to the past! Study all opinions too before you come to any conclusions. Take nothing on faith—" Fra Andrea choked on the last word and added hastily— "nothing, that is, but Faith itself!" He crossed himself, conscious of having once more fallen into the sin of intellectual pride. All the same, he could only rejoice at the thought of saving one more brand from the fire of ignorance. Flat like a plate, indeed! A thousand miles! "Now what else do you want to know? Ask me anything. If I do not know offhand, I can look it up."

Too late, the boy saw the trap into which he was falling. If he was not careful, this mad priest would launch him on some new course of study! Thankfully he saw Bartolomeo come poling up the canal. Fra Andrea, however, was waiting for an answer and Vanni hated to disappoint him. He cast about in his mind for some question, something innocuous and safe, to ask. The question he had asked Danieli would do.

"How big *is* the world, Padre?"

"An interesting question!" Stirred by interest, the Little Brother hitched up his robe another inch or two. "I shall have to look it up." Good. Vanni waved encouragement to his Uncle's gondolier, now slowly approaching the dock. "One or two Greek philosophers, I know, investigated the subject. No doubt their findings are preserved in the libraries at Alexandria. I shall write to my friend Ibn Haud there—he is an Infidel of course but a most learned man—to see what he can tell us."

That should take at least two months.

"Meanwhile," went on Fra Andrea happily, "I can give you a book by Edrisi on the subject."

Basta!

"Here I am, Master Zuan," said Bartolomeo. Yes, groaned Vanni to himself, too late!

"It is in Greek," Fra Andrea called after his departing student, "which is all to the good, since you are now really

too old to construe Greek fairy tales. It will be excellent practice, whether or not you find what you are looking for."

So that was how Vanni came, for the first time, to consider
the size of the earth—a question which at that time held no
real interest for him at all!

Edrisi was produced at the next study period.

Great Geographers of Greece. Happily Fra Andrea arranged the stained and carefully mended pages of manuscript before Vanni on the library table. "Edrisi, incidentally,
was a Moor who lived in Sicily in the twelfth century, and
this is one of the few writings of his that have come down to
us. It is many years since I read it, but I feel sure there is in
it some mention of earth measurement. To work now, and
see what you can find."

Resignedly, the boy reached for the dictionary.

He learned from the title page that the manuscript contained brief accounts of the lives of four Greek philosophers
—Eudoxus, Eratosthenes, Posidonius, and Pytheas—men who
had lived in the Mediterranean world five centuries before
Christ!

"So long ago?" exclaimed Vanni. "Surely they wouldn't
know much in those days about anything."

"My dear Vanni!" The friar hastened to enlighten the boy.
"The ancients, let us face it, were far better informed on almost everything than we are today. Take medicine, take
geography, take biology, astronomy, mathematics—take
poetry and drama. In all things—except religion, of course—
far and away beyond us. Now I know what you are going to
ask. What happened to all that knowledge? How was it lost?
And why is it only now being rediscovered?"

It was no good saying such questions hadn't even crossed
his mind. He saw that Fra Andrea was quite capable of both
asking and answering his own questions.

"When the Barbarians came down from the lands beyond

the Alps and shattered the final remnants of the Roman Empire, all the Greek and Latin learning was scattered and much of it lost for good. A little was preserved in the archives of the Church. Much more was saved by the Arabs, the Moors, and by the Jews. It seems the Infidels were better able to appreciate its worth than we! To make matters worse, in those days the Church assumed knowledge where she had it not—in purely temporal affairs. And that, my son, is how ignorance and pride breeds tyranny—for I blush to tell you that until quite recent times men were burned by the Fathers of our Church for claiming the earth was round! Oh, with the best possible intentions, I assure you, and the greatest conviction! Happily we now begin to realize our business is with matters of faith, not the physical sciences. And so, if we do not actually assist in the progress of mental enlightenment, at least we do not now hinder it to such an extent."

Fra Andrea beamed encouragingly.

"You have chosen an excellent time in which to be born, Vanni—just when we are starting to emerge from intellectual darkness, now when the lost works of the old Greek scholars are being rediscovered and copied all over Italy. Once more we taste the delights of Aristotle and his brethren, once again wander through bright fields of speculation! We may even be entering upon another great Age, like that of the Greeks—who knows? Read Edrisi therefore and soon I shall have something more for you." And the good man bustled away, plotting fresh ways to procure academic treats for his reluctant pupil.

During the next six weeks, Vanni worked his way laboriously through the *Great Geographers*. First, there was Eudoxus who had lived three centuries before Christ and who had mapped the stars, explained their motions, and written a geography of the world as it was then known. He had besides—yes, here it was—measured the circumference of the earth. Four hundred thousand *stadia*. Vanni worked the sum in his head and got, roughly, forty-six thousand miles. He grinned. Wait till he told old Danieli that! Danieli and his thousand miles!

Now that he'd got his answer, he felt even less interested in Edrisi and his friends. However, with Fra Andrea monitoring each step of his way, he had to stumble on, first through the essay on Eratosthenes, skipping a bit until he was stopped by a word or two. He read back. *Basta!* Eratosthenes had also calculated the earth's circumference and had got a different figure, one only half the size of Eudoxus! He'd better find out now if the third fellow had measured too. He had! Posidonius' figure was the lowest. Vanni shouted for the friar.

"They all measured and got different answers, Fra Andrea! Eudoxus got forty-six thousand, Eratosthenes twenty-five, and Posidonius a little over seventeen!"

"It is up to us then," said the friar calmly, "to find out which is correct."

"But how?" asked Vanni, dismayed. "If *they* couldn't agree—"

"Slowly, slowly. Only the world was made—and by God—in a matter of days. Set the problem aside for the moment. Finish Edrisi. Later, something may come up to cast fresh light on the subject. It may be necessary," added the friar jovially, "in the end, to go and find out for ourselves by traveling around it! Now how far have you got? Pytheas is next, I see. You will enjoy Pytheas."

To the boy's relief, Pytheas had nothing to say about the circumference of the earth and, indeed, the fourth biography was a pleasant surprise. Pytheas was not only a philosopher, he was a practical seaman! All Vanni's old delight in heroes revived and he began to construe rapidly and with pleasure.

Pytheas of Massilia made his voyage in the days of Alexander the Great. He was sent by his city to find the people "who lived at the back of the Northland." Though the motive was commercial—to find the men who supplied tin and amber to the Phoenicians and so cut the profits of those fat middlemen—yet the city had been inspired to choose a captain who was also skilled in mathematics and astronomy.

Vanni read how this clever Greek, eluding the Phoenicians at the portals of the Mediterranean, slipped out into the Western Sea and sailed north to the barbarian islands of Britannia and Ibernia. Landing on the coast of Cornwall, he found the tin miners and described them as a friendly, energetic folk living in mud and straw huts, threshing their corn in barns because of the cold wet weather, and making a very good local beverage called beer.

The tin miners told him of a mysterious land called Thule, six days' sail north of their country, where the nights were sometimes only two or three hours long and where the inhabitants lived on wild berries and made mead from bee's honey. Anxious to see this far-northern land for himself, Pytheas set sail once more. Gradually the air became gray and full of moisture and the water sluggish until at last it was so dense that the sailing galley could not move forward. It was as if land, sea, water, and air were all mixed together in a kind of "sea-lung," as Pytheas called it. Disappointed, he turned back, crossed the Channel, met the sellers of amber on the continent and finally found his way back by the Garonne River to his own city.

The boy, charmed and excited by the tale, was reminded of Odysseus, but from now on he knew fairy tales would not content him. Pytheas' voyage was real. It had actually happened. He must hear more of Thule!

"Here is a letter which should interest you, Vanni." Fra Andrea came hurrying across the library with a roll of script in his hand. "I have heard from Ibn Haud! He thinks we can forget about Eudoxus. That figure is much too high. He points out that the Arab geographer, Alfragan, also made measurements of the earth and his figure agrees better with that of Eratosthenes. He says, however, he does not wish to be dogmatic. He points out that Ptolemy supported Posedonius, and who, after all, can argue with Ptolemy!"

"Ptolemy?" the boy asked vaguely, his mind still on Pytheas.

"You have not heard of Ptolemy?" exclaimed the friar, "the greatest geographer of them all! Ptolemy, my son, was an Alexandrian of the second century who—" He paused, gave the boy a sharp look, then continued without change of expression. "—who used to turn backward somersaults every day of the week except Sunday!"

Vanni nodded intelligently, as if he had heard every word, and after a pregnant pause, asked—

"Did anyone ever reach Thule?"

Fra Andrea swallowed words of accusation and reproof, knowing after a decade of teaching that it was useless to drive a boy's imagination. It must be led.

"We don't know," he answered.

The boy's eyes began to sparkle.

"Remember, Vanni, the word Thule is now essentially a literary word meaning 'the land farthest north.' The place Pytheas went to find might have been any island or mainland north of Britain, and it *may* since have been discovered and settled, as Iceland was."

"But where exactly did Pytheas go?"

"Some six days' sail north of Britainnia—isn't that what it says? Or Britain, as we say today—"

"I know what the book says," said the boy impatiently, "but where *is* Britain?"

Fra Andrea stared, surprised, until he realized that the boy had no notion at all of where Britain lay in relation to

Italy, nor for that matter where Italy lay in relation to any other part of the globe.

"You have never seen a map!" The friar whistled soundlessly. "Dear me! And I am not sure I can show you one of any value."

V

Maps

"Naturally there are in Venice many excellent maps and charts, but they are not for public inspection." Fra Andrea shook his head sadly. "Map makers are a secretive lot, Vanni, and the Republic encourages it. They consider it poor business, I suppose, to give away trade secrets. Yet knowledge should be freely given to the world!" He thought for a moment. "How I should like to show you a map even now being drawn for a certain foreign government. One hears rumors that it is a map of the entire world, quite the finest ever drawn. The draftsman is a member of the Camaldolite Order —Fra Mauro—but unfortunately he is bound to strictest secrecy. Only the Doge and the Council even know for certain the name of this foreign government." *

   * Portugal

Vanni stirred impatiently. He did not want to hear of maps that were unavailable, but of ones that were. He wanted to see where Pytheas had been. He wanted to know where a future voyager ought to go to find Thule!

"Maps, when they are for sale, moreover, are very expensive. However, you will find plenty of maps in our religious houses, though I won't say how valuable most of them are. Come with me and we'll see what we can find."

The boy followed to the scriptorium, a room empty save for an elderly Brother who peered short-sightedly at a manuscript Gospel and made notes and sketches on a slate.

"Now there," said Fra Andrea softly, "is what I meant about Church maps. Fra Spezia is of the Old School, believing one ought to get all natural information from Scripture. He puts the Aegean and the Red Seas together on a string, like the beads of a rosary, with Jerusalem as the center bead. He then draws the Mediterranean as a vertical under it, and

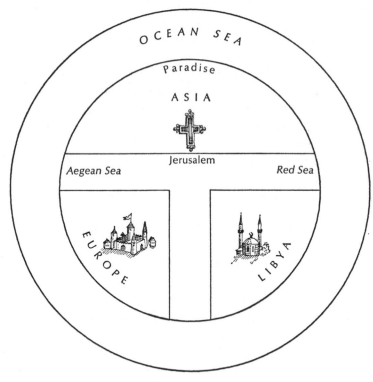

T and O Map

what does he get? The letter O, with a T inside it. 'Ah-hah' says Fra Spezia, 'the O is the world, the T the waters dividing it. Orbis Terrarum!' Not only did God create the world, you see, He even shaped it according to its Latin initials. Marvelous!" The irony in his voice was tinged with contempt. Fra Andrea was a kindly man, except when faced with fuzzy and illogical thinking. The boy smiled, appreciative of the friar's humor, but only half aware as yet of his vast good luck in having got the wise and witty Fra Andrea for a teacher instead of a Fra Spezia.

A small, irregular piece of sheepskin was laid before him reverently by the Little Brother.

"This may not look like much, my son," said the friar, "but it is very old and one of our greatest treasures. It may have been made in the fourth century after Christ. It was certainly drawn by someone, most likely a Greek, who knew more about the world than the people who came after him. It may even, for all we know, have been made by Pytheas."

The boy stared at the map, fascinated. It was a poor affair, certainly, not more than six inches wide, ragged around the edges, the words on it almost illegible. But there were the three continents—Europe, Libya, Asia, clearly marked—and that central sea could be none other than the Mediterranean!

In that moment, for Vanni, the word was made flesh.

"Where is Venice?" he asked breathlessly.

The Little Brother pointed to the neck of the boot-shaped peninsula.

"And here is Genoa on the other side."

Vanni's eyes dwelt for a long moment on Genoa. It didn't look so far away on the map!

Now he could see the track of the *Golgotha* and the way they had come to Venice, down the leg of the peninsula and up the other side.

"Padre! Where is Barcelona?"

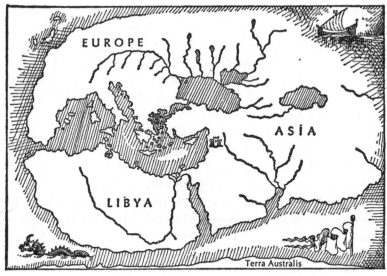

World map, A.D. fourth century

"Roughly here—"

"And Alexandria?"

"Here, near the mouth of the Nile."

Now at last he could see the way the grain ships sailed on those voyages which, according to Emilio, took as long as two months. But now he saw they were not the farthest points away from each other. The Pillars of Hercules lay well west of Barcelona, and from Alexandria it was twice as far again to the east coast of Asia! The world was enormous!

His eyes went back to the Pillars of Hercules. Through that narrow passage Pytheas had slipped, despite the watchful Phoenicians, and sailed north to—

"Those islands?"

"Britain and Ireland."

"And that dot up there?"

"Thule?" Fra Andrea smiled indulgently. "It is possible."

Vanni laughed aloud with excitement, imagining himself

up there in the mists of the Frozen Sea. How had Pytheas felt on first beholding the sea-lung? How aggravating to have to turn back short of his goal! Oh please, San Giorgio, he prayed childishly, let Thule remain undiscovered until I am old enough to sail a ship! What a triumph to discover the land that Pytheas had failed to find. He looked at the map again, contentedly.

"So that's the world. The whole world!"

"What makes you so sure?" Fra Andrea's question fell like a pebble into the little pool of silence, and Vanni jumped with surprise. "Have you forgotten the world is round?" Fra Andrea took up the map and very delicately bent it back in a curve, until the two sides met behind. Then the boy understood.

"Oh—you mean there's the Ocean Sea as well!"

"That, certainly."

"What else?"

"Islands perhaps, like Thule. Strabo, however, believed that the inhabited world was all one large island in one great sea." Vanni, reminded of Thule, began to lose the thread of the discussion. "He did not agree with Hipparchus, for instance, who thought that there might be two seas, with land between. We know only that no one has ever crossed the space between Western Europe and Eastern Asia. Men tried, they say, in the time of Christ, but turned back—not because there was any land in the way, but because of running out of food, or simply from fear and loneliness. Aristotle, mind you, states his belief that the sea between Europe and Asia is actually of small extent, but after all, he could not know for certain any more than we do." Fra Andrea, carried away by his subject, paced rapidly, hitching up his gown to alarming heights. "It is a most interesting question, you know, Vanni, one closely related to the size of the earth. Until we know that measurement, we cannot begin to know how much water or land lies between the two shores." He had lost Vanni, however. The boy's mind was on maps. Having had one taste of seeing the world in line and ink, he wanted more. Where to find them?

"You want maps?" asked Danieli. "I can get you maps."
"Danieli! Where?"
"Guido Pestrelli. His brother makes them for a group of merchants whose names one doesn't mention, seeing they are known to operate outside the law at times. For a price, Guido might copy one for you and sneak it out of his brother's shop."
"I'll pay anything!" A risky offer, since Vanni was always short of money. His small allowance from Uncle Luigi was generally spent the day he got it.
"Never give a huckster what he asks at the start," lectured Danieli. "You must bargain with Guido, he'll expect it. I don't know if I ought to have told you. He's a slippery lad. All those Pestrellis are. What sort of map did you want?"
"I don't care, just so long as it's a map! Where can I find this Guido?"
"He's mixed up with a queer lot of people, Zuan—toughs and smugglers. You'd better let me handle it—"
"No! You don't know what I want. Michiele will go with me. Just say where I'm to find this Guido."
"The best place is a certain *trattoria* in Burano, one that's only open after curfew though. I'll have to take you there myself, I suppose."
Vanni had no objection to breaking curfew. He had long since discovered how easy it was to leave his Uncle's *palazzo* unseen by way of the balcony, and to keep one eye open for the police, "the Lords of the Night" as they were called. Michiele, however, was unable to think of a way to elude the watchful eyes of the Brothers and so was left behind.

The *trattoria* was obviously a place for drinking rather than eating, and it had the air of a thieves' meeting place. The atmosphere at first made little impression on Vanni, his mind being wholly on maps. Danieli, however, was frankly eager to get the business over with, and leave. In the smoky light of oil lamps, shadowed faces turned from them after one sharp look.

They passed between wine-spattered tables to one in a far corner where a young Buranese sat alone. Guido Pestrelli was a thin, white-faced creature who never looked one straight in the eye. He received their proposition with a show of reluctance, which Vanni decided was affected to boost the price.

"I don't know if I can manage it," he muttered.

"Say one way or the other," pleaded Vanni.

"Well, I can't guarantee anything."

"It doesn't have to be a big one." By now, Vanni had decided what he wanted. "Just as long as it shows the whole of the Mediterranean, in detail."

"You'll take what I bring you and no complaints?" Guido gave him a sidelong glance. "I can't take chances. My brother'd kill me if he found out." The boy said it simply, not in a spirit of hyperbole but as if it were a fact of life, as perhaps it was. Lives were cheap in certain parts of the Venetian Republic.

"I'll pay you five *scudi*, all I have, for whatever you bring me."

Danieli groaned silently at such inept bargaining.

It was the boy's first lesson in business. The map Guido produced a week later in the *trattoria* was of dreadful workmanship. It was a *portolano*—a sea-map—and not a good one. It showed a little of the Mediterranean east of Italy and only a small piece of the African shore. All detail was lacking.

"You've cheated me!" the boy said at once.

Heads turned, and Danieli moved apprehensively.

"It's the best I could do," said Guido, backing away prudently. "I warned you."

"Pay him," whispered Danieli. "He'll have friends handy!"

In bitterness of heart, but obeying for once the voice of common sense, Vanni paid and took away the map. He showed it eventually, with shame, to Fra Andrea and told him the whole story. The Franciscan shook his head mournfully.

"It's a *portolano* of sorts. But even to my untrained eye, it is highly inaccurate. See—he's made the peninsula of Italy run directly north and south! Also, the peninsula appears as large as Spain and France put together. That cannot be right."

Vanni scowled at the map, disillusioned. His faith in maps and charts, until then a holy one, was severely jolted. It was perhaps a good thing. He would not be so uncritical in future.

"But why would Guido's brother draw such an inaccurate map, Fra Andrea? Surely the merchants would never accept this!"

"I can only presume that our young Guido copied it incorrectly, on purpose, to protect himself. If his crime was discovered, he could say it was all right, the map he had sold you was inaccurate and would only mislead."

Vanni pressed his lips together with rage and shame.

"I ought to have known better. You told me good maps were valuable. I shouldn't have expected to get a good one for only five *scudi*. There's one thing though," —the thought cheered him somewhat— "I've never seen a *portolano* before." He spread it out, his eye taking pleasure in the decorative details—the colored rhumb lines, the compass roses, the vignettes of cities and sea monsters. Something else occurred to him. This pretty picture, faulty though it was, was essentially an instrument designed to be a working tool for the master of a seagoing ship. Perhaps if he studied its principles, he could master the tool for himself.

He and Michiele worked it out together. Basically a set of sailing directions drawn in chart form, it was constructed on a base of known courses from port to port, with the distances and principal landmarks. Sets of thirty-two rhumb lines radiated from various compass points and the coast line between the base points was drawn in freehand, the outline emphasized by names of ports written perpendicular to the coast. Important harbors like Venice and Genoa were written in red, the rest in black. Very little inland detail was shown—a few major rivers, one or two mountain ranges. In the end, the two boys saw how a shipmaster could find his way all around the seas simply by referring to his compass, then laying a ruler across a line and steering along it.

"It's easy! Let's try it!"

"Try what?" asked Michiele blankly.

"Make a *portolano* and follow it! We'll draw one of the route from Uncle Luigi's house to the monastery. If we ask nicely, Fra Andrea will find us a compass." That devil's tool of Emilio!

That was the start. What began as a distraction soon became an absorbing hobby. The two boys knew already how to orient themselves by sun and stars. Now, with a compass, they could place themselves with fair accuracy east or west of North. They began to work out distances, using paces on land, oar strokes on the canals. In the end, after many false starts and some help from Fra Roberto in simple geometry, they were able to draw a fairly accurate portolan-type map of the route.

"Very good!" Fra Andrea was pleased to see the boys tackle something and actually finish it, though he would

have preferred to see them studying advanced astronomy
or the theory of circles in the original language.

Finding and copying maps now became a veritable passion with Giovanni Caboto. He copied anything and everything he could find, drawing continually until he could draw
with ease and accuracy freehand. Michiele had had to desert the cause, though not of his own free will. To Michiele's
groaning dismay, the Brothers were now busy preparing him
for his studies at the university. It looked very much as
though he would end up a priest and physician after all!

Vanni had been nearly five years in Venice now, and was
sometimes startled to notice how rarely his thoughts turned
to his home. He had word regularly from Genoa, of course—
of Emilio still plying his trade on the Gulf, of Piero already at
work in his father's warehouse, and of his sister Lisetta about
to be married—but it all began to seem far away. He felt as
though he had lived in Venice all his life, and in actual fact
as he grew older, he got very fond of the city. One could not
help being stirred by its vigor, its color, its wealth and importance. Insensibly, he had settled at last into his new life.

When he was not studying or drawing maps, he was reading true accounts of men who had traveled and explored the
world. Of the hundreds, perhaps thousands, of these heroes
—namely, Egyptians, Phoenicians, Greeks, Romans, and
Arabs—there were few who had left truthful written accounts of their journeys in peace and war. He could not find
enough of them. Fra Andrea was able to offer only commen-
taries on the campaigns of Alexander the Great and Julius
Caesar and the journals of Christian missionaries.

"However," he added doubtfully, "there are two very
popular travel tales in circulation just now, which may interest you. One is *The History of Sir John Mandeville*, the other
The Travels of Marco Polo. Both pretend to be true accounts
of personal adventure but from what I hear, I cannot rec-

ommend either for serious study. If you read them, however, read them critically and tell me afterwards what you think."

Eventually Vanni read them, beginning with *The Travels of Marco Polo*. The copy owned by the Franciscans was a manuscript written in the Italian and so he could read it quickly, skipping the duller parts. Having skimmed through it, he shared his findings first with Michiele, meeting him one evening on the bridge near the monastery.

"It's a story about two Venetian gem merchants who went to the Far East—to Cathay and the Indies—about a hundred years ago, when for a little while the door of Asia was open to Europeans. The ruler then—his name was Kublai Khan—happened to like foreigners and welcomed merchants visiting his country. He even asked the Polo brothers to bring missionaries back to him on their next trip, to teach his people Christianity—but they brought young Marco Polo instead."

From far up the canal, the tinkling laughter of a woman echoed sweetly. Nearer, the water lapped against the stones. The tide was rising. Vanni talked on and Michiele listened, half dreaming, watching their wavering reflections in the water below.

". . . and in time the Khan made Marco his personal envoy to the provinces. That's how he got to know the country so well—Marco, I mean—so well he was able to write a book about it when he finally got back to Venice over twenty years later. He *says* everything he wrote is true, but I don't believe it."

"Why not? What did he say that was untrue?"

"Well, he told about people who worshiped cattle and believed that cows were sacred! He said that for fuel in some countries the people burned black stones dug out of the earth, and that in another place a cloth was made from rock that wouldn't burn at all, not even when thrust into the heart of the fire. He talks about cities larger than Venice and ports handling ten times the amount of pepper passing through our port of Alexandria."

"No wonder they called him *Il Milione,* Marco of the Millions, meaning the way he always exaggerated. I've seen his house here in Venice. It's still called Millions' Court. Yet it's a good story! What else did he tell about?"

"He told about a place called Cipango, where the houses were roofed with gold and they had golden paving stones in the streets. He did say he hadn't actually been there himself, but had the description on good authority." Vanni paused, pulled thoughtfully at one ear. "Maybe it isn't all lies. He sounds so—so circumstantial at times, like a sober clerk recording exactly what he saw or heard." Then he shrugged. "But other times he talks of seeing visions and hearing drums in the desert!"

When he reported this to Fra Andrea, that good man nodded thoughtfully.

"Well, as for the visions and singing drums, don't be too ready to dismiss them as tall tales, Vanni. I have heard of both. It appears there are phenomena called mirages which cause heat waves in the desert and throw up a vision of things far away. Also I have read that certain singing sounds are caused by shifting sands and the falling of sand cliffs among the dunes—it might sound to some people like drums. Keep an open mind, Vanni. Now what about Sir John Mandeville?"

Vanni threw the manuscript down, disgusted.

"I might believe in dog-headed men and sea serpents, but he writes in such a silly sentimental way about sacrificing the love of fair princesses for the sake of his Faith, and so on —truly, it sounds more like one of those Arabian tales than true history."

Life was pleasant these days. Formal lessons with his tutor

had ended, but his Uncle was allowing him to continue with his classical reading at the monastery. After these study periods with Fra Andrea, he had time to go fishing sometimes on the Lagoon or to explore the canals with Danieli, who stretched at ease in the gondola and let himself be rowed by Vanni for a change.

He might have known it couldn't last, yet when the end came, it came with such abruptness it shocked him.

"You are fourteen now," said Uncle Luigi one evening after dinner. "You have been lazy long enough. Most boys your age have been at work long ago. I cannot believe you now learn anything of value with the Franciscans. You will therefore tell the Brothers you will not see them again after tomorrow. Your time belongs to me hereafter."

If the tone had been kindlier—he was generally a reasonable boy—Vanni might have accepted the situation with good grace. As it was, his gorge rose the way it did so often in his dealings with Signore Romano.

Lazy! In little more than four years he had, apart from his regular studies, learned to read and write Latin as well as Greek! According to Fra Andrea he now had the equivalent of a university education. He had won the wrestling championship at the Gymnasium, was proficient with the crossbow, and had acquired certain other practical skills—like map drawing—though he doubted these would impress his Uncle. *You have been lazy long enough.*

He cast about in his mind for a way to make his Uncle eat those words. It would have to be something subtle, for he could not risk dismissal since there was no place for him now in Genoa. He must think of something—something to give the lie to his Uncle's judgment, something also to compensate for lost delights.

VI

The Smugglers

It was dark on the Lagoon. The water was black silk and on it the boat's muffled oars spilled drops at regular intervals. The two boys pulled in silence, warmed by the exercise. Vanni's gaze swept the sky on the backward pull, glad for once that moon and stars were blacked out by clouds. Darkness was needed tonight.

"How much longer? This is hard work." Guido was grumbling as usual. "We must be near enough."

"Not quite. We mustn't look as though we're just hanging about." Strange how Guido, older and more experienced at this sort of thing, kept looking to him for decisions. Guido Pestrelli, he suspected, was by nature an order-taker. "Get the nets over and light the lantern."

"If she doesn't come tonight, we ought to ask for more pay." Guido hurled the net into the water with unnecessary noise and commotion. Resting on his oars, Vanni let the *barca* move on momentum to the place he had chosen, near enough to the fishing ground yet in position to watch the mouth of the passage. He peered back over his shoulder again to make sure no police boat followed.

If anyone noticed them from the shore, they must seem to be netting cuttlefish. Flat, small-mouthed wicker baskets in the bow contained fish caught earlier, and the furled orange sail identified the *barca* as one borrowed from the Chioggia fishing fleet. It was not unusual for fishermen's sons to go out with lanterns for sport or profit. Some species of sepia could be lured into the nets by lights and there was always a market for cuttlefish if only for the shell. The lookouts at the fort of San Pietro would think nothing of a fishing boat out here at this hour, and if they sent a boat to investigate, would find two young men in fishermen's smocks, hardly more than boys, busy with the nets. On this expedition, all precautions had been taken to deceive the Customs. It was not like their usual excursions on the Guidecca.

Vanni had been flouting the law for months now, at night, ever since he had gone reluctantly to work in his Uncle's warehouse. Through Guido Pestrelli he had met the youthful band of smugglers who operated regularly in a small way inside the Lagoon. Up to now, it had been sufficiently exciting to hang about incoming coastal craft as they anchored, and to wait for a piece of ivory or a handful of peacock's feathers to be slipped over the side. For a price, they would then deliver the goods to the seaman's home. The penalty for such activitiy was heavy, but that was no deterrent to Messer Caboto. It was adventure he looked for. Anything which added to the risk added to the fun! Also, in a perverse way, he felt he had found a way to get back at Uncle Luigi.

Tonight the two youths were stepping out of the amateur class to play a small part in a much larger operation. The danger and pay would be proportionate, and if they acquitted themselves well they might be given more responsible jobs in the future. They were to meet and deliver a message to an unnamed pilgrim galley returning from Jaffa. Word had been brought down the coast from Istria that the ship was in that port and was leaving next day if the wind served. Weather permitting, she should be in Venice in two or three days, contriving to arrive around midnight. She would enter the Lagoon through the Malamocco passage and anchor to wait for the morning visit of Customs. As always, she would be on the watch for signals. Lights and passwords had been arranged long ago for just such an emergency.

This was the second night the two boys had watched and waited. With plenty of time to think, Vanni added speculation to knowledge and worked out what he thought was happening. Pilgrim ships usually passed through Customs at Venice with a minimum of bother. Most of the passengers carried, apart from clothes and bedding, little else but small souvenirs from the Holy Land. An unscrupulous captain could easily introduce among the deck baggage of the pilgrims some bales of Eastern silks, stripped of their wrappings and sewn up in canvas like the regular luggage. A good many illicit parcels must have passed into Venice in this fashion and no one the wiser. This time something must have gone wrong and the authorities were suspicious. The organization in Venice had therefore decided that the goods must be jettisoned before the *dogana* men came aboard. They would hardly take the risk of delivering the message themselves; they must remain above suspicion. This accounted for the hiring of two comparatively raw youths as their agents. Grown men of the *bravi* type—the Venetian word for hired rogues—would look dubious out here. Boys of fourteen or fifteen were expected to do outlandish things.

They had been given their instructions by a man whom Vanni, at least, had never seen before, and neither knew the name of the *patrone* of the ship, nor if the message was for him personally or for one of the crew acting on his own initiative. They did know, however, that if they were caught in the act of signalling, their youth would not save them. Anything endangering the city's commerce called for swift and dire punishment.

Ah, by San Marco, how angry the smugglers would be, finding they must throw those precious silks overboard! Days, perhaps weeks, might have been spent in bargaining with the Infidel in the bazaars of Baghdad or Damascus and much money spent for them.

"Why are you laughing?"

He shook his head. Guido had no sense of humor.

"Nothing."

Through a gap in the Lido, Vanni strained his eyes seaward, fancied he saw a moving shadow. Excitement stirred in him. She would come tonight, he felt sure. The wind was fair from Istria and other ships had arrived earlier in the day. Still, whether she came or not, it was joy to be out here on the Lagoon in a boat, with the scent of the sea all around him, away from the crowds in the Rialto. These nights helped pay for the drudgery at Uncle Luigi's, the cleaning, packing, measuring, counting, and breathing in of spice dust. It was exciting too, creeping out of the house after dark, slipping like a shadow down to the canal where a companion of the night awaited him, rowing to the rendezvous with muffled oars, risking at any moment a police challenge.

The ruthless severance of his relations with Michiele and the Franciscan still rankled. It seemed to him that Uncle Luigi was jealous of his friends and wanted to separate him from them for good, for he had made it as difficult as possible for his nephew to see them, keeping him busy during the day, ordering him to his room at night. Of course Vanni had easily contrived to slip out via the balcony to pay a visit now and then to the monastery. Then by accident he had met Guido again and was introduced to the Brotherhood. After that, his life grew as full by night as by day. He was no longer lonely. And quite frankly he had no time for anyone else. Entirely caught up in the novelty of his new associations, he enjoyed to the full the companionship and the delicious moments of clutching fear. He felt proud to be a part of what he considered a sophisticated and distinguished company—a *brave* company bound together in deathless loyalty, risking freedom, even life and limb, in the cause of Adventure! True, it might have been more satisfying if their deeds had benefited mankind and so made them famous— but there seemed to be no Iberian maidens to rescue these days! Smuggling was the next best thing.

He hardly missed Michiele and the friar. It did not occur to him that they might be sorely missing him.

"He could come once in a while, surely." Michiele's hurt showed easily through the tone of resentment. "He hasn't been to the bridge for six weeks." The bridge was their usual meeting place.

"His Uncle, I believe, has forbidden him to leave the house."

"That wouldn't stop Vanni. No, I have seen him on the Grand Canal with his new friends." Michiele's lips were held tight to keep them from trembling. "He could surely have left them for a moment to come and speak with me. He only waved."

"Perhaps he had a reason." Fra Andrea spoke with determined cheerfulness. No use showing that he too was concerned about the boy. As a matter of fact, the friar had more than a suspicion of what Vanni was up to. He knew some of the youth's present companions. Also, there were other boys from the Rialto district who brought tales to him at school. It was a great pity. Such waste! Fra Andrea hated waste, particularly the waste of a good mind. Eventually he felt compelled to take action. He went, as it happened, to see Signore

Romano the same night Vanni went to meet the pilgrim galley.

In his elegant study, the merchant received Fra Andrea with frigid politeness. Not one to be put down by looks or tones, however, the friar came straight to the point.

"You cut off the boy's studies too abruptly, Signore, inflaming the natural tendency of his age to rebellion. At the same time you separated him from his one real friend—and now see what has happened!"

"Zuan has many friends. Patricians!"

"And what has happened?" the friar repeated. "Vanni has turned to less suitable companions and possibly less suitable recreations. His whole life could be ruined."

Signore Romano looked as outraged as his inexpressive features allowed.

"Zuan's future is altogether assured. As my protege, possibly my heir, he will be a rich man some day."

"Ah, that!" Fra Andrea brushed aside money and position with a gesture. "I am not talking of money but of something more important. Vanni has a very good mind, an *educated* mind. He has also an open-heartedness and honesty unusual in this day and age, and I fear for him because of it. I fear his impulsiveness and energy. True, he is being foolish, but it is up to us who care for him to—"

"Us?" The merchant got up and walked to the window. "Zuan has been put in *my* charge, may I remind you. I believe I know what is best for him. What do you mean—" he turned sharply, "by unsuitable recreations? Zuan goes nowhere when his work is finished."

Fra Andrea hesitated. He did not like the role of informer, and yet—

"If he is upstairs now, Signore, why not call him down, ask him what he does in the evenings?"

With a forbidding face, the merchant rang for a servant,

sent the man upstairs with orders to fetch Messer Caboto. There was silence in the study until the man returned, nervous, stammering.

"The boy is not there, sir."

Signore Romano grew quite pale with fury.

Signorina Baretti was then called and admitted that she had often seen the boy climb from his balcony to the roof and so from there down to the street. She had thought it only natural, she explained nervously, that boys should slip out at night and hadn't thought it worth mentioning. The Signore sent her off in tears and turned a bitter gaze on the friar.

"Very well. It seems you know more of my nephew's activities than I do. Where is he?"

"That I cannot tell you, I'm afraid," said the Franciscan in all honesty. "I know only that he has been slipping out at night with undesirable companions."

"He will be punished!"

This was to be expected, but it was not precisely what Fra Andrea wanted. He resorted to guile.

"And so he should be, Signore. Such ingratitude, after all you have done for him! The boy does not deserve so good an uncle. It is a pity he was not born a poor man's son. Then he might have learned what hard work is, and so appreciated his present advantages."

"Very true!"

"A fisherman's son, perhaps. A few trips to sea would have opened his eyes, but of course it's something he need never—"

"I do not agree, Fra Andrea! It is not too late!"

"Oh? How do you mean, Signore?" asked the friar innocently.

"He shall go to sea tomorrow if I say so," the merchant said angrily. "And I do say so. He will go on one of my ships as a servant, and my captain will have orders to treat him exactly as he would any of the other grommets!"

"Poor lad," sighed the Franciscan, "but of course the situation does call for something drastic." He nodded solemnly while Signore Romano congratulated himself on finding such an excellent solution to his problem. It was an added satisfaction that in sending Zuan to sea he would also be breaking up this association with the Franciscan and his beggarly apprentice. He was sure now of what he had always suspected, that Fra Andrea had more influence over his nephew than he himself had.

The Little Brother walked home, feeling he had done all he could for the present. He hoped he had not left it too late. He could only pray . . .

At that moment, Vanni was shivering with excitement.

"There she is!"

"That's not a galley!"

"Wait and see!"

"Not ours, anyway."

"Bet you twenty *baiocci.*" Not a large bet. A *baiocco* was the smallest coin of the state.

The moving shadow detached itself from the gray bulk of the Fort, and a signal light flashed between ship and shore. The ship was giving her name and number in code to the lookouts. Now she showed the familiar buglike shape of the galley, but whether she was the one they were looking for, or another, still remained to find out.

Vanni lifted the lantern and waved it gently from side to side, making sure the ship would hide the light from any watching eyes at the Fort. The galley came on. If she was not their quarry, she would pay no attention, would sweep past. The tempo of the oars visibly slackened and two small lights appeared at the bow, one above the other.

"Give me the twenty!"

Guido swore.

"Now, while she's letting her anchor go," said Vanni with a swift glance toward the shore. "Now's the time."

Guido produced a red cloth and threw it in front of the lantern, turning its yellow light to a ruby one, while Vanni passed a piece of sacking in front of it once, twice, three times. Three red glows in the dark—"abandon cargo." One brief flash from the ship meant "message received." The job was done.

"Come on," said Guido. "Let's go."

"Wait!"

Vanni had his head cocked, listening. With the clarity of sound on water, they heard a round of low oaths, then a small splash. Vanni chuckled. The cargo was going overboard and the men out there were savage at losing it. In the last moment or two, the galley had drifted down to them and was now less than a cable's length away. The boy could see the vague shapes of crewmen leaning over the bow and then, in the silence, he heard a hoarse whisper.

"You there! In the boat!"

"Don't answer!" Guido's tone was sharp. This was not in the bargain. "We've done the job we're being paid for."

In principle, Vanni knew Guido was right, but he was curious. In calling out like that, the men on the galley were taking a risk. Why? What if the oarsmen heard? No, the *galeotti* would be down below now, guzzling wine and bread in preparation for a night's rest. The pilgrims? Asleep, most likely. Still, it was dangerous. There must be a reason, and Vanni wanted to know what it was.

"We can go on pretending," he told Guido and called out "Buy some fish, signores? Nice fresh cuttlefish!"

"Come aboard! Let's see what you've got."

"Don't you drag me into this!" whispered Guido furiously.

"I'm not here—see? Say you came alone. I want nothing to do with this." He dove under the nets, out of sight.

Vanni shrugged, a little surprised, more than a little contemptuous.

He sculled with one oar over the stern until he reached the side of the ship, and a rope came plopping down out of the darkness. He used it to help himself up and over the side. Dropping on deck, the first thing he saw by the light of the binnacle was a water cask with the name *Vesta* burned into its side. So the ship was the *Vesta*. He saw a group of men as dim shapes in the half-light. The dress and attitude of the central figure made Vanni sure it was the *patrone* himself. He had the patrician manner, the cold deliberate speech.

"Who are you?"

"Zuan Caboto." He wondered if his name was known.

"Who is with you?"

"As you see, *patrone*, I am alone."

"Good." The captain sounded pleased. "I have a parcel here I want taken ashore." The man drew a small package from his doublet. It was flat, wrapped in canvas.

"I might have been seen boarding your ship," said Vanni with belated caution.

"You came to sell fish. I'll take all you've got."

"There's a full basket in the boat. I'll send it up on the line. There's a chance I might be stopped by the patrol on the way back!" He felt the thrill of dealing on equal terms with a brave *patrone*, his companion, after all, in crime!

"Then you must drop the package overboard. It is weighted and will sink. But try not to be caught. All I own," the *patrone's* voice was grim, "is tied up in this! Take it to my house in the Salvi district." He took out a purse and spilled a handful of silver carelessly into Vanni's hand. "You'll have as much again if you deliver it safely. Betray me—" his voice dropped to a harsh whisper—"and you will regret it!"

Vanni stiffened, offended. Surely the *patrone* knew he was a brother-smuggler and would sooner die than betray a comrade. He thought for a moment of refusing the commission altogether, but that might look like cowardice. He held out his hand.

"You have nothing to fear from me," he said loftily.

"Go from the dock at San Antonia, down the Little Merceria, toward the Alto bridge. Turn left just before it and just past the Inn of Gold you'll see a two-story house. Knock twice, then three times, but make sure first you have not been followed. That is important! No one must see you go in, is that clear?" The man's eyes glittered in the half-light. "Don't give the package to anyone but my servant, not even to my wife. Ask the servant's name before you hand it over and do not part with it unless he says 'Tedesco.' Have you got all that?"

"Yes."

"Say to Tedesco, 'The *patrone* told me to give you this and in return you will give me the usual.' Repeat that."

Vanni did so.

"Say it just that way, or you won't get your fee. Now be off, and remember, if you're stopped, throw the parcel overboard. If you play me false, my friends will see to you."

Without troubling to answer, Vanni turned his shoulder to the captain, effectively cutting off further insults. He put a leg over the bulwark and at that moment heard a voice from the darkness of the deck, speaking in a foreign tongue.

"I say—confound it!" The voice added in Italian "What's going on here?"

VII

Sir William Thorne

The *patrone* swore briefly under his breath.

"What's all this bumping about in the middle of the night?" demanded the newcomer. "Is that you, Captain Fontana?"

"Yes, Sir William," answered the *patrone* in a deliberately light tone. "There is nothing to worry about."

"I was asleep, dammit. The row woke me up. Who's that you're talking to?"

A bulky figure in the loose costume of the pilgrim with the red cross on its breast, stepped into what light there was on deck. The *patrone* picked up the binnacle lamp and shone it with an appearance of candor on the youth in the fisherman's smock.

"Fisher lad looking for a quick market, Sir William." He turned to Vanni. "I won't pay more than two *soldi* for the lot. If it's not enough, be off!"

"I suppose it must do," muttered Vanni sullenly.

The lamplight hung between boy and pilgrim, and they stared at each other for a moment. Vanni saw a red face, a fleshy nose, inquisitive blue eyes. The stranger's speech was

Italian, but Italian so heavily accented it could hardly be understood. He must be a German, or a Frank.

"Blast it, I've a good mind to go ashore with him! After three months in this ship, I could do with a decent bed."

"Customs and immigration, sir, in the morning."

"I know, I know! Humph! Get on with it then, but not so much noise. I want my sleep." And he stumped away.

"Barbarous Briton!" muttered one of the men.

"Do you think he heard?" asked another.

"It doesn't matter if he did," snapped Captain Fontana. "He can't prove anything, and it's not in his interests to report us. All he can think of now is getting home to England. He won't want to get mixed up in anything that might cause him extra delay." He turned to Vanni. "That's all. Do as I told you, precisely."

Vanni thought as he slid down the rope that Fontana couldn't be as clever as he'd thought, to trust a Briton! From all the boy had heard of that rude North Country, the men there were a set of ignorant rogues. He sent up the basket of fish on a line. Guido was still an unmoving lump among the nets as he cast off from the galley. In ten minutes, the big ship had faded into the darker background of the land. When Guido finally emerged, he asked without shame—

"What did they give us?"

Vanni spilled half the silver coins into the other's hand. "As many more if we get this parcel safely to the captain's house."

Guido's eyes gleamed like a cat's in the darkness and he made no further comment. They rowed together quietly, seeing no sign of a patrol, no movement anywhere on the water, seemingly alone in a dead world. The fresh sea scent gradually faded. The danker smell of the canals came to meet them. Dimly, the two o'clock bell sounded. They stopped momentarily to rest their arms.

Vanni looked at the parcel, shook it cautiously. There was no identifiable sound, but that only meant the contents were well packed. What article of trade could lie in so small a compass and yet be so valuable—so valuable that the *patrone* had risked sending it ashore with an inexperienced youth rather than casting it overboard with the silk? Precious stones? Pearls, perhaps, from the far-off Indies, or some rare spice that had traveled for months across Asia!

What would he do if the police appeared? Drop it overboard, as the *patrone* had ordered? Why not hide it? Drop it among the cuttlefish in the basket, then drop the basket overside on a line? Fishermen often dragged their catch home in the water that way, using the sea for temporary cold storage. On the other hand, if the package contained spices, the sea water would do it no good. Perhaps it was as well that they met no patrol on the way back. Slipping past the mouth of the largest canal, they docked in the shadow of an old church.

"Come on, let's get it over with," said Guido.

They crossed the dock, feet pattering on the silent stones, and passed through an archway into the Little Merceria, the street of shops, sister to the big one in the Rialto district. Everything was shut up tight. Vanni began to suspect that "the Lords of the Night" went to bed like other people as soon as curfew sounded. He thought one was actually in more danger from the occasional *bravo* and similar cutthroats of this somewhat run-down section of Venice.

"How much more do we get, did you say?"

"The same again. I'm to say to Tedesco 'Give me the usual.' "

Guido stopped short.

Surprised, Vanni looked back. Guido was a motionless statue in the half-darkness.

"What's the matter?"

"I told you we should have come straight back!" The voice held panic. "You go on alone if you like. It doesn't need two of us."

This was a surprise. Guido was generally well up to the front when it came to collecting money.

"What's got into you, Guido?"

"I'm—I feel ill!" Guido's voice actually trembled. It was a lie, naturally, but Guido lied so often it was more of a surprise when he told the truth. "I'll—I'll wait for you at the boat." He faded off into the darkness without another word.

For a moment Vanni thought of going after him, then he shrugged. He could manage the rest alone.

He walked as swiftly as he dared down the dark street. Only an occasional smoky oil lantern hung outside a shop or private house. Strange, Guido's desertion. What had he been afraid of? For he had been afraid, Vanni was sure of that. He'd been all right until—until he heard what the *patrone* had told him to say. What was so fearsome about that? A little ambiguous, perhaps. The usual . . . Why not the exact amount, or even "a handful of silver"? At first the *patrone* had said he would get the same as he already had been given. Now it seemed he was to receive "the usual," whatever that was. Was it more than a handful of silver, or less? If less—suddenly Vanni stopped short. He was struck by a cold, ugly thought. The usual!

The youth tried to dismiss the idea as nonsense. Guido would have warned him. Wouldn't he?

Vanni's mind went back to the boat and Guido's unwillingness to follow him aboard the *Vesta*. Why? Guido hadn't even known the name of the ship or the captain. But—what if he hadn't wanted to know? What if knowing such things were—dangerous! Guido knew a lot more about the organization through his brother than he, Vanni, did! Perhaps he knew the name "Tedesco."

How trusting Captain Fontana had been, come to think of it. First, to put a valuable parcel into the hands of a completely strange boy was bad enough, but to let that boy see the name of his ship, even overhear his own name spoken—that to a man like the *patrone* was almost like suicide. What if Vanni had been as dubious an agent as Fontana had seemed to suspect? What if, after delivering the parcel and collecting his fee, Vanni had gone straight to the Lion's Mouth, one of those sinister little boxes left by the secret police to receive anonymous messages? Fontana would not have lived to enjoy the proceeds of that little parcel.

So he had made sure that, once the parcel was handed over, there would be no opportunity for Vanni to lay an information against him because he, Vanni, would be dead!

Now the boy began to remember whispers concerning bodies found regularly in the canals, stabbed or strangled, disfigured beyond recognition. He began to tremble. For the first time, he glimpsed the wide gulf that separated him, the romantic amateur, from men like Pestrelli and the *patrone*, the professionals. Vanni had glamorized them to suit his own fancy. He saw them clearly now—criminals and cutthroats, without honor even among themselves.

What next then? The usual!

But what if he was all wrong? What if it was all in his imagination? He must be absolutely sure . . .

He began to walk forward again, slowly. If he was judging them falsely and did not deliver the parcel, he would be failing in his promise. And what would he do with the parcel? But if he was right about Fontana, he was now walking to his death. How to be sure? A vague plan formed in his mind.

He walked more quickly. Glimpsing water ahead, he knew he was near the canal. Yes, there was the bridge, and there the Inn's gilded sign under a lighted lantern. Finally—he very nearly turned back—there was the gloomy second-

storey house. Vanni forced his quaking legs to carry him up
to the door.

There, after a deep breath, he knocked twice, then three
times. He waited, his heart in his mouth. Presently he heard
faints sounds from inside and footsteps came slowly down
the interior stone staircase.

As the door opened, Vanni stepped back, seeing nothing
but feeling an animal presence. A sibilant whisper asked
what he wanted. Vanni swallowed, made an effort to keep
his voice steady.

"I'm—from the master of the *Vesta*."

"So?"

"He told me to ask the name of his servant."

There was a pause, then a harsh—

"Tedesco!"

So there it was.

"I've got—a parcel." His heart fluttered painfully. "And a
message."

"Give it here then. What's the message?" The boy imagined a stealthy hand reaching for a knife!

"The *patrone* said—" He tensed, then shouted it, "You're
to give me the usual!" Then he hurled the package into the
darkness, and was off running back the way he had come.

No voice called after him in protest as might have been
expected from an innocent man. Instead, there was the sound
of pursuit—heavy steps striding after him, breaking into a
run. So Guido was right! There was no doubt left now.

Light splayed into his path as he tore past the Inn and
turned the corner. A moment later, that same light rocked
and leaped up, sending the shadows capering ahead of him.
He knew that Tedesco must have seized the lantern off its
hook as he passed, and this was frightening. Up to now, the
advantage had been with Vanni. In the darkness he had
planned, with a short head start, to step aside in the first

doorway and let the pursuit go by—but now Tedesco could seek him out with the light. Now, therefore, he could only hope to outdistance the man in a straight run down the Merceria where the buildings were pressed tight together and no side alleys offered escape routes. In the Square, if he got there first, Vanni might find a place to hide.

The feet pounded closer and closer. In the youth's frightened imagination, Tedesco seemed to have legs eight feet long. Vanni ran as he had never run before, praying he wouldn't stumble. The street seemed endless. If he hoped to save his life, he must go faster, for he would need extra seconds to hide when he reached the Square. He called from his aching legs one last spurt of power and burst into the Piazza.

Seconds later, Tedesco pounded in after him and Vanni tried to hold his aching breath. The *bravo* looked huge in the darkness as he stopped short and looked around.

Tedesco must have realized at once that the boy could have gone anywhere from this point, to the right through the arcade, to the left in among a score of pillars, or behind and around the church. He might even have raced straight across the Square and reached the canal by now. And he might still be here, quite close! The thought went through his slow brain that if he went looking for the boy with his lantern, his quarry could slip off in the opposite direction. He was a stupid man and there was no one to give him orders. He could think of no ruse, no scheme. Defeated, he went back down the Little Merceria.

Vanni breathed again. The pain around his heart grew easier. Still, even after the steps had quite faded, he remained where he was, hidden behind the statue in front of the church. He had been within a hand's reach of Tedesco when the man stopped. Pressing himself against the cool marble, on the alert for a surprise return, he counted the

seconds. But Tedesco did not reappear. Vanni heard only
the beating of his own heart. At last he slipped into the shadows around the church and made for the canal. The boat was
still there, but Guido was not. Vanni was not surprised.

The boat must be returned to the fisherman who had
loaned it. Wearily Vanni took up the oars again.

All sense of fellowship with smugglers, young or old, was
gone by now. He felt betrayed. Treachery was a fact of life,
evidently, one to be reckoned with even among so-called
friends. He saw that one shared a roof with criminals at one's
own peril. Danieli had warned him. What a fool he had been!

Vanni arrived home as dawn was breaking to find Signorina Baretti waiting for him, seated in his room half-asleep.
She got up, slow and accusing, as he closed the balcony
curtains.

"You have got me into trouble with your Uncle. I have to
tell him now what time you got in." She paused in the doorway, sour with reproach. "I'm too old to sit up all night."

"Good night, Signorina." He could not care about the old
witch now—nor about his Uncle, nor about anything. He
flung himself fully clothed across the bed and fell instantly
asleep . . .

He was late for breakfast next morning. Uncle Luigi had
gone to the Rialto, leaving word for him to follow. Still, the
boy ate without haste, unable to feel any real concern at the
moment for what his Uncle might say or do. It was too late
now for remorse, too late for worry. He felt only a deep
lethargy.

Stepping out of the gondola near the bridge, he was still
in this strange remote mood, taking in the colorful scene
about him as if for the first time—

Everywhere movement and color—merchants in black
gowns with crisp white collars, presiding over booths of silks
and satins, red, yellow, and green brocades, trays of gems

and goldwork. Red flowers in the window boxes, sun blazing down the front of the houses in slanted rays. The graceful *loggias* looking at themselves conceitedly in the mirror of the canal, and the old wooden bridge crowded with people—hucksters selling fruit and fish and vegetables from market gondolas under the bridge, porters and servants darting in and out among dark-visaged Moors, blond Germans, red-hatted Jews, and the foreign merchants pressing up to the money-changers to exchange the coin of their country for the *soldi, scudi,* and *ducati* of Venice. And under the bridge, the swans swam upstream in lordly pride.

Amid all the noise, the cries, the laughter, Vanni moved quietly, feeling empty and rather peaceful. What might happen next was beyond his control. Meanwhile, he was alive—when he might have been floating, dead, in some lonely canal. With regret he stepped at last from the bright warm air into the chill of his Uncle's warehouse and stopped short, all his senses alert again, sending frantic signals. There, seated on a bale of goods, was the red-faced Briton he had last seen on the deck of the *Vesta!*

After the first shock of recognition, Vanni saw it was useless to pretend he did not know the man. He began to be appalled at what one word from Sir William might mean to him. Uncle Luigi was rigidly law-abiding. If he were told by the Briton that the *Vesta* was smuggling, he might feel it his duty to notify the police, perhaps even force Vanni to play the informer! The men on the *Vesta* would be betrayed and never know it was through no fault of his. He had one hope —if he ever expected to walk again through the streets of Venice in safety—and that was that if the Briton had recognized him he would at least know nothing about the smuggling.

"Ah-ha!" growled Sir William in his terrible Italian. "So it's our young fisherman—all dressed up this morning in

gentlemen's clothes. You wouldn't be Signore Romano's son?"

"His nephew." How could he make this man keep silent? What was a likely excuse for being on the *Vesta* last night? Could he say he had played fisherman for fun? On a bet? Before he could open his mouth, the red face spread in a knowing grin.

"Does your uncle know you spend your nights with smugglers on the Lagoon?"

"Sir!" Vanni cried in agony, glancing around in terror. "My Uncle—"

"All right, all right, don't worry! I won't give you away." The blue eye nearest Vanni twinkled. "I see you're a spirited lad. I was myself at your age. But you're a fool to get mixed up with professionals, especially—" he glanced around at the piled-up bales. "—especially when it's unnecessary. If you'll take my advice—though I suppose you won't—you'll get out of it and spend your talents and energy on something more worthwhile."

The relief was so great Vanni could hardly speak.

"I'm already out, sir! Last night was the last, believe me! I—" But there was no chance to continue. Uncle Luigi was coming in from the street with outstretched hand.

"My dear Sir William, forgive me for keeping you waiting." Catching sight of his nephew, Signore Romano's face darkened. "See to the invoices, Zuan, and do not leave here without permission. Now, Sir William, if you will come with me, we will see about your money."

"I don't mind if I do," said the Briton, and went out without another glance at Vanni.

Would the man keep his word? After his recent experience, Vanni felt he could trust nobody. And now for the first time he saw the danger he was in, apart from the possible vengeance of Fontana. If Uncle Luigi were really angry, he

might send him back to Genoa in disgrace. He imagined the pain and disappointment of his parents, the embarrassment of Piero, now his father's sole heir. All day he was kept in suspense. Only after a late and silent dinner in the *palazzo* did Uncle Luigi finally speak.

"You must be punished." Vanni braced himself. "I am going to send you to sea." He must have seen the boy jump. "No, it's no use pleading with me, Zuan. I have made up my mind. I intend to send you on one of my own ships as an ordinary grommet and you may expect no favors through being my nephew. I shall instruct the captain to keep you at work every hour of the day." Vanni stared at his Uncle in disbelief. "You have only yourself to thank for this."

Out of the jumble of words, Vanni caught only the phrases "send you to sea" and "on one of my own ships as an ordinary grommet." And he still couldn't quite believe it!

"You have shirked your duties, Zuan," the merchant continued in his soft clipped tones. "You have deceived me by slipping out at night. You have defied me! Perhaps in a year or so you will have learned a little more humility."

Vanni had all he could do to keep his face solemn and still when his whole being felt like shouting and dancing.

He was going to sea!

Glory to San Giorgio! He wasn't going to be sent back to Genoa! He was going to be sent to sea!

VIII

The Grommet

Life grew suddenly rare and wonderful for young Caboto. From the deck of a real ship, he would now discover what the real world—the Mediterranean world, at any rate—was like.

How had he missed seeing such an opportunity for himself? He had always known that his Uncle, in partnership with other Venetian merchants, chartered a ship from the Signory once or twice a year to trade with the cities of the Levant, yet it had never occurred to him that he might ship with the crew himself, perhaps because he had always associated "going to sea" with being grown up and independent. Naturally he had never confided his secret ambitions to his Uncle. He soon discovered Fra Andrea was chiefly responsible for his good fortune. Signore Romano mentioned it himself.

"It is your fine Franciscan friend you have to thank for this, Zuan. He let me know you were up to mischief. He has evidently received confidences from you which, with proper family feeling, ought to have come to me." There was a tinge of hurt there. "Even now, if you will tell me where you were last night, I may overlook your fault." How a Venetian hated not to know what was going on!

"I am pledged to secrecy," Vanni repeated stubbornly, thinking it was perhaps just as well that he was leaving Venice, to be out of reach of the Pestrelli brothers and their friends for a while. "I did not tell Fra Andrea what I was doing. I don't understand how he can possibly have guessed."

Signore Romano's expression relaxed a trifle, pleased that the friar was no wiser than he himself was. He then jumped to a conclusion which might easily have been justified in the Venice of his day.

"Amorous adventures, I suppose," he said tolerantly. "You exaggerate the importance of such matters."

Deciding that his Uncle was now not quite so angry, Vanni ventured a question of his own.

"The man from Britain. You know him well, Uncle?"

"I know Sir William Thorne in the way of business and have for years."

"You trust him absolutely?"

Signore Romano's lip curled.

"One trusts no one in that fashion, Zuan, as you will in time discover. Why?" He eyed the youth with sudden sharpness. "Do you know any reason why I should *not* trust him?"

"No sir, of course not."

"Then why are you so concerned about his reliability?"

"I'm not," Vanni replied evasively. "It is just that I have been told these Britons are all vulgar, unscrupulous men, yet Sir William seemed a gentleman, and honorable."

"He is perhaps less of a barbarian than most ultramontanes." This word "ultramontane" was one used to describe a people who lived beyond the Alps and so beyond the pale of Italian civilization. The merchant was highly amused at his nephew's idealism. One did not grant anyone the possession of an honorable nature, not at least on such short acquaintance. Well, the boy would learn. "Naturally he is a long way from being civilized according to our standards."

It was all right then. Sir William had not betrayed him to his Uncle, so had probably not reported the *Vesta* to the authorities either. Now the Briton was on his way back to his cold rough island on the edge of the world and Vanni would never see him again. The secret was safe. So, promptly and lightheartedly, he dismissed the whole affair from his mind and went to see Michiele and the friar.

He came on Michiele first, mooning about in the monastery garden when he ought to have been making up lists of herbs and physics in the pharmacy. At sight of Vanni, the sad face widened in a delighted grin. The reunion was jubilant, and there was no hint of reproach on Michiele's side. Vanni, aware of his long desertion and remembering what Michiele's friendship had meant in those first lonely months in Venice, felt enormously guilty. He did not deserve such a friend! He vowed to himself that he would make it up to Michiele some day.

"Is it true, Vanni, you are going to sea?"

"Yes! In the *Santa Lucia*, one of the newest galleys from the Arsenal. Rico Aredan is the *patrone*, Messer Stegano is sailing master. We sail first to Istria, then to Crete and then to Constantinople. I will sail in the track of Odysseus, Michiele, think of it!"

Michiele thought of it with mixed pleasure and woe.

"I'm glad for you, my friend, but I won't see you for months."

"Ah, but think what a lot I'll have to tell you when I get back."

"I wish I were going too."

"But you have your own affairs to see to, Michiele. You must work on the Plan while I am gone." Earlier, Michiele had confided his intention of rebelling against the Brothers'

decision to make a medical priest of him, even if it meant
running away. Vanni had suggested a better plan. His idea
was to work separately on the sympathies of each Brother in
turn and thus gain the support of the majority. If Michiele's
plea was still refused, time enough then to consider running
away. "You will be a barber some day, I know it! Your experience in medicine will be all to the good too, since Fra
Andrea says that in some countries a barber is also a surgeon."

"I'll sign on your ship some day then," cried Michiele,
cheering up, "as barber and surgeon!"

"Good! But you must be firm now, or all is lost."

"I'll try."

"Ah, Michiele, one day we shall go in search of adventure
together, you'll see! Together we will seek glory!" proclaimed Vanni in his grandiloquent way. "Each in his own
fashion—you in the profession of your choice, I in mine. If
Uncle Luigi will let me alone, that is," he added, coming
down to earth, "for a year at least. I want to learn all I can
in the time I have."

"What's the *Santa Lucia* like?"

"She's a galley, of course—that can't be helped. The law in-
sists that we ship valuable goods—bullion, glass, spices, and
so on in state-owned transports. But she's modern, Michiele,
not like the old *Golgotha*. She's a trireme with a stern rudder, oars all on one plane in groups of three in the new fashion, with three men to each oar. We have 114 rowers, fifty
fighting men, and fifty seamen, including six apprentices of
which I am the oldest but most junior." He shrugged ruefully. "But I don't care. I'd sooner go as the least person in
the ship than not go at all. She has three masts, all with
lateen sails, and they tell me she goes like a racer, reaching,
with a good stiff breeze on her beam. Once a galley like the
Santa Lucia ran home from Southampton in thirty-one days

—imagine it! Twenty-five hundred miles. That's more than fifteen miles an hour!"

"Will you go to Southampton sometime, I wonder, with the Flanders Fleet?"

"Possibly, if I'm lucky."

"Then you can see where Pytheas sailed!"

"I must pray that my precious Uncle doesn't decide I've been punished enough after a voyage or two, and hustle me back to the warehouse. That would be the real punishment if he only knew it. Anyway, I shall see Constantinope on this voyage, and possibly Alexandria if—"

"What's this about Alexandria?" asked a new voice, and there was Fra Andrea smiling and hitching up his robe in the old familiar way. Vanni rushed at him, hugged him gratefully.

"As if you didn't know! Padre, how did you manage it?" The friar waved this away with twinkling eyes.

"I? It was your Uncle, Vanni, who decided a spell at sea doing an honest day's work for a change would be good for you, and of course I agreed with him." The boy was not deceived. He looked at the kind dark face in much the same way he had looked into Emilio's five years earlier. What would life in Venice have been like without Fra Andrea and Michiele? And why was it that sincere gratitude was always so hard to express! Was it because one used up all the stock phrases in everyday politenesses? Vanni took refuge in describing the ship and the course she would sail.

"If we do not get sufficient cargo at Constantinople, we will go on to Alexandria. I had hoped to cross the Black Sea to Trebizond, but Uncle Luigi says the political situation there is not good." Fra Andrea looked grave at this reminder of the constant threat of Turkish power on their borders, but it also reminded him of something.

"I must give you a letter to Ibn Haud in case you do get to

Alexandria. It is just possible he has found something new since I last wrote to him."

"New?" Vanni stared blankly for a moment, then remembered. "Oh, earth measurement. I'm afraid I won't have much time for that sort of thing now, Padre. I'm a working man, you see, with a lot to learn about things that really matter." Fra Andrea raised his eyebrows dubiously. "But I shall certainly go to see your friend. I must ask him if there were any men like Pytheas in Arabia who made voyages of discovery in ancient times." Vanni sighed with pleasure. "It seems to me that life is beginning at last!"

Fra Andrea shook his head ruefully. He had always hoped that one of his brighter pupils would choose the way of the books, but it seemed Vanni was not to be that one. The youth was not cast in the scholar's mold. He was a doer, not a dreamer. Ah well, the world needed both sorts. The Little Brother had to confess to himself that he was sorry, partly because he himself had grown fascinated with the academic problem they had begun together to investigate. By San Antonio, who *was* right? Eratosthenes or Posidonius?

"Remember," he told his graduate student, "always ask questions! Study the past to discover the future. If something comes along, casting light on the earth's dimensions, I shall put it aside for you."

"Thanks, Padre." The smile of affection took the sting away from the carelessness of the words. Now the good friar proffered a gift—a short commentary on *The Travels of Marco Polo*, for which he apologized. "It is in print, I fear. There is no manuscript copy." In spite of his generally modern outlook, Fra Andrea still could not quite believe that this monstrous new mechanical device of printing could really equal the accuracy of devout scribes working with pens and brushes to the glory of God.

So it was good-by to Michiele and Fra Andrea. It was off

with the lace-trimmed doublet, off with jeweled cap and velvet shoes——and on with a plain woolen shirt and breeches, and most of the time no stockings at all. The single earring given to him by Michiele five years ago was carefully fastened to his right ear, pierced for its reception by Michiele himself. Then away to join the *Santa Lucia* in all the pride of near-manhood.

At the last moment Uncle Luigi decided to accompany Vanni to the quay where the tender would take him out to the ship. Signore Romano was now showing belated signs of concern for this nephew of his, possibly his heir, who was going out into that dangerous and unfriendly element, the sea. Was he perhaps putting his largest investment in jeopardy? Or had he grown insensibly fond of the boy? True, Zuan was not now the sullen child who on arrival in Venice had so filled him with misgiving. No, the Signore flattered himself, due to his generosity and supervision, the boy had grown into an assured and handsome youth. Vanni's qualities of candor and enthusiasm, often deplored by the close-mouthed Venetian, nevertheless were attractive qualities which drew all sorts of people to him.

As they traveled by gondola to the docks, Signore Romano delivered a lecture.

"Never expose yourself to cold and damp, Zuan, which leave the vital forces too weak to combat disease. There is a virulent type of fever which afflicts many going to the East for the first time. You must try to be in good condition to throw it off. Avoid stenches, Zuan, since many physicians today suspect a connection between foul odors and illness."

Vanni wondered how he was to avoid cold and exposure at sea, or the noxious odors inevitable in a ship carrying more than three hundred men in a confined space.

"Avoid the breath of evil people," went on Uncle Luigi, "and here is a pomander of amber and cloves which you must keep about your person at all time. It will help ward off the plague. Above all, Zuan, do not put yourself in any physical danger, such as climbing the ship's masts. I have seen sailors doing this in the course of their duty and con-ider it most dangerous. If these risks must be taken, let others crowd in ahead of you. It is better to be cautious than dead. Again, on shore, wear your dagger at all times and take care not to wander far in a strange city where you may fall in with thieves and cutthroats. But if for some rea-son you find yourself in such a situation, be sure to strike first!"

There was much more of this typically cynical advice, most of which went in one ear of the prospective seaman and out the other. Vanni was relieved when Bartolomeo brought the gondola up beside the tender at the quay. Uncle Luigi, however, had not yet finished.

"You will look up my agent in Constantinople, a man named Fragini, and give him this letter. I want him to show you the city and explain to you the business situation. It will be valuable knowledge for you when you return to Venice to take up your proper career. Very well then." He kissed his nephew solemnly on both cheeks. "Good-by, Zuan. I shall see you again in three months or thereabouts."

"Yes, sir." Vanni took his seabag from the gondolier, who called up with a broad grin—

"Good luck, Master Zuan! Watch out for the women in those foreign places!"

Young Caboto took the horny hand thrust out to him and shook it heartily.

"I will, thanks, Bartolomeo. Take care of your rheuma-tism!"

Free at last. In the tender, he did not look back.

As they approached the *Santa Lucia* he had a fine view of her. She was over 150 feet long from stem to stern post, a

The Santa Lucia

galeas sotile, that is, a galley with oars in groups of three but on a single plane, thus able to sit low in the water. Like the ordinary *fusta*, she had a covered bridge between the oarsmen amidships, called the *corsia*. This not only gave strength to the vessel fore and aft, but its roof provided a fighting platform for the soldiers. Vanni was to learn that it also provided the only completely sheltered place on the ship for storing perishables such as rope and water casks and ammunition. The next deck down on either side of the *corsia* roofed the oarsmen's benches and one entered the *corsia* by hatchways, descending by ladders to the hold. There was no forecastle, as on the *Golgotha*, but the poop or aftercastle was hung with costly and colorful awnings which provided shelter for the officers and gentlemen.

Closer, he saw the red cross painted on the stern. This was the mark of the compulsory load line set by the authorities—an innovation which was strictly observed. The mark was only a hair's breadth above the water, showing that the hold was filled to capacity. Cargo space was limited on a galley and only very valuable goods were ever carried in them. English wool, German silver, Venetian glass and lace were carried on the outward voyage, spices on the return one. Sometimes a quantity of bullion had to be carried to make up the unfavorable balance of trade. She was armed to meet the possible threat of Saracen pirates.

On the three masts, the huge triangular sails hung un-furled. In a good breeze they would bell out in massive wings, but here in the Lagoon on a hot afternoon they hung from the tilted yards, limp and wrinkled. The Lion of St. Mark was displayed on the main staff and on lesser staffs hung the various standards of the merchants. He picked out his uncle's, a golden salamander on a green ground, and was reminded as they passed beneath the deadly battering ram

at the bow that the galley could at short notice be turned
into a warship of the Republic in time of war.

With a faster-beating heart than usual, Vanni climbed
through the entry hatch on the port side and threaded his
way through the last-minute bustle on deck, inquiring for
the Steward who on these ships included in his duties the
overseeing and training of the grommets. Vanni was told to
mount the *corsia* and walk to the end of it, which he did. He
was aware, as he walked the length of the platform, that he
was under close scrutiny from the man at the end. Eyes
downcast as befitted the least member of the crew, Vanni
reported as instructed.

"Ah yes, Caboto, of course." The voice had the richness
of a sweet pudding. The boy raised his eyes and saw a
plumpish man with a pock-marked face and eyes like black
raisins. To his surprise, the man gave a slight bow.

"I am Scalzi. I am sure we will be friends."

This confused Vanni. Was it usual for a Steward to bow
to a grommet? No, he decided, vexed. It must be that he was
to receive special treatment as a relative of one of the owners. He would have preferred to be accepted and judged on
performance! He gave Scalzi an even deeper and most re-
spectful bow in return and murmured, "Yes, sir."

"Go below now," said Scalzi with a kindly smile. "You will
find the other grommets somewhere about the galley. Tonio
is the senior boy. Ask him to show you where to stow your
gear. Then tell him I want all of you on deck."

"Yes, sir!"

Finding Tonio was not difficult, but Vanni's reception this
time was quite different, definitely cool, either because he
was slightly older than the senior boy or because he was related to the management.

"Put your bag in that cubbyhole and mind you have your
name marked on it plain. We don't like those who poke

about in other lads' bags, saying they made a mistake!" The senior boy could not have been more than thirteen, yet already he had the workman's slouch, partly his natural heritage, partly the effect of two years' heavy work before his bones were properly set. An even smaller boy now jumped out from behind Tonio with a vacuous grin and announced that he was Piccolo. Both boys had strong Neapolitan accents and Tonio seemed to exercise a special patience with the younger boy. Vanni delivered the Steward's message.

"Fat old Scalzi wants all hands on deck," growled Tonio. "Hop to it, lads."

The new apprentice was set to work with the others, cleaning the deck on the heels of the departing shore workers. The cargo was all in now, all guests ashore, and the sun was sliding down into a gilded Lagoon. The towers and domes of Venice glittered in the last glorious rays.

With water drawn on board in a canvas bucket, the newest grommet worked with a will, finding the chores a novelty —a novelty, he guessed, which would soon wear off! He sloshed with more zeal than effectiveness and his joy burst forth in one unguarded moment beside Tonio.

"Isn't it marvelous! Soon we shall be at sea!"

Tonio gave him a sour, sideways glance.

"What's marvelous about it?"

"You don't think it's exciting to be sailing off to strange ports in the country of the Infidel?"

Tonio shrugged and spat on Vanni's clean piece of deck.

"I've seen them, and they're all the same, full of Saracen cutthroats. A wicked lot! And wait till you find out what the sea's like before you say it's marvelous. There's nothing good about the sea—mind what you're doing there—not so much water!"

The new grommet was silenced. Tonio, though younger, was certainly the more experienced. All the same, Vanni doubted he would soon change his own views, not with the joy of it all surging in his veins. In view of the other's sneers, however, he'd better keep his more lyrical opinions to himself after this. It was clear, if Tonio was a sample, that the ordinary seaman had no romantic illusions about the sea. Possibly in time it would become to Vanni, too, no more than a way of going from one place to another. He hoped not.

Now the apprentices were shooed off the deck by the sailors getting ready to weigh anchor. The overseer began to beat the rowing time and soon, with a faint night breeze to assist the *galeotti*, the *Santa Lucia* slipped out with the tide, leaving Venice and the Lagoon behind.

By the twentieth hour, they were far from shore. With no duties at the moment, the grommets retired to their corner by the galley to play at dice or to sleep. Vanni joined them, cheerfully ready to be friends, and asked Tonio to tell him about Constantinople. What was it like?

"A big old ruin full of Turks," answered the senior boy shortly.

"So long after the Siege?"

"What do you know of the Siege?" The question was scornful. "It happened before you were born." The scoffing was the defense of the uneducated man against the scholar, but Vanni was unaware of this, interested only in the old Byzantine city.

"Three years after, actually," he corrected Tonio. "I wish I *had* seen it. Imagine being able to watch those Turkish ships sailing over the land, with the sailors—"

"Sailing over the *land*? What kind of crazy talk is that?"

"Why, didn't you ever hear about it?" Vanni was honestly surprised. It was a most important event in history, the fall of Constantinople, one of the most important to date. Eager to inform, he began the tale his tutor had related to him on one of the few occasions when that dour man had spoken eloquently without launching into Latin. "You know, of course, that the Greek Christians at Constantinople held out for a thousand years against all their enemies—Goths, Slavs, Bulgars, Persians, and Saracens—and the Turks were especially savage about their failure to take the city. So in 1453 they made their heaviest attack, using artillery stronger than any used before. Poor Constantinople! This time she stood alone. Only a few ships came from Genoa and Venice to help her defend the great chain that stretched across the harbor mouth, protecting the city. Still, for weeks she held out, beating the Infidel back time and time again. Then the Turkish commander, Mohammed, thought of a way to bypass the Christian defenses by transporting his ships across the peninsula, to the inner harbor, and this is how it was done."

Though Tonio and his companions stared loftily into space, they were listening with attention.

"Lengths of timber were placed end to end on the Bosphorus shore over the heights of Para to the edge of the Golden Horn, forming a slipway greased with oils and fat. Then, on this slipway, ships were hoisted by means of ropes and winches and teams of oxen, and hauled along by thousands of men. What a picture, Tonio! Think of it, ships traveling by moonlight across fields of flowers, sailors boarding their vessels as each came to the top of the hill, then as they rolled down, unfurling the sails and trimming them as if they were on the high seas! Others, sitting on the rowing benches, held their oars in their hands and pretended to row, while the overseers ran up and down the track spurring their men on with whistles and shouts and whip-cracking. And so the Turkish vessels slid across the country just as if it were the sea—and when the Christian sentries looked out next morning there were seventy-two Turkish ships riding at anchor in the channel of the Golden Horn!"

There was the tribute of silence for a moment, then Tonio asked with assumed carelessness—

"What happened then?"

"It was the end for the Christians. The Infidel fell on them, killing, destroying—and indeed when Mohammed himself saw all the ravage and destruction, a great sadness came over him and he repented the pillage. 'What a town this was,' he said, with tears in his eyes, 'and we have destroyed it!'"

"Damn Turks!" said Piccolo cheerfully.

"Later the Sultan gave himself to the study of philosophy and that's how so much of the old Greek science was saved. The works of Ptolemy, for example—"

But Tonio and his group had no interest in the works of Ptolemy. Anyway it was time to put this cocky interloper in his place.

"Where's the dice, Piccolo? Come on—let's play!" And they formed their circle so close he was left outside.

Accustomed to being liked and accepted by most people, Vanni was surprised and hurt, but at once determined not to show it. He wandered off alone, whistling, to look over the ship.

For a while he watched the *galeotti*. Most of them, he guessed from their looks, were Slavs and none too clean in their habits. He went on to look at the pattern of sails and running gear, trying to understand how it all worked, but stumbling over a sleeping sailor on deck he was driven with curses back to the *corsia*.

"Ah there you are, Zuan!" The plummy voice of the Steward came out of the darkness and Vanni thought he was to be reprimanded, but the Steward's smile was apparent in his voice. "You wish to learn about the ship, is that it?" The bulky shape came closer. Why couldn't Uncle Luigi have minded his own business! This sort of special treatment would do Vanni no good with the other grommets. He could hardly turn, however, and walk away from a superior officer.

"I was only wondering, sir, about the crew—how many there are and where they sleep and so on."

"Let me make it all clear to you," said the Steward agreeably. "First, there is the *patrone*, our military leader, who is in charge of the soldiers—" But Vanni already knew that.

"Surely Venetian ships, sir, are safe from attack?" He was really shocked at the idea of anyone challenging Venetian naval power.

"Not entirely, dear child. We pay heavy bribes to the Turks to be left alone, naturally, but there is always the odd renegade, and our cargo is a valuable one." Scalzi came closer. "Then there is the sailing master, Stegano, a mariner of great experience who is in charge of our pilotage and navigation. The mate, who is also the pilot, relieves the master on alternate watches, and he has several officers under him. Besides forty petty officers and seamen, we carry 114 oarsmen, all free paid men who can be depended on in an emergency to drop oars and take up weapons. Six apprentices complete our crew."

"Thank you very much, sir." Vanni made a move to retire, but somehow Scalzi was between him and the *corsia* entrance.

"You ask where they sleep," went on Scalzi. "The officers live splendidly in the sterncastle and the soldiers sleep anywhere, on deck in fine weather, in any sheltered spot below when the weather is foul. The *galeotti*, of course, sleep at their rowing benches. Seamen and apprentices, who are on duty in two watches of four hours each, also sleep on deck in fine weather, but when there is a storm they do not sleep at all."

Vanni saw his chance and dived into the *corsia*, but Scalzi was right behind him and, walking down the passage,

he pressed so close his sleeve brushed Vanni's hand. Why
did it give him such a feeling of uneasiness? The man meant
well, obviously—

"These galleys, you know, are fair-weather craft, and reducing sail in a storm is a great labor, needing all hands."
Scalzi talked faster as the boy walked more quickly. "The
yards themselves must be lowered and hoisted, and the spars
are as heavy as the canvas."

Vanni was conscious of an odd fear of physical attack.
Vague thoughts of the Pestrelli brothers sending an agent on
the ship to put him out of the way were dismissed as nonsense. Anyway there was nothing to be afraid of. He could
handle Scalzi if he had to—the man was nothing but a blob
of flesh!

"But perhaps you are not interested in all this? Perhaps,
like me, you enjoy books and appreciate art—" Now the man
had his hand on Vanni's arm and the boy was having all he
could do to keep from brushing it off. "It's a lonely life at
sea, for a man of my sort," went on Scalzi eagerly. "If you
like, when we get to Constantinople, I'll show you around
the city, introduce you to people like ourselves—"

Vanni broke away and made for the sanctuary of the galley where he could see the boys still at their game, and all
the time he found he was trying to shut out the sound of the
Steward's voice.

"I have friends among the Turks. With me to speak for
you—" Scalzi said rapidly in his ear. "After all, it is your first
visit—"

"No thank you!" Vanni said with flat emphasis, and at that
moment caught a look from Tonio, so knowing, so derisive,
his heart caught. "I have friends in Constantinople." And
he sat down abruptly beside the grommets.

The snub was too direct, too obvious to be overlooked,
and made in front of the other boys. Scalzi stood very still

for a moment, then his lips drew down in a grimace of mock scorn. His color, however, was high as he strode away. Piccolo jumped up and ran after the Steward, calling affectionately—

"Scalzi, wait! I'll come with you, Scalzi!"

"Come back, little fool!" cried Tonio, but it was no use. Tonio glared at Vanni as if he were to blame. "Now see what you've done."

"I?" A wave of heat passed over Vanni, a kind of shame. Why should he feel so excited? Unpleasantly so!

"Never mind." Tonio turned his shoulder, and they all went back to their game, shutting him out.

Vanni sat there, still a little shaken, knowing only under the surface of his mind why Scalzi's friendliness had repelled him. But he knew now that Uncle Luigi was not behind it. Signore Romano was far too fastidious to have dealings with a man like the Steward.

Vanni had made an enemy, but it couldn't be helped. He would obey Scalzi's orders, of course, but hold himself free to choose his friends. Vanni looked at the circle of grommets disconsolately. It seemed the friends he would have chosen would have nothing to do with him. Never mind, he would make them accept him! He had simply to show he was as good a seaman as any of them—or better!

IX

Constantinople

A fair wind that night helped carry the *Santa Lucia* down the Istrian coast. Next morning they put into the port of Parenzo to augment their stores with salt, local mutton, and salad herbs, then sailed for the isles of Lesina. Ship life settled down to a routine.

In this routine, Giovanni Caboto found himself the busiest person on board. Everyone ranked higher than himself and so everyone down to Tonio gave him orders. From dawn to dark, and sometimes later, he scrubbed decks, cleaned pots and pans, carried wine and water, cooked for the seamen and was running continually to the call of master and officers, as well as the Steward. Scalzi seemed deliberately to save all the hardest and dirtiest jobs for him, and the finished work was never satisfactory to that vengeful man. Other members of the crew, discovering the new boy to be a willing donkey, foisted extra chores on him too when they could. He had, moreover, to take his regular turn each third watch at the sandglasses. Though it was a welcome period of rest for his body, he was always in dread of falling asleep, and

Heaven help the grommet who failed to turn the sandglass sharp on the hour and sing out the time!

Somehow, perhaps because he was so utterly determined to show his quality, Vanni managed to ignore his continual fatigue. Dirt and foul conduct, he found, bothered him most, for in living with Uncle Luigi he had become somewhat over-nice in his habits for shipboard life. He was careful not to show his feelings, however, knowing the others would laugh at his squeamishness. More than once he was obliged in the middle of a meal to make for the rail. Luckily it passed for natural seasickness.

In the eyes of the other grommets, Vanni's willingness to tackle any job that offered was considered a scandal. Such thoroughness showed up their own slackness and, instead of winning their respect as he had hoped, he was now definitely in their black books. There might have been open quarrels and fighting, but young Caboto was a head taller than any of them, and quicker and stronger to boot. They had seen him at Parenzo wrestle a quarrelsome adult beggar off the ship and dared not tackle him even in a group. He was, too, a relative of one of the owners. So they ignored him, which hurt Vanni more than any physical blow.

Still, he survived the first leg of the voyage with his courage intact and without shaming himself. His tiredness vanished like magic on arrival in the Golden Horn. Constantinople at last! The ancient city of Byzantium! Determined to dodge his Uncle's agent, Messer Fragini, who would doubtless meet the ship, Vanni slipped ashore early to have a look at the city.

He discovered that Constantinople, like Genoa, was walled, but these walls (where they were not broken down or heavily damaged with artillery fire) were much larger and higher than those of his home city. Inside the walls were buildings, some collapsed to rubble, spires cropped of their ornamental tops, broken stairways and crumbling roofs, looking all the more dismal in contrast to the shining new Moslem mosques. The Turks had not, apart from erecting religious buildings of their own, done anything to repair the city in twelve years, apparently. Vanni found it lonely walking by himself and in the end went back to the ship, meaning to snatch a sleep while the chance offered, but he ran into Fragini waiting for him on deck. Naturally, the agent had been told by the captain that a nephew of Signore Romano was on board. There was nothing to do but hand over his Uncle's letter.

"Welcome to Constantinople!" cried Fragini, a brisk smiling man in his early thirties. "You must come ashore, Messer Caboto, and live in the Venetian colony while the ship is in port." He smoothed down his black velvet doublet and looked around the ship with polite distaste.

Vanni did not argue, deciding it would be a change at least, and he would be leaving no friends behind to miss him. The Steward gave permission for his departure with indifference and Vanni slept that night in a proper bed again.

The house seemed a *palazzo* after the ship. The stairs were somewhat broken, true, and the roof let daylight through in places, but with rich tapestries and silken hangings the Venetian had contrived to cover the worst of the damages.

"It's a hovel," apologized Fragini cheerfully, "but we have fixed things up as well as we could. Perhaps now you would like to take a tour of the city?"

Apart from the ravages of war, Constantinople was as Sir John Mandeville had described it in his *History*—"a full, fair city." It must have been astonishingly beautiful in the days of the Greeks, with the golden arm of the Hellespont encircling two parts of the town in a splendid panorama of land and water. That "most fair church, most noble in all the world," Santa Sophia, stood intact, reminding Vanni of the

Cathedral in Venice. Santa Sophia was now, of course, a Moslem shrine and in front of it lay the heap of stones where once had stood a statue of the Emperor Justinian on horseback. Once too there had been an apple of gold in Justinian's hand, said Fragini, but in the course of time the apple had fallen out and disappeared and legend said that it represented the lands lost in the time of the Fourth Crusade, chiefly through the treachery (alas!) of her sister republic, Venice. Now—Fragini shrugged—not only the apple, but the hand, the whole man, was gone.

The agent pointed out to Vanni the ruined stables of the brave Constantine and the gymnasium where the Greeks had once wrestled and jousted, and the youth felt resentment rise strong in him against Islam. This had been a Christian city, disobedient, true, to the Church of Rome, but the lone bastion of the Faith when Rome was a city in ruins.

"The old Greek palaces are now inhabited by Turkish soldiers," said Fragini sadly, "who care little if the rain comes through or the walls are cracked, so long as they can find a dry place to stable their horses and make their own beds. The upper storeys they leave to be overrun by rats and mice. The Turks cannot understand why we bother to fix things up. They themselves avoid magnificence except in their public buildings, for they feel that to go to such expense in furnishing one's home is a sign of pride and vanity. They regard their homes as a traveler regards an Inn. If one is safe from thieves and protected from heat and cold and rain, one requires no further luxuries."

Turkish soldiers, Vanni noticed, were much in evidence everywhere, and not only in the city. Fragini took him briefly outside the gates and showed him camps lying thickly across the plain. The boy was amazed at their extent.

"It is Turkish policy to have armies twice as large as ours," said Fragini with a twist of the lip. "This superiority in

numbers gives them additional courage. Also, it allows them
to attack from more than one direction at once."

"What is the matter with them?" Vanni stared curiously
at a group of Saracen soldiers sitting quietly on the ground
in front of their quarters. "Are they ill?"

"Ill? Oh! You mean the silence and tranquillity." The
agent laughed. "Yes—no shouting, no quarreling, no violent
merrymaking as in our own camps. Well, it is the way of the
Turks—of all Mohammedans for that matter—to be quiet and
well-disciplined. Their religion forbids them to drink strong
liquors, which we must admit too often leads to violence
among our mercenaries."

"How clean everything is! No dung-heaps, no rubbish lying about."

"Cleanliness is another of the Mohammedan rules. It is
set down in the Koran, in fact, that they must bathe regularly and extensively. They are a strange people," said Fragini, thoughtfully, "loyal, brave, clean, able to stand hard-
ship without complaint, asking little in return for their
services. They make excellent soldiers."

Vanni marveled at how different things could be from
what one had heard and imagined. It was true what Fra
Andrea had told him, one should always wait for a second
opinion, should always question generalities, should if possible go and see for oneself. Loyal, brave, clean, uncomplaining—all admirable qualities which he would not have thought
to apply to the Turks. He had pictured them as savages, still
looting and oppressing the surviving Christians. Yet here in
actual fact was a city quieter and more orderly than Venice.

He watched as Fragini exchanged polite gestures with a
Turk, dignified and handsome in a green turban and military tunic, standing near a camp gate. A horseman came
clattering up the road. He wore a white turban and yellow

shoes, and was elegantly mounted on a saddle with fine silver trappings.

"A Janissary officer," whispered Fragini. Vanni had heard of them—Christian youths brought up in the faith of Islam to form an elite corps of Saracen troops.

This one looked neither to right nor left, but courteously drew up to let a group of citizens cross the road in front of him. Not the rude tyrant Vanni had been led to expect. Then he saw the spear in the horseman's hand, the scimitar and steel club hanging from the saddle horn, the sword at his hip—and a chill passed over the Venetian youth. The Turk might seem outwardly civilized and peaceful, but the power and the savagery were there, waiting. The scimitar, the club, the camps, the feeling of silent readiness. Yes, the Turk was a sword hanging over the head of Christendom, and no one in Europe had better forget it!

"Well, where do you want to go now?"

"To the bazaar!"

Fragini chuckled.

"Every Venetian ends up there."

"There is something I want to buy," explained Vanni, "a gift for my Mother. I have been told that the silk of Constantinople is much finer than the stuff they manufacture in Genoa."

"Naturally, since it comes from Cathay, the home of silk. Come this way for silk—provided there is any here to buy."

They picked a torturous path through side streets while the agent expanded on his subject.

"In Christian times there was no lack of good silk to be found in Constantinople. It came in from Cathay and Persia by way of Trebizond mostly—at a price, of course. Even then we had to pay outrageous bribes to the Assyrians to get it through. Of course we simply passed the added expense on to our customers. They had to pay. Where else could they buy? It was possible, you know, in those days," he added wistfully, "to ship six cargoes of spices and silks to Venice, lose five on the way by shipwreck and piracy, and still make a good profit when the sixth was sold."

"And now?" Vanni was interested in spite of himself.

"And now," sighed Fragini, "we Venetians are no longer the lords of creation. We no longer have our special privileges but must pay heavy taxes to the Turk as well as the usual extortions. There is a limit to what people will pay, even for spices—so our profits are lean. Also, war between the Turks and Persians has of late interrupted deliveries— so that is why I said 'provided there is any silk to be found in Constantinople.' "

"Is it as bad in Alexandria?"

"In most respects it is worse, I think. The Mameluke rulers, though Moslem themselves, go in deadly fear of the Turks, just as we do. They keep raising their exactions while they can, determined to bake bread while the oven's hot! Ah well, we all get our profit in the end—a little anyway. Trust a Venetian for that, eh?"

The Constantinople *souk* was a busy and colorful market place with a straw roof for shelter against the burning Eastern sun. A large part of it was occupied by farmers selling the produce of the countryside, but at the far end there was a section for the use of foreign traders. Vanni made at once for this section.

"Not too much enthusiasm, my young friend," warned Fragini, "or they'll put the price to the skies. If you like, I'll handle it for you."

"Oh, no thanks, I can manage," Vanni said confidently. This was something he wanted to do all on his own. It was a project he had had in mind ever since leaving Venice, for he knew the ship would stop at Genoa on the next or some future voyage, where he would see Emilio and his family again for the first time in seven years. This might be his one chance to get a nice piece of Eastern silk at a good price. He was well supplied with money, having with him his ill-gotten gains from smuggling. What better way to spend it than on gifts for his loved ones! "I'll pay what I must, even if I have to use all the money I have with me."

Fragini shook his head dismally.

"And you a Venetian!"

"I was born in Genoa."

"A distinction without a difference! However, as you will. If you will excuse me then, I see a young friend over there. I'll bring him along to meet you when you're finished."

Vanni turned to the booths. He did not need Fragini. One did not need language to bargain. That was a language all men knew. He had a little Latin and Greek, as well as two Italian dialects, for any emergency. He could certainly manage a simple purchase among this crowd of Turks, Syrians, and Persians.

He picked up a dress-length of heavy blue silk which caught his fancy. It was the color of Mamma's eyes. He looked questioningly at the vendor, who shrugged, waiting for him to make an offer. Belatedly cautious, Vanni mentioned an insignificant sum which caused the man to throw up his hands in horror. Vanni shrugged, dropped the silk, and turned away with assumed indifference. He then devoted himself to examining silver filagree work at the next booth.

At that moment he was nearly knocked off his feet. A man in Eastern dress thrust past him roughly. Vanni caught a glimpse of a yellow burnoose as the man hurried on without apology, paying no attention to Vanni's indignant cry—

"Look out! Mind where you're going!" But by then the man had disappeared in the crowd.

Vanni shrugged, turned back to the stall, his hand reaching again, in spite of himself, for the enticing blue silk. He couldn't bear it if someone else bought it when his back was turned. He haggled with the man for a bit, but then impatience got the better of him and he paid what the man asked. The silk was his. It had taken all his money, but he didn't care. The other gifts could wait.

As the merchant handed him the rolled-up silk, Vanni felt a commotion near him and turned to see a foreign merchant pointing an accusing arm in his direction, jabbering excitedly. Several people in the milling crowd turned to stare, then to watch and see what happened. It didn't seem serious to Vanni at first. The merchant, who looked Syrian or possibly Lebanese, planted himself in front of the Venetian youth and began to harangue him angrily. Vanni shrugged and smiled at the people watching, drawing them into the joke.

"*No comprendo!* I don't understand. I am a Venetian."

The man's voice rose, shrill and meaningless, and the crowd—mostly Turks—pressed closer, completely surrounding boy and merchant. Vanni began to feel uneasy. If only he could talk to them, answer their questions, find out what the trouble was. He knew he must not on any account show fear, so he drew himself up to his full height, staring around arrogantly, at the same time siezing his chance to spot Fragini and draw his attention—but he saw only a sea of foreign faces. From among them, he picked out the man in the yellow burnoose, who had reappeared on the edge of the crowd and was watching closely. The eyes, half-shadowed by the yellow hood, peered out like shiny raisins. Scalzi!

The moment Vanni's eyes fastened on him, Scalzi—if it were he—turned and hurried away. It was Scalzi, Vanni was sure of it! The bulk of him. The eyes. And the Steward had said he had friends among the Infidel. They would let him borrow their clothes. But what mischief was Scalzi up to?

Something malicious, something harmful to him, Vanni. Had Scalzi made the crowd believe, somehow, that he had broken one of their laws? How he wished now for Fragini beside him.

Vanni spread his hands in a gesture of bewilderment, which only resulted in the Turk, or Assyrian, holding out a demanding hand. For what? Money? He had none left. He showed the man, held out his empty purse. This made the man angrier than ever. San Giorgio! What was keeping Fragini?

Someone pushed him from behind, deliberately he thought, and he reacted instinctively, flinging angrily around on his heel to see who had done it. As he turned, something shot out of his sleeve and fell in front of the angry merchant. There was a short breathless pause and Vanni felt every eye fastened first on the article on the ground, then on himself. He saw the thing too, a chain of gold hung with a red jewel, a valuable and distinctive-looking gem, and knew the people imagined he had stolen it and hidden it in his sleeve!

The merchant snatched it up and showed it around triumphantly. There was a low murmur from the crowd, a threatening sound, and Vanni's heart began to pound. There was nothing he could do, no way to prove he hadn't stolen the jewel. What would happen now? Would they call the police or deal with him themselves? The former, he hoped. Waiting for the police would take time. That was his only hope, to play for time until Fragini returned. He played for it now by acting out puzzled bewilderment and horror, pointing to the jewel and shaking his head. They stared back at him with hating eyes.

He thought of offering them the ring he wore, but guessed it was not half the value of the ruby that had fallen from his sleeve. Besides, to offer it in payment would be admission of guilt, and he was innocent.

A queer ring of silence shut them off from the general hubbub of the *souk* which passed by, unheeding, uncaring, and now they crowded in on Vanni, pressing against him. His hand reached futilely for his blunt, boy's dagger—

"Don't move!" The voice rang out warningly. Thank God! Fragini!

The agent, talking rapidly and persuasively in Turkish, was forcing his way through to Vanni. As he reached the boy he asked quickly, "*Che é successo?*"

"That pendant fell out of my sleeve. I never saw it before in my life!"

Fragini did not even turn his head, but went on talking to the Turks, spreading his hands eloquently, smiling, shrugging, even laughing. Tension relaxed a trifle. Then Fragini took out his purse and the Assyrian's eyes narrowed. The crowd began to melt away, shrugging cynically, and the bargaining began. Vanni's knees felt weak. During the quarter-hour of bargaining that went on beside him—animated, impersonal, until at last the jewel and the money changed hands—he managed to regain his composure.

"I thought I was in real trouble," he confessed to Fragini.

"*Calma, calma!* One soon learns to manage these people. They'll stop anything to bargain," said Fragini, but the sweat stood out on his upper lip. It would have been serious for him if Signore Romano's nephew had been killed or even carried off to a Turkish jail. "I explained that you were a stranger and that the jewel must have caught in your clothing as you passed the stall, by accident."

"It was no accident!" Vanni looked around for the yellow burnoose, in vain. "It was planted on me deliberately, but since I cannot prove it I had better mention no names." The agent nodded swift agreement. He had no desire to be dragged into fresh trouble on Vanni's behalf.

"Come now, I must introduce you to my young friend."

Fragini beckoned and a youth who had been standing on the edge of the crowd during the commotion now came toward them. He was an elegant young gentleman with a pale face and tight lips. He wore the new and fashionable slashed doublet and a special kind of cloak worn by Florentines.

"Amerigo," said the agent, "this is Master Caboto of Venice. Messer Caboto, Messer Vespucci. Since you are both visiting Italians and both learning to be merchants, you should have much in common."

Vanni thought the fellow looked a fop and, conscious of his own crumpled doublet—it had suffered sorely from confinement in a seabag—thought he saw a sneer on Messer Vespucci's face.

"We had better return now to the *fondaco*," said Fragini. "I must see if I can find a purchaser for this pendant."

"If you will wait for your money," Vanni told him, "I shall be glad to pay any price you ask for it."

"No need, my boy, I think I've got a bargain. Depend on it, I shall have my profit. I've earned it, I think."

"You have, indeed! I thought for a moment that crowd would turn and tear me to pieces."

"So did I," said Vespucci casually. Vanni looked at him, incredulous. So the Florentine had seen, and just stood by— not even called for help for his compatriot.

"He's a clever boy," Fragini told Vanni later, "from an excellent family. He is certain to make a name for himself!"

Most probably. All the same, Vanni could not warm to the Florentine. He and Vespucci were never more than polite to each other during the *Santa Lucia*'s stay in Constantinople. Vanni was glad, in fact, when the ship was ready to leave—this time for Alexandria.

X

The Storm

Two days out of Constantinople the wind failed and the *galeotti* were obliged to row all night and most of the next morning, toiling down the island-spotted coast with infinite labor, while still the air remained lifeless. The heavy sails hung without movement and the heat became a torment. The insistent drum could no longer speed the stroke of the weary oarsmen.

"There will be a storm," prophesied Tonio with gloomy relish and a side glance at the new apprentice. "Now we will see how marvelous life is at sea."

Vanni too sensed the storm in the offing. It would come suddenly when it came. These summer gales seldom lasted long, but could do tremendous damage. He had experienced one on the Gulf with Emilio, a mild one, and had gloried in it. He waited with impatience to see what the great galley could do in heavy weather. He had stripped down to loin-cloth, yet sweat ran freely from every pore of his body. A breath of air, a cloudburst would be a relief.

It was the mate's watch and he was obviously uneasy. They were off a lee shore and far from any safe harbor. Or-

dering the main and mizzen struck, the mate left the foresail
in position, hoping that if the wind came from the right direction he could take brief advantage of it to beat up to
windward of that dangerous shore. If it came from the opposite direction—well, it was a gamble either way.

Black clouds crept overhead and now what blue was left
in the sky was of a hard metallic color. All waited, excited,
uncomfortable, frightened, each according to his nature, for
the storm to come. Vanni thought he would feel happier with
that huge fold of canvas buttoned tight to the yard, but pre-
sumably the mate knew his job. Not all on the ship were
ready to leave their safety entirely to the officers. Some of
the timider spirits were already muttering the names of their
favorite saints.

With no wind to steady her, the Santa Lucia heaved and
side-slipped in a greasy swell. The overseer was getting some
response now from his rowers, yet it seemed as if in spite of
their efforts a strong and secretive hand was dragging the
ship toward land. A breeze must come soon!

It came, but from the wrong direction, wafting in from
the south as hot as air from a kiln. Then the squall raced
down to them over the water, striking the ship a hammer
blow, setting the oars to clashing wildly. At once the vessel,
with the wind full behind her, drove toward shore. There
was no time to reef. The ship needed power, the power of
the wind, to pull away. She must be brought around.

Holding tight to a brace, Vanni watched with interest.
The master was on deck now, taking command. A lateen-
rigged ship, good in so many ways, was difficult to put about.
Smaller vessels could tack to windward and for short tacks
keep the yards on the weather side of the mast—Emilio's
boat could do this easily—but a large vessel like the Santa
Lucia could not. Her masts not being stayed forward, the

strain caused by setting the great sails aback could tear them out. She would have to wear 'round.

In the ensuing struggle, the ship lurched into the trough of a huge wave and the crew lost hold of the tack-tackle. In a flash they were strewn about on deck, some knocked out by the fall. The mate shouted for extra hands. Little Piccolo, willing enough but hopeless on account of his size, was one of those who answered the call. He was simply shoved aside by the men in their headlong rush. The ship heeled, the boy lost his balance and staggered backwards, ending up in the scuppers. His senseless body was washed back and forth in the receding wave, in company with an equally senseless mariner. Vanni saw them both. Letting go his hold on the brace, he plunged across the deck, hoping to grab the boy before the next wave came. He was too late! A second wave, larger than the first, came tumbling down on the three of them, sweeping Piccolo out of his reach. A ton of water seemed to strike Vanni in the small of the back and he was slapped to the deck. When, half-stunned, he got to his knees and looked around, the boy Piccolo was gone. The sailor too. Shaken, clinging to a rope, Vanni crept back to the shelter of the *corsia*.

The crew by this time had got the yard hauled over and now with great straining were setting up shrouds and tack-tackle on the new weather side. The sail was sheeted home on the new tack, the men leaned en masse on the tiller, and the ship slowly turned her stern to the land, safe for the moment.

It still needed a dozen men to hold the tiller with the ship plunging and shuddering from end to end. The rain came, sideways in torrents, and they had to shield their eyes to see. Dazed by the continual motion, sickened by the memory of the drowned men, Vanni clung to his hold, no longer welcoming the storm. Never had he even imagined the implacable hardness of a mass of water striking against a ship's side. The sound was not fluid but solid. How long could a vessel withstand such blows, especially one like the *Santa Lucia*, built for speed, not weather. What a fool he had been to imagine a seaman's life romantic? Here was no romance—only cold and sweat, fear, desperate danger and quick death! Once the ship rolled over so far and stayed so long he thought it was the end. Was this then to be his first and last voyage? Was it God's will that he should die without having lived to make his name known in the world? Slowly the *Santa Lucia* righted herself.

Above the noise he could hear the groans and cries of men vowing to have masses said to the saints if by any chance they reached shore alive. Some were singing hymns, others praying.

The wind whipped around again with frightening speed and, in the steerage, men scattered like leaves. Released from the rudder's constraint, the vessel swung broadside and the great sail went wildly free. The yard splintered.

Then, with the suddenness of the storm's arrival, a lull came. The wind fell away and everything, by contrast, seemed peaceful, with only the torrential rain playing its tune against the ship's gear. Men could move without exerting all their strength against the wind. It was the miracle they had prayed for, the time the crew needed to get the rudder under control. The oarsmen did not need to be urged to put forth their full strength now. They knew their own lives depended on it.

The lull was over all too soon, but when the wind came again, it was not so strong and it blew from a favorable direction. Numbed and battered, Vanni felt the change with the rest and sobbed with relief.

Gradually the waves smoothed and the oars bit the water two times out of three. The thunder still rolled unceasingly and the rain still fell, but a thin light showed in the eastern sky and it was slowly spreading. A hoarse cheer came from somewhere aft. They were to live, it seemed, after all! Now there were actually patches of blue sky showing, and men fell on their knees, if they were not there already, to thank Heaven for their deliverance—

"Grazie, San Paolo e San Pietro! Grazie a Dio!"

The rain ceased, pattering away to nothing, and the sun shone. Sky and sea looked suddenly as fresh and radiant as a new-minted coin, and the mate ordered the crew to work clearing the wreckage. Vanni, aware of someone coming to stand beside him, turned and looked into the gray face of Tonio.

"So now you know," said Tonio.

"Yes." Vanni wondered if his own face was as pale as the senior boy's. He knew he had been more frightened in this last half-hour than he would ever admit, but it was over now, already receding into the distance. "It was wild, wasn't it?"

Tonio's face wore an odd look of mixed grief and embarrassment.

"That was a good thing you did," he muttered.

What good thing? Vanni had only held on and prayed, like the rest. He said so.

"Piccolo, I mean. I saw it all."

Ah, poor Piccolo. Vanni had forgotten him already!

"But I couldn't help him. I didn't reach him in time." Again the failure smote him.

"You tried anyway. You're all right, Zuan," Tonio said with a solemn air, and Vanni stared at him, understanding. This was the senior boy's acknowledgment that things had changed. Vanni would now be accepted. How peculiar life was! He had struggled to earn his companions' regard by efficiency and hard work and they had called him a fool. Now in one unthinking moment of natural action—an action which had failed of its purpose too—he was a hero to them. It was all a little disappointing—and sad. Poor Piccolo.

The *Santa Lucia* put into the nearest port to make repairs and those of the crew not needed for the work were sent ashore to get them out of the way. To Vanni, the little town offered few attractions and he had seen all he wanted to see in half a day, so he found a quiet place on the beach and stretched out with Fra Andrea's commentary on Marco Polo —an inquiry into the truth of that traveler's account of Cathay, in which it was pointed out that some of the Venetian's seemingly wild statements had been corroborated by Christian missionaries visiting the East around the same period—

"What's that you're reading?"

Vanni glanced up, startled to see Messer Gabriel Duchesne, one of the ship's officers, a serious, rather sarcastic young man who kept his mind on his job. Vanni jumped to his feet.

"You want something, sir?"

"No, no! Go on—read. I didn't mean to interrupt."

"That's all right," said Vanni hastily. "It's just to pass the time. It's a commentary on Marco Polo."

Messer Duchesne looked blank.

"Marco Polo?"

"A Venetian merchant who wrote a book about his travels in the land of the Great Khan."

The other looked at Vanni with something like respect. He had early in the voyage picked young Caboto as the most useful and willing of the grommets. Later he had noticed the boy's interest in the running of the ship and had occasionally condescended to explain an order from the officer of the deck or to point out a landmark on shore.

"That's in the East."

Vanni nodded.

"You haven't read the book yourself, sir?"

For a moment the Burgundian hesitated, then he shrugged and admitted in a dry voice that he was unable to read.

"I ran away from home when I was eight." He smiled sardonically. "What folly, eh? I speak French, Italian, and the *lingua franca* of the ports, but can read only a little French and Latin not at all."

"That's a pity." Vanni avoided Gabriel's eye, a little embarrassed.

"Yes," said the officer soberly, "it is a pity, since I wish very much to become a qualified shipmaster some day."

"But you can be that without reading!"

The young man's lip curled.

"Ah yes! I can learn with compass, lead line, and a good memory to blunder my way about the Mediterranean and the Black Sea, but I wish to do more than that. I wish to be able to read the sailing directions on *portolani* and understand the pilot books of all the oceans. I sailed once on a Portuguese ship from Lisbon to Morocco." Gabriel hesitated again, then added lightly, "I do not intend to spend my whole life on inland seas."

"But there's nothing much outside the Mediterranean, is there?"

Momentarily the Burgundian surveyed Vanni with speculation, then his eyes grew veiled. "Perhaps not, Caboto. Yet I have an ambition some day to sail my own ship down the coast of Africa."

Vanni felt no particular interest in Africa, knowing little about it, but he thought again how peculiar life was. Here was a man, with the practical knowledge Vanni yearned to have, while he himself had the learning the officer lacked. An idea struck him and he rushed into speech without reflecting that he spoke to one of the ship's officers.

"Why don't we make an exchange?" he cried. "You teach

me to recognize the capes, the river mouths, the bays, as we come to them, tell me about tides and phases of the moon, about using the stars to find position and how to find the depth and nature of the sea bottom—and I shall teach you to read the pilot's books. We could take the *Compasso da Navigare* for a start—" Here he stopped short, appalled at his own daring, expecting a blast from Duchesne. But the Burgundian's face was alight with interest.

"*Mon Dieu!* Why not? It is a bargain!" He thought rapidly. "I believe I can borrow the ship's *Compasso* while we're in port—" And so the two, as opportunity offered, shared their knowledge.

Meanwhile the *Santa Lucia*, repairs completed, moved briskly on her way to Egypt as though no storm had ever touched her.

XI

Alexandria

Alexandria! Ancient center of Hellenic culture, once proud rival of Athens, Alexandria was now a Moslem city ruled by Mamelukes, the slave dynasty of Egypt.

Here still, as in the days of the Ptolemies, libraries flourished and the old Greek knowledge mingled with the intellectual genius of the Jew. Conquest sat easily on non-Moslems. There was no effort, as with the Christians, to persecute or convert. Jews especially were granted basic protection as "readers of the Book," though obliged to pay special taxes and to suffer other penalties. In most respects, however, they were better off than under Christian rule.

It was perhaps the Christian traders who suffered the severest humiliation. Venetians and Genoese had to swallow their pride to live in Alexandria. Obliged to stay in factory compounds called *fondaci*, they were even at times locked in after curfew! The Venetians had two such compounds in Alexandria and Vanni moved into one while his ship was in port. Once again a letter from Uncle Luigi to his agent assured the new grommet's release and his acceptance at the *fondaco*. Since the *Santa Lucia* was anchored in mid-harbor, living ashore made it easier for him to explore the city. Also, he wanted plenty of time for a visit to Fra Andrea's friend Ibn Haud.

On the first morning, Vanni fared forth to see the town, warned when he left the compound to be sure to return before sunset. His first stop was the bazaar. It was an exciting place, the *souk* of Alexandria, full of strolling, examining, bargaining shoppers. Vanni mingled with them, giving himself up to the sights and sounds and smells. Wherever he looked, he saw exotic Turkish carpets. There were brocades from Persia, leathers from Cairo, sword blades and lamps from Damascus, and sad groups of slaves from the Caucasian Mountains. There was the smell of incense mixed with that of spice and camel and dust. There were the gutteral cries of Arabs exhorting their customers to buy, the peeping of caged birds, and in the background a snatch of music, music full of wild repetitious rhythms, the music of the desert.

In the spice stalls, strident voices were raised from time to time in futile anger at high prices. Pepper aroused the greatest contention, for pepper was the monopoly of the Sultan and the price went up with monotonous regularity. Yet the buyers paid in the end, for pepper was the most precious spice of all, and in short supply.

Around noon, Vanni left the *souk* and inquired the way to the Library, feeling a stir of interest at the thought of making his first personal contact with the horrid Infidel. He found Ibn Haud in the geographic room, and the reality was disappointing. It was like being back in the Franciscans' library in Venice—the same familiar smell of wax and mold and leather and papyrus, the same dust motes dancing in the sunny air over sheaves of manuscript. In some ways Ibn Haud even resembled Fra Andrea, with his dark skin and eyes, his mild scholarly demeanor. His costume was different, of course—a white *djellabas* instead of a brown robe—

and his Latin was heavily accented. Still, from his abstracted gaze to his ink-stained fingers, scholar was written all over him.

"Yes, yes," he murmured, skimming rapidly through Fra Andrea's letter of introduction. "So you are the young man interested in cosmology. There is nothing new since my last letter, I'm afraid. You wished to study the science of earth measurement, eh?"

"Not exactly. I—"

"And how is my old friend? In good health, I trust?"

Vanni began to assure Ibn Haud that Fra Andrea was fine, but again was interrupted.

"Excellent. Now what else can I do for you, young sir?"

"I wondered if you could tell me about any Arabs, sir, who traveled—" Ibn Haud had his hand cupped about his ear, head straining towards Vanni, and the boy saw that the man was deaf. He raised his voice accordingly—"Arab travelers who explored your country?"

"Travelers?" Ibn Haud frowned.

"I have heard," Vanni shouted, "that your people were great voyagers in olden times. Fra Andrea thinks he heard somewhere that one of your people sailed completely around Africa."

"Indeed? There was Ibn Battuta, a great theologian who traveled widely a century ago. I believe there is an account somewhere of his travels, though I cannot at the moment think where to put my hands on it. I shall look it up, if you like."

"If you would, please—"

"I beg your pardon?"

"I said yes, please!"

"Then there was a man named Masudi, and another Ibn Haukal, but I fear I know nothing of them besides their names. If any of my people found their way around Libya, I have not heard of it. Are you sure it wasn't a Phoenician? My interests, I must tell you, are purely academic. In fact, I have no time to read travel tales. If you wish to know what the world is really like, *effendi*, you should read Ptolemy, but perhaps you have already—"

Vanni shook his head, mumbling that he had heard of Ptolemy of course. Actually, Fra Andrea had offered him the *Almagest* to read one day, and Vanni had found it excessively dull. It was all about astrology and concentric circles and transparent spheres, not at all the sort of thing he cared about. It seemed, however, that the scholars had no more patience with the study of practical seamanship than he himself had with scientific treatises. The gap between scholarship and firsthand experience was wider than he had suspected.

"Ptolemy is highly regarded by our scholars," observed Ibn Haud. "Do you intend to become a cosmologist?"

"Oh no!"

"Astronomer?"

"No."

"Geographer? Historian, perhaps?"

"None of those." Vanni cast about in his mind for a word to describe what he intended to be. "Traveler" was hardly the word. "Explorer" sounded pretentious. "Merchant" came nearest the truth, but to mention that word would be to concede a kind of defeat. He shook his head, troubled.

"I don't know yet."

He did not, naturally, mention a desire for fame and fortune, considering that these were the natural aims of all men and therefore obvious.

"I'm interested in maps," he said loudly.

"Maps?" Ibn Haud shook his head regretfully. "I must tell you at once that this is not the place for maps. My people were never very concerned with map making. What you want to see is the *portolan* work of the Jewish cartographers of the last century. You will find the Catalan Atlas in the Palma Maritima in Majorca, you know. Abraham Cresques was a great artist and his work is said to be accurate. If you should find yourself in Palma, go to see the maps for yourself. But I would still advise you to read Ptolemy."

"Perhaps—" Vanni shouted as persuasively as one can, when loudness precludes a note of cajolery, "perhaps, sir, you would give me a letter to the people in Palma."

He left the Library at last, somewhat hoarse, but with the letter in his pocket. Ibn Haud had, moreover, promised to have the account of Ibn Battuta ready to show him the next time he came to Alexandria. Not having eaten since morning —Ibn Haud apparently did not eat at midday or had forgotten about such mundane matters—Vanni found a cafe where he was able to buy bittersweet coffee and small almond-covered cakes, enough to stave off the pangs of hunger until he returned to the *fondaco*.

It was growing late by then, but he thought he would walk the long way back around the western harbor where he would see the Arab fishing boats, called *feluccas*, which he had noticed in the approaches to Alexandria. A boat of any sort still had the power to stir his senses. He wanted to examine the *feluccas* at his leisure and did so. They were beautiful, and looked both fast and efficient. They were small, rigged like Emilio's boat with a large triangular sail, and he yearned to hold the tiller of one of them in his own hand. He knew if he could choose his life merely for pleasure, it would be easy. He would simply acquire a boat of his own and sail it wherever he wished to go!

Strolling and dreaming, he pictured himself in the dim future crossing some wild stretch of ocean, accomplishing some vague feat which would lead to the plaudits of the multitude. Yet for the first time, he was discontented. It was not enough any more to see the thing in general terms. He wanted now to see his plans in the particular—

Vanni woke suddenly to the fact that he was passing a certain mosque for the third time. Vexed, he retraced his steps to the harbor and taking a correct bearing this time, eventually found his way back to the Venetian *fondaco*. It was long past dark by then, and the gates were shut and locked. He rapped tentatively at first, then harder, and finally when there was no response he attacked them in a fury. A figure came hurrying to peer through the gate bars.

"It's no good, you know, you can't get in. We're locked up for the night and there's no key. You're one of the Venetians from the *Santa Lucia*, aren't you?"

"Yes, and I must get inside. All my things are there."

"That is unfortunate, but it makes no difference. You'll just have to go back to your ship." The voice sounded harassed, but firm. "I can't let you in and that's all there is to it." Seeing the youth glance up at the wall, he added quickly, "I wouldn't if I were you! The wall's not only spiked but guarded. Try the monasteries. There's one down the road half a mile or so, run by the Dominicans." And with that, the figure slid away into the gloom. Oh excellent! A fine way for the Mamelukes to treat their best customers! Once again Vanni was observing at firsthand the iron hand of Islam.

He found the monastery easily enough and was admitted. His host, Father Ferenco, treated him coolly at first, and Vanni decided it was because he had announced himself as a Venetian. He was beginning to notice that *La Serenissima* was not popular abroad. However, the atmosphere warmed a trifle over supper.

Vanni asked his host about the Infidel, frankly interested. At first the good Father answered everything in a calm, unbiased way.

"Yes, Moslems believe in one God as we do, and are com-

pletely submissive to His authority. They also put perfect
reliance on the ritual of prayer. They live, however, by the
Koran, which they claim contains the revelations of Mohammed, and turn to Mecca—their principal holy city—to
pray." He said it was true that neither Christians nor Jews
were persecuted, but in this restraint Fra Ferenco saw no
special virtue. "They practice tolerance as a matter of ex-
pediency, be sure of that!" His face darkened. "The Moors
are our rulers, at least for the moment! The sword of the
Crescent hangs over us all, but too few of us see the danger.
If our people were more alert and self-sacrificing, we could
unite against Islam before it is too late." His voice rose in a
wave of emotion. "We must cease fighting among ourselves
and combine against them, or lose all! You look skeptical,
my son. What, tell me, is to prevent Venice going the way
of Constantinople?"

"We would fight."

"Yes," agreed the priest sourly, "you might fight—you with
your great Navy and your hired soldiers—if your commerce
were threatened, not otherwise! And not on your own territory if you could help it. He would be a fool indeed who
expected Venice—or any of the city-states of Italy, for that
matter—to fight for a common ideal. The spirit of the Cru-
saders is dead, alas! There is only one hope left now."

"And what is that, Father?"

"It is for our Christian nations to join forces with the
teeming millions of the East, the subjects of the Great Khan,
the men of Cathay and the Indies!"

"But—" Vanni was bewildered. "There has been no contact between his people and ours for nearly two hundred
years."

"Then it is time," said the priest fiercely, "we made contact
with them again!"

"But *why* do you think those heathen people would help us against the Moslems?"

"Are they heathen?" asked Father Ferenco, fixing Vanni with a tense glare. "*I* do not think so. We have every reason to believe that they are Christian like ourselves. Our missionaries went there, you know, in the years the country was open to visitors—men like Plano Carpini and Brother William of Rubruck, and others. Christian merchants too, like the Polo brothers, were in touch with the Great Khan. He sent messages by them to the Pope, begging him to send Christian missionaries and oil from the Holy Sepulcher."

Vanni was startled to hear the priest quote Marco Polo. Father Ferenco must have some faith in the traveler's veracity! Vanni pulled thoughtfully at his gold earring.

"Didn't the Great Khan die at the time of Marco Polo's departure from China, just before the Ottoman Turks descended on Europe?"

"Yes, but the seed was planted by then!" cried the good man with fanatical certainty. "By now it will have produced a great harvest. Do not forget that Nestorian Christians dwell there, as well as that great Christian King, Prester John, and they would be certain to propagate the Faith in Cathay and the Indies. We need only fight our way past the Turks, regain contact with our Chinese allies, then launch a great attack on Islam from the rear. We will then utterly destroy the whole Islamic empire from Spain to Persia and regain Jerusalem!"

Vanni was impressed by the Dominican's vehemence. His imagination made an effort and he saw himself fighting in some Far Eastern war, striking a blow for the Church and in the process winning fame and fortune. Yet the vision did not stir him as it should. For one thing, it would not be easy to fight past those efficient Turkish troops at Constantinople.

"Do you know, Father, where I can find any stories of men

who explored Africa and Arabia in ancient times, especially
by sea?"

"Well," said Father Ferenco, a little taken aback by the
sudden change of subject, "there was Herodotus who explored the Red Sea and looked for the source of the Nile. If
you are interested in geography, you ought to read Ptolemy
of course."

Ptolemy again. These scholars were all alike. Personally
Giovanni Caboto did not care in the least if the spheres revolved around the earth carrying sun and stars with them, or
if it was the other way about! He had no interest any more,
either, in whether the world was twenty or forty thousand
miles wide, or how much of it was water, how much land.
He wanted only to read of men like Ulysses and Pytheas and
Ibn Battuta, men from whom he could learn, men whom he
could emulate. Instead, he was put off with an ancient Greek
who had done nothing but draw circles. He found there was
nothing in the Dominicans' library describing the actual
journeys of Herodotus. Well, there might be maps.

"Maps?" wondered the priest. "Yes, we have maps."

These were chiefly of the *mappa-mundi* variety, so deplored by Fra Andrea, but one was a copy from the famous
Catalan Atlas showing a part of Asia, with pictures of men
and camels crossing a section near the Black Sea and he
wondered if they were meant to show the Polo brothers on
their way to the court of Kublai Khan.

Then his eye was caught by a different sort of map, one almost hidden under the larger ones. It was a simple sketch-
map of the world—without pictures, uncolored, blurred in
places. Two things about it, however, excited him. First, he
had never before seen the east coast of Asia depicted. On
this map it was shown as a straight coast running north and
south down to a deep bay or strait running due west, enclos-
ing an archipelago of islands. The Spice Islands? It was pos-

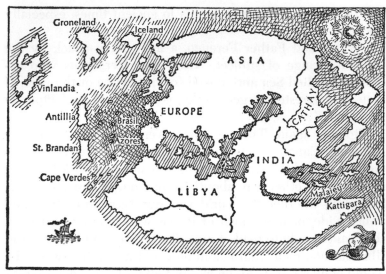

Alexandrian map

sible! Secondly, off the western shore of the tripartite
continent lay three fairly large and completely unfamiliar
islands, two smaller ones, and groups which might be the
Azores and the Canaries. The names on the three northern-
most islands were difficult to read. The nearest to Europe
was marked "Iseland"—of course, Iceland! The next to the
west bore the name "Groneland"—he'd never heard that
name before—and the most western island of all looked like
"Vinlandia." Interesting. No Thule—unless of course Thule
was the old name for Iceland.

His eyes slid south to two small islands marked respec-
tively "Antillia" and "Isle of St. Brandan." Again, names he
had never heard before. With Father Ferenco's permission,
Vanni made a hasty copy which the Dominican allowed him
to take away.

"It is said to have been made in the tenth century," said
Father Ferenco, "and came into our possession some years

ago through the kindness of a Swiss monk. I can't swear to its accuracy of course, but I hope it will be of use to you." All his initial distrust of Vanni seemed to have disappeared.

Next morning on leaving the monastery, remembering to drop some ducats in the poor box, Vanni congratulated himself on having learned so much on this one voyage. He had discovered something about pilotage and something of the spice trade, and a good deal about the Turkish menace. He had, as well, added a new map to his collection. He would have much to tell Michiele and Fra Andrea when he returned to Venice. How they would hang on his every word!

But on arrival home, it wasn't quite the way he had imagined it. For one thing, Michiele had finally persuaded the Brothers to let him become a barber, and he was now apprenticed to a shop in the town. His hours were long and an apprentice was given little free time.

"Wait until I have a shop of my own, Vanni! Then we'll have all the time in the world to talk."

In the second place, Danieli had managed to buy his rented gondola, was now an earnest businessman making every moment count, and was about to be married. Fra Andrea, though he welcomed his old pupil warmly and spent a whole afternoon listening to his adventures, had new pupils making demands on him. It was the same with others of his friends. All seemed to have made other plans in his three-month absence, formed other contacts.

Vanni consoled himself in the shops and became quite a notable peacock, spending large sums on clothes. Fortunately Uncle Luigi approved of such spending and contributed generously, even urging him to acquire a proper sword and dagger. Was he not a man now? And did not feminine glances follow him along the canals of Venice?

It seemed to Vanni that his uncle treated him at last with

a faint tinge of respect. One day as a special mark of favor, Signore Romano invited his nephew to admire a private collection of bronzes.

"It is a finer one than the Pope's," said Uncle Luigi with quiet pride. "All these treasures will be yours some day, Zuan, if you please me and work hard." Hoping his uncle could not read his mind at that moment, Vanni tried to estimate what such a collection would bring at auction. Enough to buy a ship?

"Have you had enough of the sea yet, Zuan?" Catching the mocking look in his uncle's eye, Vanni's mind snapped to attention. How to reply in the negative without showing that Uncle Luigi's act in sending him to sea had been anything but punishing? But the merchant did not wait for an answer. "Do not try to deceive me," he added dryly. "I have long been aware that you enjoy the seafaring life. Your face, Zuan, will never adequately conceal your thoughts." Vanni's heart sank with dismay. "It is obvious from the reports I receive from your officers that you are able to work hard when you wish to. I trust you will exert yourself similarly in working for me." So it was all over. "However, I have no objection to your continuing at sea for a while longer—" Vanni breathed again. Signore Romano added with sarcasm, "—since I am able, I find, to do without your valuable services at present." Why did Uncle Luigi always spoil things? For a moment, Vanni had actually felt friendly toward him.

Running down to the canal later that day, he saw a child seated on the wall at the edge of his uncle's property—their neighbor's daughter evidently. Vanni glanced at her casually as he stepped into his uncle's gondola and saw her gazing at him with a child's solemn intensity. He smiled, waved lightheartedly, receiving a startled look in return—and immediately forgot about her. After that, however, he kept seeing her about from time to time. He seemed to keep stumbling over her, in fact, and was amused, perhaps a little flattered, by the child's obvious devotion.

Soon he was off to sea again. He sailed twice more as grommet in the *Santa Lucia*, from which happily Scalzi had resigned his post. The third time he was signed on as Able Seaman Caboto—swift promotion, which he knew he owed to his uncle. Not all the hard work in the world would account for his jumping so soon over the heads of Tonio and the others. What he did not know, however, was that a word from Gabriel Duchesne to his captain had tipped the scale.

"My third officer tells me," said Captain Stegano, "that your nephew has acquired proficiency with a compass and understands something of pilotage and sea charts. He is being wasted in his present position."

Surprisingly, the grommets did not hold the promotion against Vanni. In their minds they were satisfied that he had got the job through influence, but they had expected no less. It was the ways things were done. One or two fawned a little, hoping for future favors, but Tonio treated the new able seaman as he had always treated Vanni since the storm. As a special condescension, however, he invited Vanni to go ashore with the grommets in Barcelona. This was an honor that had not so far been offered, and Vanni accepted partly because for the first time in his seagoing experience he was feeling a little homesick. This may have been due to the fact that the ship was going to Genoa after Barcelona.

At the last moment he wondered if he had been wise to accept the grommet's invitation, but by then it was too late to back down.

XII

Barcelona

"We don't go ashore to play marbles, you know!"

Tonio was in high spirits as they set out.

"Our sort of fun may be too rich for your blood, Caboto."

"We'll see!" Vanni resolved not to be outdone by these boys in sophistication. He must follow where they led or be shamed forever.

So it was that at a late hour that night he found himself in a grubby wineshop, the fourth they had visited, feeling utterly tired and bored. What pleasure did they find in tramping from one bar to another, drinking in silence, or whispering together in a corner? They flatly refused to talk, and Vanni suddenly realized that the ship was their only mutual interest. Was he being supercilious? He tried not to be, did his best to fall in with their mood of suppressed excitement, but it was no good. He felt bored. He yearned for his bed.

In the next *bistro*, he disgraced himself by falling asleep, and before buying his round of drinks. Tonio shook him awake disgustedly.

"And it's not midnight yet! Come on, we're going to a different sort of place this time."

Vanni followed, feeling stupid and heavy, but still dogged. He was not only tired, he was unused to taking wine without the addition of water, or with food, and his head swam a little. He trudged after the other five with his eyes only half-open, feet stumbling on the cobbles, vaguely conscious of dark evil-smelling alleys. He kept telling himself he must keep up. It was a matter of pride. After all, he was at least a year older than most of them. He was a man now, a wage earner. Jingling the coins in his purse, Vanni remembered it was his turn to buy. As they stumbled at last through a dark doorway into a dimly-lighted room, he announced loudly that this time it was his treat. He wondered why they laughed.

He saw that they were in the confines of a small room smelling of wine and perfume and something else—dirt, he thought. There was no proper bar in the place, but seated on benches against the wall were girls—women, rather—who turned and eyed the newcomers with set smiles. Vanni's stomach gave a lurch, and quite suddenly he knew he'd had enough.

He was not altogether pretending when he doubled over, clutching his stomach—

"Excuse me. I'm ill," he mumbled, and fled, followed by a gust of delighted laughter. He didn't care now—he no longer wished to impress. He had known about such places, of course, but he hadn't expected the reality to be so—so unclean! That was his weak spot, his fastidiousness. Never mind, he was simply thankful to have escaped.

Now all he had to do was find his way back to the ship and get some sleep. Fortunately, his head had cleared.

Which way to go? It was nearly pitch-dark in the alley. The houses and shops on either side were close-shuttered, the people inside fast asleep. It must be long after midnight. No one would be about except drunken seamen, thugs, and pickpockets! Vanni quickened his pace. He had only to find the Plaza del Rey and then he could orient himself. Absolutely nothing to worry about.

A hundred yards down the alley, he saw the welcome glow of a street torch up ahead, promising a plaza or open space, but when he rushed toward it, he found only another street leading off at an angle, as dark and empty as the one he had just left. Now he began to recall stories of seamen slugged and robbed in just such places. He must find his way back to the ship as quickly as possible!

That tumbled-down wall—he seemed to remember it. Hadn't it been on his left as they came up from the harbor? He put it on his right now and plunged down the black street. These ruins, he told himself to keep from thinking of other things, must be part of the original Roman wall around the old city. There was a newer wall now beyond it, for the city had grown.

Once every hundred yards or so, he came to another lighted torch. One showed a colonnaded Roman doorway, another revealed a modern-looking chapel, but neither were familiar. He made himself walk, not run, but was ready to shout with relief when he saw an open space ahead. The Plaza del Rey! He burst into the square at a fast trot and stopped short.

This wasn't the Plaza del Rey. It was a smaller square, one he had never seen before. He was lost!

But this shivering of the flesh was cowardice. He couldn't be lost in the very heart of Barcelona. He stiffened his back. There were people within sound of his voice, probably quite near if he could only see. Was that a footstep? That shadow! *Basta*! Something soft touched his foot and he had all he could do to keep from crying aloud—but it was only a rat.

He turned first this way, then that, afraid to go either forward or back. To his fevered imagination the city seemed to stretch endlessly in every direction. Courage dwindling, he looked desperately around. A faint spark caught his eye and he looked up. The stars! At once his heart calmed, his pulse steadied. Old friends. Once again he had forgotten them!

There was the Great Bear padding serenely across the northern sky. A simple matter to pick out Polaris and to remember that the North Star had been on his left as he walked off the ship. He could laugh now, ashamed of his recent panic. Keeping the North Star on his right, Vanni set out confidently and almost before he knew it walked into the Plaza del Rey. No mistaking the Castle of Aragon looming in the background, the guards walking sentry duty under lighted lanterns. From here he could see the spire of Santa Maria del Mar outlined against the sky—a church on the water front!

The stars. He must not be so forgetful another time.

The other boys turned up on the *Santa Lucia* shortly after his own return, a little anxious, having reflected that they might be blamed for losing an owner's relative. It was all right though—they found him sound asleep on deck.

"We won't take *him* again!" grumbled Tonio.

From then on, Vanni had to explore the ports alone and by day. He spent his evenings on deck in the warm moonlight, gossiping with older mariners who had lost their taste for stews and grog shops and liked to drink their wine in comfort on the ship, and to talk of old voyages and brag about youthful adventures. One man, an Istrian, claimed to have sailed as far north as Britain once when he was younger. Vanni asked what it was like, this barbarian island on the edge of the world, but the sailor had never been ashore there. He had stayed huddled on his ship.

"Cold?" he shuddered reminiscently, and took a draught

of wine to warm himself. "By San Antonio, I never was so cold in my life." An Irishman off another ship who was visiting a friend on the *Santa Lucia* murmured tolerantly—

"It's not so bad in summer."

"It was summer I was there," exclaimed the Istrian, "with rain or fog every day!"

"It's true what they say, by San Marco," swore the Irishman's friend, "the farther north, the worse the weather."

"Not at all," argued the Irishman. "There's a port on an island north of Britain where it gets pretty warm in summer."

"Thule?" asked Vanni eagerly. The Irishman gave him a puzzled stare.

"Thule? Never heard of it. I was going to say Iceland. It's warmer there sometimes than it is in Ireland."

"And it's north, you say, of Britain?"

"More nor'west."

"How far?"

"Three or four days, with a fair wind."

"Four days *north*, Brian?" His friend gave a snort of disbelief. "Neither man nor ship can live that far north, everybody knows that."

"Holy St. Patrick!" cried the Irishman, fed up with Southern arrogance. "I've been there meself, haven't I?" They murmured doubtfully. "There's fishing up there, I tell you, all the way to Iceland."

"Is the water open all around the island then?" asked Vanni. "All year, I mean?"

"Well now, maybe you'd find slush off the Arctic ice—or a few icebergs floating about in the real cold weather, but ships sail in the fishing trade all the year around."

Slush off the Arctic ice! Sea-lung?

Yet it could hardly be Thule if the water was open all year, unless of course conditions had changed since Pytheas' time.

"The South is best," said the sailor from Rimini, sententiously, "best for everything. People are better here—smarter, quicker. Those in the North are a slow and awkward lot."

The Irishman's eyes began to glitter.

"They're great with their fists though, Pasquale," Brian's friend said warningly, "especially the Irish."

Pasquale took the hint.

"Sorry, my friend. No offense." But Brian fumed.

"The men of the North are quick enough when they want to be! Didn't they nearly conquer the world once?"

"What!" They stared at him.

"The Irish monks tell of it," said the Irishman, "how, in olden times, the Norsemen—Vikings they called themselves—came over the water in their serpent ships to rob our monasteries and carry off our womenfolk. And after that they went raiding and robbing all over Europe, as far as Italy, a priest told me. Some of you might even be descended from those wild men. That boy there—he's fair and blue-eyed enough to be a Viking himself!"

They all turned and looked at Vanni reflectively.

"In their best days," said Brian, "the Vikings sailed wherever they pleased. Nobody could stand against them, not even the Irish!"

Had these Vikings ever found Thule on their voyages, Vanni wondered. He lost track of the conversation for a while, dreaming of a voyage north to look for Thule—until he heard them talking of the Ocean Sea. Opinion was divided about the Ocean Sea. Some of the men feared it because they might be swept west with no wind to bring them back again, others because the sea itself broke off short some distance west of Europe. All agreed, however, that it was the breeding place of storms and sea serpents.

"I knew a man once," said the Istrian mournfully, "who

sailed west from Lisbon and never was heard of again, which is what comes of going to look for lost islands."

"Islands, is it? Then you'll have heard of St. Brandan's Isle! A great navigator St. Brandan was who, hearing of this isle in the West called Brasil, nothing would do but he must go and see it for himself."

"Did he find it?" Vanni asked.

"He did," answered the Irishman, "and discovered it to be the isle of Paradise itself, at the end of the world. And there St. Brandan abode, drinking with the saints at the fountain of life, to the end of time."

"How does anyone know what the Isle was like if he never came back to tell of it?" But the Irishman pretended not to hear.

"Some men call it "Brasil" and others the "Isle of St. Brandan," he said. "It's well known!"

St. Brandan! That was one of the names on his new map.

"And have you heard of the Isle of the Seven Cities?" asked the Istrian, "the one discovered long ago by Spanish refugees fleeing from the Moslems?"

For a while the talk was all of islands—of Antillia which men claimed to have seen often enough in the western ocean but had never got close enough to land on, and of fabled Atlantis sunk beneath the surface of the ocean by the wrath of the sea gods.

"The King of Portugal offers money and land to anyone who'll find those lost islands," said the man from Rimini. "A mariner could make his fortune that way."

"And sail off the edge of the world doing it!"

"But that's impossible," cried Vanni, unable to contain himself any longer, "since the earth is round and there's a force which draws all to the center—" He faltered to a stop, seeing how they all turned to look at him.

"Round!"

"The earth *is* round," he insisted.

The Istrian smirked gently.

"Who told you that, boy?"

"A very learned Franciscan! Anyway, you only have to look at a ship coming in from sea—" But they laughed him to silence.

"Did that friar go around the earth himself? No? I thought not. Then how would he know?"

"If you ever saw an eclipse of the moon," Vanni began half-heartedly. It was no use. They wouldn't listen.

"If the earth was round, Zuan," said one of the men cheerfully, "those that live on the bottom side of it would walk on their heads!"

"You can see for yourself, anyway, it's as flat as a pancake."

"Besides, the priest says it's heresy to call the world round."

"Do not feel badly, Zuan," said the man from Rimini in a kindly tone. "We do not make fun of you, only of those who speak in jest of things they do not understand. How long are you at sea now—six—eight months? Wait until you are as old as I, boy, and you will know better." And the Istrian added—

"You've never heard a *seaman* say the earth was round!"

"I did once," said the Irishman unexpectedly. "He was a Genoese I met in Savona a while back."

"A queer seaman then!"

"He was queer to be sure, always quoting the Bible—something about six parts of the earth being dried up and only one-seventh of water left. And he swore up and down the earth was round."

The Istrian crossed himself anxiously, and the rest smiled indulgently.

"He must have hailed from the Alps!" said Brian's friend hilariously.

"I told you he was Genoese. Now what was his name—

Cristophe—Christo—Christopher Columbus, that was the name!" Seeing Vanni's puzzled frown, he asked if he knew the fellow.

"I've heard a name like that—somewhere," answered Vanni, "but I can't think where."

The Irishman shook his head sadly.

"Of course he was mad, poor fellow."

"Naturally!"

Vanni wanted to tell them they were wrong, that they didn't understand, but Gabriel Duchesne came up just then and shook his head at him.

"You could never convince them," the Burgundian remarked later, "not if the captain himself swore to it on the Holy Cross. They are too old to change. Also, like me, they have no education."

"But, Gabriel, you don't believe the world is flat."

"I did when I was your age, *mon ami.* A captain I sailed with, a learned man, had one hard time to convince me. But after that, I used my eyes. Name of a name! One has only to watch the stars, how they descend to the horizon as one sails south."

"Just what Aristotle said!" Vanni thought for the first time —how lucky to have had Fra Andrea for a teacher! If the Little Brother had not made him work hard and get a proper education, he would have been like these men—stubborn, bigoted, ignorant.

"Education is a great blessing," sighed Gabriel as if he had read Vanni's mind.

"You're doing fine," said Vanni comfortingly, "you'll soon be reading the *Compasso* without difficulty."

"Possibly. But never will I be able to read whole books like your Aristotle and your Marco Polo."

"You're not missing much in Marco Polo. He told awful lies, Gabriel."

"What sort of lies?"

"Tall tales—like the one about people in the East digging black stones out of the earth and using them to make fires."

"But that is true."

"What!"

Gabriel nodded calmly.

"One winter I sailed to Jaffa with a cargo of pilgrims. Our Captain went to Damascus on private business and took me with him. There I saw the black stones and was told they came from the East."

If Marco Polo had told the truth about this, perhaps other things were true—the ten thousand elephants clad in cloth of gold, for instance, and the marvelous island of Cipango off the coast of Cathay. He must read the book again, carefully this time. Perhaps, after all, Polo was another traveler like Pytheas from whom he might learn.

"What was that talk of islands as I came up?" Gabriel asked now and when he had heard, his thin face lost its cynical wisdom and grew wistful.

"Ah yes, *mon Dieu*, it is true that the Portuguese reward the discoverers of islands. I shall tell you a secret now, *mon ami*, for years I have dreamed of being one of them! It is not the coast of Africa I yearn to sail on, but the sea to the west where so many men have made their fortunes. Those who found Madiera and the Azores, the Cape Verdes and the Fortunate Isles became rich men." His eyes glowed with desire. "There may be other such islands farther west!" So this was Gabriel's secret. This was the ambition that separated him so sharply from the other crew members.

"It is the only way I know for a man like me to become a landowner," he said, "wealthy and respected."

So then Vanni told him that he too had island-hunting in mind.

"In the North though, where Pytheas sailed, not in the

West. We will join forces, Gabriel!" he cried. "I shall help you find your Antillia, then you can come with me in search of Thule, or at least Brasil!"

"Stranger things have happened," said Duchesne seriously.

XIII

Return to Genoa

Islands were forgotten when the ship arrived next day in the port of Genoa. Vanni was home again, after nearly eight years. He ran up the well-remembered streets, out through the gate under the tower of San Andrea and past the weaver's house where the boy Colombo had lived. At the thought he stopped short, overtaken at last by the name "Christopher Columbus." The man the Irishman had mentioned might have been that same Colombo. What a small world, after all! Then, striding on, he thought only of his waiting family.

"*Madre mia!*" He burst into the house with a shout.

After the first excitement had subsided, Vanni's mother and sisters stood back, gazing at him with wonder.

"So tall!"

"Look at him, Mamma! So handsome!"

"You have grown, my son!" The tears began to flow all over again.

"What did you expect?" he laughed, his own tears flowing as he hugged her again. "I am seventeen—a man!"

"Man indeed!" she scoffed, smiling and wiping her eyes.

"You are *mio bambino,* my first-born!" She fussed over him, petted him, and admired his gift, and he was so happy he ached inside. He basked all morning in her praise and in the affection of his sisters. Piero came in from work and he was so big he seemed at first a stranger. Then he grinned and the brothers fell into each other's arms, talking, laughing, pounding each other on the back. The house with all these big people in it seemed so much smaller than he remembered. His sisters though were prettier, and Lisetta brought a baby to show—his namesake, Giovanni.

At last the women all rushed away to the kitchen to prepare a special meal for the returned hero. Vanni's mouth watered in anticipation. Mamma was a famous cook and it was a long time since he had tasted her *lasagna* and *vitello scaloppine.* Piero had to go back to the warehouse, but Papa stayed to talk business with Vanni, wanting to know all that went on in Venice. Vanni told what little he knew, and heard that Signore Caboto had given up trying to compete with Venice in the spice trade. He and Piero now dealt in less exotic but safer commodities.

"People like your Uncle have had it their own way too long, Vanni," prophesied his father. "I see a change coming. There is a limit to what people will put up with, you know. Venice is beginning to be hated everywhere."

"Other countries are jealous, that's all!"

"Nevertheless it reflects on business. Do you know that we are now getting pepper from the coast of Guinea in Africa? Soon we will not need Eastern stuff."

His son smiled confidently.

"Oh yes, I have heard of that vile malagueta. It does not compare with Indian pepper, Papa, surely!"

"Perhaps not, but all the same, if Venice is not careful, she will price herself right out of the market."

"But that is impossible!" Vanni felt himself a veritable ex-

pert all of a sudden. "Venice will always prosper—at least, as long as she has a monopoly of the spice trade—and she won't lose that if she can help it. If people want spices, they must pay for them."

His mother, entering to put away her blue silk, heard Vanni and paused in the act of opening her carved household chest to listen.

"If they can't afford to buy," her son said airily, "let them do without—or be satisfied with onions and garlic grown in their back gardens!"

Carefully, Signora Caboto laid away the silk, closed the lid of the chest, and rose with an odd expression on her face. Her son observed it and wondered, but all she said was—

"Dinner, Vanni *caro*, will not be for three hours yet. Why don't you go to the beach? Emilio has been asking after you."

Vanni jumped up, then paused, with a glance at his father. "If you don't mind, Papa?"

"Go on," said his father indulgently. "I know you won't be happy until you've seen him."

So, once again, feeling the years roll back, Vanni stood waiting on the beach while Emilio's boat came bobbing around the end of the mole.

"Emilio! It's me—Vanni!"

The fisherman waved back, pointed to the skiff on the beach, and brought his old gray boat up smartly into the wind in the way he had taught the boy so long ago. They met in the cockpit of the larger boat, embracing and exclaiming. Settling down over the remains of a bottle of wine to talk, Vanni thought that neither Emilio nor the boat looked a day older. One thing at least had stayed the same.

Emilio wanted to know everything, where he'd been and what he'd done.

"So! You are a proper seaman now! And to think it was

just the other day you asked me what was out there in the Gulf."

How satisfying to be with Emilio again! The old fisherman, unlearned though Vanni now knew him to be, would always fill a special place in his heart. He asked about Gino.

"He is doing very well," said the father with pride. "Now he is second mate on a grain ship. Six *bambinos* he has! Maria and I, we live with them, so I do not have to fish much now, just enough for the family."

"That's good." Vanni laid his hand with a loving gesture on the old gray tiller. "You have the best of it, Emilio, as I used to tell you. I still think a fisherman's life would suit me best of all."

"No, no, Vanni. You have learning! You must do more than haul fish. You can be a merchant like your Papa and your Uncle, and make much money."

"I suppose so." Vanni sighed. "I hate the thought of being shut up in a warehouse for years and years—until I'm rich enough to buy a ship and sail off in search of an island."

Emilio grunted disbelievingly.

"Island? What island?"

"One of those said to lie in the North, perhaps even a little west of Iceland!" He told Emilio about Thule and Pytheas and about Gabriel's idea to collect a reward some day from the King of Portugal.

"Of course," he said, a little pessimistically, "there may be nothing out there at all but sailors' imaginings. I fear I was born too late, Emilio. Practically everything of any value has already been discovered. Marco Polo found Asia, Herodotus explored Asia Minor, and Ibn Battuta touched at every Moslem capital in the East, as well as exploring Africa. Pytheas discovered the North and someone or other explored the Atlantic islands. Perhaps there are no more islands left, none at all for me to find!"

Emilio nodded sympathetically.

"Life does not always give us what we ask. I wished as a boy to be a farmer, Vanni, to grow almond trees and grapes, but in the end, as you see, I am a fisherman like my father before me."

"I shan't end up like *my* father," said Vanni fiercely. "Or my Uncle! *I* shall do something important in the world."

"You were always a stubborn one," chuckled Emilio admiringly. "I believe you will do as you say."

Emilio, as always, was a great comfort.

Later Vanni helped the fisherman tidy the boat and carry home the catch.

"Do you ever hear anything of that red-headed boy?" he asked Emilio as they walked along. "You know—the weaver's son?"

"Colombo? The family moved to Savona a while back, but I have heard the lad is a seaman now, like you, which does not surprise me. I always said the pair of you were as like as two peas."

At home, they awaited him, expectant.

"Dinner is ready," said Mamma. "Sit down in your old place."

Vanni suspected nothing. His sisters wore their usual expressions. Piero kept nudging Papa and laughing, but Vanni thought nothing of it. He was too anxious to enjoy Mamma's good food again. He took his first mouthful of *zucchini* and lettuce and was disappointed. This was not the salad he recalled from his childhood, but perhaps it was like the house, not so fine as he had carried in his memory.

The plates were taken away and his mother's famous *vitello scaloppine* put before him, with a side-dish of *lasagna*. This was what he had been waiting for. He took a large mouthful and—spat it out!

"Ugh! Horrible!" he gasped. "What is it?"

"It's veal from a calf killed only two months ago," snapped his mother. "Why is it horrible?"

"It tastes rancid!"

"Naturally it tastes rancid!" Vanni stared at his mother incredulously, saw that her eyes were snapping with mirth and triumph. "It was not spiced like the rest of the meat, so of course it tastes rancid. Try the *lasagna* now and see how you like *that* without pepper and spice!"

Then the whole lot of them exploded into laughter.

"If one cannot afford spices," mimicked his Mamma, "one must do without—eh, *carissimo*? Lisetta! Bianca! Take away this garbage and bring in the proper dinner!"

XIV

Inspiration

He told Fra Andrea about it when he got back to Venice.
By then he too was able to laugh at the joke.

"You cannot imagine how awful it tasted, Padre! Even the
wine was made without sugar, bitter as gall. Of course we
had a fine, properly-spiced dinner eventually, but it was a
lesson to me. If I never realized before the importance of
spices, I do now. Messer Fragini's remarks about the great
profits to be made in the trade now make more sense, and I
can see how certain countries would be only too pleased to
find other sources of pepper."

"Until some way besides smoking and drying is found to
preserve food," agreed the friar, "and as long as man has a
sense of taste, spices will be most necessary. Does this mean
you are going to be a spice merchant after all?"

"*Basta*! No! Or at least only until I can find a ship. Then I
shall join forces with Gabriel and go off to find an island!"

"Gabriel?"

"Gabriel Duchesne. I told you about him, Padre—the Burgundian officer."

"Yes, yes, I remember now. So you and he intend to look
for an island!"

151

Vanni explained how the King of Portugal was encouraging voyages of discovery by offering rewards and how, as soon as they could, he and Gabriel would join in the search.

"Excellent! You must prepare well. Much specialized knowledge will be needed."

Vanni grinned quietly to himself. With Fra Andrea, education was, as usual, the answer to everything.

"That reminds me," he said, "I have been rereading *The Travels of Marco Polo* and, Padre, I am sure now that every word of it is true!" Seeing Fra Andrea's dubious look— "Some of the 'impossible' things he claimed to have found I have since discovered actually exist. And as your commentator says, much of what he wrote is duplicated in the Relations of the missionaries who went to the East a little later on. But only Marco Polo speaks of the island called Cipango, which lies in the Sea of Chin off the province of Manjii in Asia and which is said to be very rich in gold and pearls. Now if Gabriel and I could only find an island like that on *our* side of the world!" He shrugged. "But I suppose we must be satisfied to find a hump of sand and a few trees in the Ocean Sea. Once I get the ship, it will be easy enough, simply a matter of sailing west." Fra Andrea gave his robe an angry hitch.

"*Madre mia!*" he growled. "You are like all young people. You think great things may be accomplished with little effort."

"But you yourself have taught me all the geographic knowledge I shall need—"

"I have taught you almost nothing!" cried the friar in an unusual passion. "You have taken but a small step in the world of real knowledge. Use sense, Vanni. If it were so easy, dozens of men would have discovered your islands before this!"

Vanni sobered.

"I suppose so."

"Lazy men do the easy things. Nothing worthwhile is accomplished without effort!" Vanni had never seen the Little Brother so worked up. "You must learn seamanship. Not the Mediterranean variety—conditions in the Western Ocean may be quite different. Also, you must know how to navigate when out of sight of land for long periods. That will require a knowledge of astronomy and mathematics. There is no sense in going off unprepared, simply to make a fool of yourself. You know nothing about the Ocean Sea!"

"I've seen maps," he protested.

"Maps! Good heavens!" exclaimed Fra Andrea, forgetting everything else on the instant. "Maps, of course—come quickly! I've something to show you!" And he rushed to his own room off the library.

Vanni followed, amused at the Little Brother's growing absent-mindedness. He saw the remains of lunch on the table. Evidently Fra Andrea had been eating when he heard of Vanni's arrival and had completely forgotten about his meal.

Fra Andrea laid a large printed book in Vanni's hands triumphantly.

"Ptolemy!" he crowed.

Oh no, thought Vanni—not Ptolemy again!

"Padre," he said as tactfully as he could, "I am not really interested in studying astrology and the principles of circles."

"You are thinking of the *Almagest*, Vanni, a book on astronomical matters. This is Ptolemy's *Geography*."

"Oh?" Vanni opened the book at random and saw a page covered with lists of names and figures. "What are these?"

"Latitudes and longitudes of some eight thousand different places on the earth."

Vanni knew of course that latitude was the distance on

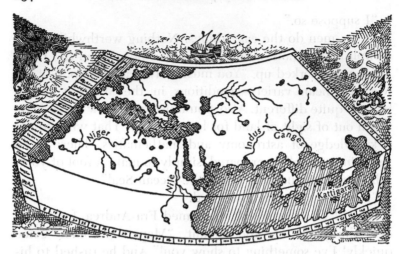

The world according to Ptolemy

the earth north or south of the Equator and that longitude
was the distance east and west of a prime meridian.

"Very interesting."

Fra Andrea gave him a sharp look.

"By San Marco, such enthusiasm! Are you no longer interested in maps then?"

"In maps, yes, but what have these figures to do with—"

"Give me patience! They have everything to do with maps.
These figures are the very foundation of the art of making
accurate maps of the whole world! Look at these!" Fra Andrea shoved his meal aside and reverently laid out a sheaf
of manuscripts. Maps! Vanni bent over them eagerly. This
was more like it. The top one showed the world from Spain
to the Far East, with Asia running entirely off the page. The
Indian Ocean, he saw to his surprise, was surrounded by
land!

He noticed these things first, then saw where the map
differed from any others he had ever seen. Instead of being

drawn flat on a single plane, the outline of Europe-Asia-Africa was drawn in a frame somewhat the shape of a lampshade so that at the Equator it was widest and diminished in width toward the north and somewhat also to the south. Then, instead of rhumb lines crisscrossing in portolan fashion, there were vertical and horizontal lines crossing each other here and there, with latitude and longitude marked at the sides.

"It shows the earth as it really is!" crowed Fra Andrea.

"Then, instead of locating places by bearings and distances as on *portolani*," said Vanni, groping to understand, "one would locate them by latitude and longitude—once they were known."

"Precisely! *Portolani*," said Fra Andrea putting on his lecturer's tone, "assume a flat surface, which does not matter greatly in a sea like the Mediterranean where latitude varies so little. But once you move up the coast, to Ireland say, then because the world is round errors grow progressively greater. You know, of course, how difficult it is to put a plane surface on a round one—" He took an orange from his plate and tried to wrap a map around it. "You see? So what Ptolemy did was to *project* a round earth on a flat surface in *astronomical* terms, using the same sort of network used by astronomers in making star charts. Ptolemy even used an astronomical instrument called the astrolabe to make his measurements."

"But first he made a—a grid of co-ordinates of latitude and —wait a minute! Are these latitudes correct?" Vanni knew how difficult it was to work out accurate latitudes. To work out longitude was almost impossible.

"I shouldn't like to swear to their accuracy," Fra Andrea admitted. "I believe that Ptolemy, being no traveler himself, got most of his figures from explorers and merchants, and worked out the rest by estimating distances on the basis of travel time. So we must allow for error. But the point to remember is this—when, in time, we do know for certain all longitudes and latitudes, we can with this system draw an almost absolutely accurate map of the whole or any part of the world!"

The friar had no reason now to complain of lack of enthusiasm. Vanni went rapidly through the other maps, comparing them in his mind with those he had seen in the *portolani* tradition, and he saw that Fra Andrea was right. These maps were by far the best he had ever seen. The method itself was revolutionary. It would be invaluable to seamen charting unknown seas and islands. Another idea struck him.

"It should be possible to draw those co-ordinates on a sphere too, and get an even more accurate picture of the world!" He snatched up a table knife and Fra Andrea's orange and began to cut the shape of Europe-Asia-Africa in the skin, using Ptolemy's map as a guide.

"Think of it, Vanni," said Fra Andrea happily, "a method of making maps invented twelve hundred years ago by a man who never went out of his library! And the whole thing lost until this century."

The orange was small, the knife point blunt, and Vanni knew he could not divide it into Ptolemy's 360 degrees. Nevertheless he wanted to see how the world looked in the round. There were problems. Where did Asia end? Ptolemy's map did not show the coast of Asia at all. Vanni recalled the map he had found in Alexandria and he cut that shore line roughly from memory. But when he had finished his globe, it was still unsatisfactory. He was disgusted to see that the shores of Spain just about touched the extreme limits of Asia.

"Well, that can't be right. I haven't left space enough for Cipango."

Fra Andrea chuckled richly.

"How can you know how much space there is?"

"I can't, of course," said Vanni slowly, staring at the orange. "I'd have to know the width of the Ocean. And I

Cabot's "orange"—first inspiration for route, 1464

can't know that without knowing the width of Europe and
Asia together."

"You see?" Fra Andrea accused him joyfully. "You need to
know more! You need to know, for instance, the earth's circumference!"

"So that I can subtract from it the land area and see what
is left for the Ocean!"

"Precisely. The same old problem. Posidonius or Eratosthenes?"

Vanni thought of the Greeks all those centuries ago, calculating that the earth was round, making their globes and their maps according to the spherical theory, and trying to measure the world at the Equator. If only one of them had got it right and could prove it without shadow of doubt, then he would know roughly where to leave off cutting the orange skin. He would know roughly how far Cipango was from—

He caught his breath. If the sea was anything like as narrow as it looked on the orange, there was hardly any distance at all between Spain and Cipango! He had never looked at it this way before.

Cipango was *not* on the other side of the world. It was only on the other side of the Western Sea!

Vanni trembled, feeling himself on the edge of something terribly important. His mind began to juggle with words and ideas—Spain to Cipango, the earth is round . . . malagueta pepper and the desperate need of spices . . . Father Ferenco and his scheme to unite with the people of Asia . . . Aristotle's theory that the Ocean Sea was narrow. Rewards for finding islands in the Western Sea . . . an extension to Cathay and the Indies. Islam. Spices. Take Jerusalem from the rear. An alternative route to the Spice Islands—

The ideas came in a rush, shouting now, crowding one another.

"You see, Vanni," said Fra Andrea, happily, "it pays to look to the past—"

"Wait!" Vanni gasped, tremulous with the fear of losing the threads—the earth is round, the earth is *round*! That was the thing to remember!

"Padre!" he shouted, and saw the friar looking at him with anxious concern. "Padre, I've thought of a way to reach Cipango and the Spice Islands without having to deal with the Turks! An alternative route! A way no one else has ever tried! West!" he cried triumphantly. "West across the Ocean Sea direct to Asia!"

Part Two

CABOT THE MAN

XV

Change of Course

More than twenty years would elapse before Giovanni Caboto could even begin to put his tremendous idea into
execution.

In the first place, he had to understand that Venice was
the last government in the world to sponsor such a project.
In his innocence he had thought the proposal of a short way
to the Indies, evading pirates and middlemen, would appeal
at once to a wealthy, forward-looking maritime power like
Venice. He had not seen what his Uncle saw the moment
the subject was broached, that such a route would mean the
end of the Venetian spice monopoly.

"Venice is too far from the Western Sea, compared with
countries like Spain and Portugal." He spoke mildly enough,
indulgent to the wild notions of an eighteen-year-old. "Secondly, our money is invested in ships designed for coastal
and inland trade. It would be unrealistic, Zuan, to convert to
ocean-going vessels. Thirdly, it should have occurred to you
that if a Venetian ship led the way across the Ocean Sea to
the Indies, foreign ships would be quick to follow and, lying closer to the sea route, could make the voyage more

profitably. Venice would merely open the way to a competition which would in the end ruin her."

"But you do believe the idea itself is feasible," reasoned Vanni. "You believe it is possible to make such a voyage?"

Uncle Luigi smiled from a lofty eminence.

"A hundred years from now, perhaps." His nephew's face fell. "Not in my lifetime, thank God. These are youthful dreams, Zuan. We have all had them. Nevertheless," he added, abruptly serious, "I trust you have not discussed them publicly."

"Only with Fra Andrea."

"Then warn him to keep a still tongue in his head. If loose talk of that kind came to the ears of the Senate, it might be interpreted as disloyalty to the State. Remember the glass laws." Vanni remembered. In essence they ensured that any manufacturer of glass who left the city or imparted his knowledge to another power could by the law of the State be hunted down and killed.

Depressed, he went to his friends for support and encouragement, but they too were dubious.

"You are too young, Vanni," said Fra Andrea, "and still too ignorant. No one in authority would listen to you."

"Particularly in a foreign country." Michiele, wanting very much to support his friend, still felt obliged to point out difficulties. It was the same with Gabriel.

"Even if you secured financial backing, *mon ami*, where would you find a ship suitable for such a voyage—or a crew?"

"Ship design is improving," said Vanni quickly, "and better ships will make braver crews."

"You will need ten years at least," said Fra Andrea with his usual optimism, "to grasp thoroughly the necessary mathematics, astronomy, cosmology, and geography."

"The world is round," Vanni persisted stubbornly. "That is the important thing. One need only sail west!"

Gabriel shook his head.

"One must still navigate. There would be storms to drive you off course. Your compass might fail you. Could you depend on compass and lead and hourglass only, as in these inland seas? Are they sufficient, do you think, to cross the Ocean Sea, fix your position on the other side, and return? I do not think so, *mon ami.* There are no capes, no landmarks, in the Western Sea."

"I should simply choose a latitude and run down my westing until I reached land!"

Gabriel threw up his hands, despairingly.

"When you do not know for certain how far you must sail?"

"A great many months if Eratosthenes' estimate of the world's size is correct," Fra Andrea reminded him. "Now if we had reason to believe that Posidonius' calculations were more accurate—"

"It would still be too far," said Michiele pessimistically. "How could one carry enough food for so long a voyage?"

"Me, I shall be content to find one small island," declared Gabriel, "not too far from the coast of Europe. Antillia, let us say!"

"I'll go alone!" Vanni cried, embittered.

"Slowly, slowly, my son. You are impatient. It is your great fault."

"Wait until you are older, Caboto," advised the Burgundian. "That is only common sense."

"One should not listen too long to common sense," mourned Vanni, "or nothing new would ever be done. I shall be an old man if I wait till my scheme is easy and practical. And by then someone else will have got there. Someone else will have found the gold and seized the spice monopoly!"

"Remember, Vanni," said the friar, "other men must face

similar obstacles, take time to gain the necessary knowledge too. You can begin now—prepare!"

"The Padre is right, Vanni. Too much is still uncertain."

"Your friend, Ptolemy, does not even show Cathay on the map."

"If only the Greeks had agreed on the length of a degree—"

"And if only Marco Polo had been able to give us exact latitudes, precise directions—"

"If only—if only! Why think only of what is *not* known! The world is round!" Vanni knew he was right and, even as he spoke, he knew they too were right. It was too soon. Very well, if learning was the only way for the moment, he would go back to the books.

All the things he had dismissed as dull and difficult now had to be learned after all, and in spare moments snatched from regular work. It mattered now if the earth was round or square, and whether or not it revolved around the sun, if the earth was twenty or forty thousand miles wide, and how much of it was water, how much land.

Back to the Greeks. Back to Pythagorus who had first worked out the principle of circles and announced that the world was round. Back to Aristotle who thought the Ocean Sea was of no great width and could be crossed in a few days with a fair wind. Back to Strabo who had "proved" there was no land in the sea between Spain and Asia because those who had tried to cross it had failed, not because of land in the way, but because of loneliness or running out of supplies. Back to Hipparchus who did not agree with him, who even thought there might be *two* seas between.

One valuable find was made by Fra Andrea through his friend in Alexandria—the methods of measurement used by the early astronomers. Eratosthenes, the librarian of Alexandria around 200 B.C., one midsummer day in Syene had noticed the sun reflected in the water of a well and decided the sun was therefore at its zenith. Arranging for the angle of the sun at Alexandria to be measured on the same day, he found it to be one-fiftieth of the great circle which was already established as 360 degrees. Then having calculated that Alexandria lay five thousand stadia due north of Syene, he multiplied by fifty and found the circumference of the earth to be 250,000 stadia, or roughly 25,000 miles. This of course worked out to a degree of longitude measuring seventy miles. But Posidonius, who got his central angle by an astronomical method and measured the distance between Rhodes and Alexandria on the basis of the time a boat needed to sail between those two places, got a degree of only forty-eight miles. Alfragan, the Arab, measuring the length of an arc with wooden rods, got sixty-six. Ptolemy, influenced by Posidonius, finally settled on one of fifty miles.

Who was right?

If Posidonius and Ptolemy, then the width of the ocean was not excessive, and when ship design improved it might just be possible to reach the other side. If Eratosthenes, then the whole idea was hopeless. What ship could ever travel more than ten thousand miles across open ocean?

Much also depended on the proportions of land to water. The Church taught that six parts of earth were dried up. Therefore, the seventh part must be water, a comforting thought to the would-be voyager. But Ptolemy said it was half and half, 180 degrees of each. Marco Polo added Cathay and Cipango to Ptolemy's Asia and made the land that much larger, the ocean smaller still.

Who was right?

For Vanni, the two shores of Europe-Asia kept moving at first farther apart, then closer together. How far west was the Far East? How long would a voyage between the two shores take? Was it possible? And if so, was it practicable?

Finally, regretfully, he decided—no. Not for the present.

Not even if Ptolemy were correct about the earth's circumference and Marco Polo about the width of Asia. Such a comparatively small Ocean Sea would still be far too large for the ships of the day. With a following wind, they might get there, but they'd never get back! They could not in any case carry sufficient food and water for such a lengthy voyage, even if crews could be found to risk it. Perhaps some day ships would be built which would sail closer to the wind and require smaller crews. Meanwhile, Vanni must set his dream aside and attend to the business of everyday living. Life was, in fact, making demands on him.

Briefly he was caught up in a war between Turks and Venetians in which Venice ultimately lost Dalmatia, Lemnos, and Morea and was condemned to pay an annual tribute to the Sultan. This was a sad blow to Venetian pride and one which she tried to assuage by forming an alliance with France to make war on Milan and Naples. Vanni played a minor role on the naval side and was happy when it was over. He returned to Venice and went to sea again as soon as his ship was converted to peacetime use, as his Uncle's factor as well as third officer. He was now in a mood to enjoy life and worry no more about the future.

When the opportunity came to realize an old dream—to sail with the Flanders Fleet to Northern Europe—he seized on it eagerly. On his return, he had much to tell Signore Romano.

"Britain is an interesting country, not so backward as we thought. Of course in many respects she's barbarian! The manners are rough and the people are always eating and drinking! Nevertheless, it seemed to me I could sense a kind of vitality, of growth. Gabriel thinks the English will one day become a nation of commercial importance."

"Not, of course," said Uncle Luigi stiffly, "to compare with Venice."

"Perhaps not. All the same, they are starting to challenge the supremacy of the Iberians in trade. A large merchantile marine is carried on from Bristol as well as Southampton and London—exporting dried fish, raw wool, as well as finished cloth, and importing wine and spices. Their mariners go to Iceland for cod—that is, when the Danes do not prevent them—and to Madiera and the Canaries for wine, Lisbon for pepper. They have merchant colonies in the Azores as well as in Spain and Portugal, and their ships sail regularly in this Ocean-island trade. By the way, I ran into Sir William Thorne again."

"Indeed? In London?"

"No, it was when we were at Southampton waiting for the Fleet to load for Bruges. I met him at the house of some Venetians I visited and he remembered me when I reminded him—er—of a ship we both knew. He sent you his regards."

"Very kind of him."

"Sir William introduced me to a Bristol cousin of his, a Master Robert Thorne, which is how I came to visit Bristol. It was Master Robert who told me about the Ocean-island trade and said that England would one day have a commercial empire on the west coast as rich as ours in the eastern Mediterranean!"

Signore Romano shrugged.

"Most unlikely, I should say."

Vanni did not argue, but there were some things these days he could see more clearly than his stay-at-home Uncle could. He was beginning to suspect that Venice as a world power had nearly reached her peak, if indeed she had not passed it. No longer did her decadent merchants risk their lives in the pursuit of trade. Instead, they stayed at home and worried over freight rates and fire insurance. Meanwhile the audacity and vigor of other nations—Spain and Portugal and England—increased.

"I should like to take a voyage along the Ocean-island route some day," Vanni mused, "from Libson to Bristol, to Iceland, down to the Azores and back again to Lisbon. Wonderful experience!"

Uncle Luigi brushed this remark aside with the scorn it deserved and suggested that it was time Zuan thought of getting married. When the young man smiled in response to his suggestion, Signore Romano saw clearly the charm which caused so many feminine hearts to flutter in Vanni's vicinity.

"No thanks, Uncle. I'm happy as I am."

"You will be twenty-one next month."

"Another ten years of freedom," said Vanni lightly, "then we will see." He knew the way his Uncle's thoughts were running. If Signore Romano decided to leave his estate to his nephew, he wished to be sure there would be heirs. Vanni, however, had no idea of settling down so soon to a life of married bliss.

"Which reminds me," said his Uncle with quiet pride, "plans for your birthday party are now being set in train. The guest list includes half the patrician families of Venice and nearly all have accepted." He had succeeded in his ambition to make his Genoese nephew fit into Venetian high society, with little aid from Vanni himself.

"Does the list include Michiele?"

"Your barber friend?" Uncle Luigi looked down his nose, but did not fail to catch the glint in his nephew's eyes.

"If Michiele doesn't come," Vanni said cheerfully but firmly, "neither will I." The name was added to the list. Uncle Luigi was not a man to waste his strength over trifles.

The twenty-first birthday celebration of Zuan Caboto began shortly after dark in the courtyard and garden of the Romano *palazzo*. From dinnertime on, gondolas came and went at the water-gate and elegantly-dressed ladies and gentlemen, mostly masked, were helped out of them. Colored lanterns swayed in the breeze and there was dancing to the music of flute and harp. As soon as Vanni could escape from the reception line, he considered his duties at an end and went in search of Michiele. Perversely he wished to make a joke of the party, possibly because Uncle Luigi regarded it with such unnatural solemnity. He and Michiele disappeared briefly into the house and when they came out they were unrecognizable.

Besides being masked, they were disguised. Over his doublet of black velvet slashed with silver, Vanni had donned a crimson satin coat which fell to his feet. With a black cape and a solemn manner, he was the epitome of the grave Venetian Senator. Michiele had covered his puce-and-gold glory with a sober black robe edged in white at the throat and was also decently covered by a black cloth cap. Assuming the grave and dignified air of middle-aged patricians, the two young men strolled through the gardens until, coming upon a pair of pretty ladies they snatched them up in a surprise embrace. By the time the ladies had got over the surprise of being kissed by a dignified Senator and a respectable-looking merchant, the two with mocking bows had departed into the crowd to compare scores. Success counted ten points per kiss, a miss counting five against and a foul (when a lady was quick enough to deliver a slap in return) ten against. Michiele was ahead by five when Vanni saw the girl in the cream silk gown.

"Wait here, Michiele. I'll be right back."

"Off to tie the score? All right! I'll wait." Smiling, Michiele returned to the wine steward's table to refresh himself after his labors, while his friend walked swiftly through the crowd toward the girl he had marked out. She was dancing the *galliard* now with a blond man in brown tunic and breeches.

Brown was a color much too subdued for a Venetian. The man must be an ultarmontane.

The girl was young and slender with very black hair, masked however, so he could not see her features. The hair alone distinguished her from the rest of the company, for blondness was all the rage in Venice at the moment, Venetian women spending hours each day on rooftops bleaching their tresses in the sun. There was, however, something besides her hair that attracted him—something in the poise of the head, the daintiness of the figure.

When the dance ended, the man offered his arm and the two strolled out and down one of the paths. Vanni followed as if pulled by strings. Stumbling over the edge of his scarlet robe, he threw it off impatiently, aware that he had no more use for it. In his own person, unmasked, he presented himself before the girl. His bow was returned. He rushed into speech—

"Will you honor me, Madonna, with the next dance?"

For a moment she hesitated. The musicians were playing the opening notes of the *pavane*, at that time in Venice a highly sensuous dance which one did not usually dance with strangers. But then, with a little nod and an upward glance at her partner, she put her hand on Vanni's arm.

"I shall wait for you here, Mattea," said the man, with a heavy Northern accent. He smiled pleasantly at Vanni.

The opening bows were performed and the dance began. The *pavane* in its original form depicts the wiles used by male and female in the course of a seduction, the man displaying himself like a peacock from every vantage point while the female seems to advance even as she retires, eyeing her partner provocatively over her shoulder. The dance ends with the lady inside the circle of the man's arms and at that point it is up to the individuals whether they kiss or separate.

Breathing rather quickly, Vanni and the black-haired girl faced each other, for a moment uncertain. Then something —modesty, perhaps—made the girl draw back. Vanni, suppressing his natural inclinations, at once released her. At the same time, however, he pleaded, "Unmask! Please!" He must know who she was!

Hesitating only long enough to give the surrender some value, the girl slowly untied the silk and the mask fell. She was lovely, but a complete stranger. Very young. Surely no more than sixteen.

The pleasant voice with its German gutterals came again at Vanni's shoulder.

"Time for supper, I think, Mattea."

The girl had been staring expectantly at Vanni, but now, a little disappointed, she turned to her escort.

"Yes, Ari, but first let me present to you our guest of honor, Messer Zuan Caboto."

So she knew who he was. Vanni bowed to the man she introduced as Messer Olafsson, all afire with jealousy. The man was handsome perhaps, but too old! His leather boots and hearty tone surely could not appeal to her. Yet they called each other by their first names. Mattea. Who was she? Why couldn't he remember her? Where had they met? He saw her bite her lip, half-smiling, half-reproachful.

"He does not remember me, Ari. How disappointing."

Miserably he racked his memory, hot with embarrassment. Where had he seen her before? How could he ever have forgotten her?

"I regret, Madonna—" he began unhappily, but his sentence was drowned out by a laugh from the odious Olafsson.

"God-a-mercy, Messer Caboto, don't you know your next-door neighbor?" Next-door neighbor! Not—*basta*—not the little Miracoli girl he had been stumbling over all the past year? It was!

"What has happened to you?" He gaped at her and she lifted her chin loftily.

"If you had bothered to look at me once in a while, you might have noticed I was growing up." She took Olafsson's arm and half-turned away, letting Vanni pay a little for his forgetfulness, then relenting—the *pavane* all over again—she eyed him over her shoulder.

"Perhaps you would like to join us for supper."

He went gratefully, almost humbly. Was this really he? Giovanni Caboto the heartbreaker of the Rialto? He felt like a country bumpkin, all arms and legs and awkward gestures. At the refreshment table he haltingly introduced a surprised Michiele.

"How do you do, Messer Ferari," said Mattea. "Do you know my friend, Master Olafsson?"

"I have not had that pleasure," said Michiele.

"Ari is from Prague," Mattea reported, and Vanni was startled out of his bemusement.

"Are you a heretic?" All he knew of Prague was that it was the center of a Church Reform movement. Heretics had been burned there, and anyone who made any criticsim of Rome was said to be from Prague.

"Of course not!" answered Mattea for him, indignantly. Olafsson smiled.

"I have read and studied the works of Master John Wycliffe, but I do not think that lays me open to a charge of heresy."

"Ari reads a great deal," explained Mattea, "but he is as good a son of the Church as you, Messer Caboto! He had nothing to do with the heresies of Jan Hus. He didn't even live in Prague then, did you, Ari?" She must be very fond of the fellow, thought Vanni unhappily, to defend him so warmly. "Ari was born in the North and lived in Denmark most of his life."

Denmark? At once Vanni thought of Iceland, and then of course of Thule. Denmark was ruler over Iceland.

"Were you ever in Iceland, Messer Olafsson?"

"I lived there as a child. My father was an Icelander, as a matter of fact. We moved to Copenhagen when I was a child. I am a descendant of Norsemen." Olafsson said it with pride, but added with a smile, "and perhaps that accounts for my strange tastes in reading. The old Vikings, you know, were pagans of the wildest sort, bowing neither to men nor gods."

The man was wrong to joke about religion! What could Mattea's father be thinking of to let his daughter consort with such a man? Vanni suddenly conceived it his duty to save her from Olafsson, knowing already that life without Mattea would be quite insupportable.

After that, in his determination to cut out the Icelander, Vanni spent most of his spare time in the house next door, feeling the need to work quickly, because soon he would be off to sea again. Yet it was nearly impossible to get Mattea alone. Olafsson was staying in the house as a guest, and in the evenings there was generally company and Mattea, whose father was a widower, was obliged to act as hostess. A few times there were just Olafsson, Mattea, Messer Miracoli, and himself—and then there was a great deal of talk between the older men. Vanni was bored but feared to interrupt. If he offended Mattea's father, her door might be closed to him.

One evening the company got on the subject of religion again, and Vanni dared to suggest that Olafsson's broadminded attitude verged on heresy. He did not take offence.

"I have no quarrel with the Church," he said, "only with those who claim to be her devoted servants. I despise men who, appointed to serve God in a small community, gad off to Court where life is gayer and more comfortable, while the people they are supposed to guide on the road to Heaven

never see them again! I say only that certain laxness ought
to be corrected, one or two changes made."

"Change is always dangerous," said Mattea's father sententiously. "You know what they say about sweeping out old
devils!"

"Changes will occur nevertheless," said the Northerner
positively. "It is an era of change we live in, Signore." He
turned to Vanni. "Is that not so, Messer Caboto? You must
see a rapid change these days in such things as ship design
and methods of navigation."

It was true of course—rigging particularly had changed
even in the short period during which he himself had been at
sea—but he resented this stranger pointing it out to him.

"A certain amount," he said with reserve.

"In geographical matters too," went on Olafsson, unper-
turbed. "Men no longer fear the cold of the North or the heat
of the Equator as they once did, now that Prince Henry's
men have made their notable voyages." What voyages?
Vanni wanted to hear more about this, yet he could not bring
himself to ask the interloper for information. Who was
Prince Henry? He'd never heard of any Prince Henry!
Olafsson went on to talk of something else, and Vanni
writhed in his impotence.

"Perhaps," said Mattea in a soft voice, "you would like to
take a walk in the garden, Messer Zuan."

He blinked, jumped to his feet, then looked toward Signore Miracoli.

"Very well," said Mattea's father, "for a few minutes
only."

All thought of voyages and Prince Henry was swept away.
Excited, with a sudden feeling of mastery, Vanni followed
Mattea into the garden and they walked down together to
the wall at the edge of the canal where he had first seen her.

It occurred to him that now was his chance to warn her

against Olafsson, showing her in a tactful way that the man's friendship might be dangerous, but he had hardly begun when she interrupted him impatiently.

"Oh, *Ari*—why are we talking of Ari? He is Papa's friend, not mine. He was kind enough to escort me to your party, of course—at Papa's request—and I must be polite since he is our guest—"

"You mean you're not in love with him?" he burst out.

She shot him a demure glance.

"I like him of course—but I couldn't possibly be in love with him. He's *old!*"

Suddenly Ari Olafsson was the most excellent fellow in the world! Just as suddenly, he and Mattea were talking on a much more fascinating subject—themselves! He told her how wonderful she was and how much he loved her and that he couldn't possibly live without her and she was crying a little, but smiling too, and saying—

"But I've loved you ever since that first day!"

After that, of course, there were only minor details to arrange, with the approval of Signore Miracoli. The wedding was set for the spring. And during the remainder of Ari's stay in Venice, he and Vanni became friends. It shocked Vanni a little, though, to hear the Northerner admit to being a poet.

"You, the descendant of Vikings, a poet!"

"They come in all shapes and sizes," said the Icelander, laughing immoderately. "What makes you think a Viking can't be a poet?"

"Poetry is an occupation for ladies and dandies."

"Oh you Venetians—all business! Listen, Master John," —Ari always called him John in the Northern fashion— "for five hundred years all the Court poets of Scandinavia were Icelanders. My people traded songs with the Earls of Orkney and the Princes of England, and wrote among other things the history of our people in verse. Have you never heard of the *Graenlendinga Saga?*"

The younger man shook his head. Never for a moment did he connect the word "Graenlendinga" with the "Groneland" on the sketch map he had found in Alexandria.

"I have little time for poetry, I'm afraid," Vanni said, adding courteously, "but you must compose a song for our wedding, Ari. It will please Mattea."

So Ari said no more about the Sagas, being much too polite to inflict poetry on a man who obviously had no taste for it. Thus, through his own lack of interest, Giovanni Caboto failed to hear about the men who had crossed the Ocean Sea some five hundred years before he himself had ever dreamed of such a thing.

Uncle Luigi was delighted with the match between Mattea and his nephew. Signore Miracoli was not so wealthy a man as himself, but was of better family and able to supply Mattea with a modest dowry. Shrewdly foreseeing that the marriage would take some of the wanderlust out of Zuan and possibly keep him at home where he belonged, Uncle Luigi made his decision. He gave the young couple not only a handsome wedding present but promised to rewrite his will in their favor.

Soon after his marriage, at Uncle Luigi's suggestion, Vanni applied for Venetian citizenship and was granted it the following year. Having resided the required number of years in the city, fifteen, and having fulfilled all the required duties, Zuan Caboto was now entitled "to enjoy for ever and everywhere the rights, liberties, and immunities exercised and enjoyed by other Venetian citizens."

With that, young Master Giovanni Caboto underwent a metamorphosis. No longer was he Vanni Caboto, the seaman nephew of Signore Romano. He was now Messer Zuan Caboto, an established citizen with a house and the beginning of a family. He was surprised to find that he enjoyed his new dignity as a married man and even, to his amusement, began to get pleasure out of telling Uncle Luigi how to improve his old-fashioned business methods. More surprising still, his Uncle sometimes took his advice.

Mattea's dowry bought them a little house in Chioggia where they spent the first happy years of their married life, busy furnishing and refurbishing it. In the course of time, they moved to a finer dwelling within the boundaries of San Jacomo de Lorio and, like homeowners everywhere, soon found themselves involved in household and property problems. In the years that followed, Caboto's time outside business was taken up with such matters as painting and repairing, settling boundary disputes and arguing over water rates, managing gardens and seeing to garbage disposal. For years he never set foot on a ship. Yet he was content.

Two sons were born to the Cabotos during this time. Fra Andrea stood godfather to Ludovico, Michiele to Sebastiano. Occasional visits from Gabriel, now master of his own little trading ship, kept Caboto in touch with maritime affairs to some extent, and at such times they talked nostalgically of their old plan of discovering islands, but there was no urgency in it now. Gabriel too had business to attend to.

"I have enough to do just to make a living. It is getting more and more difficult to procure luxury goods at a reasonable price. Merchants have even taken to studying geography these days, puzzling over the old trade routes, hoping to find a gap in the wall of Islam."

"Hopeless!" Caboto's eyes flared with some of the old excitement. "The only way is west across the Ocean Sea!"

"Not the only way, *mon ami*. I hear whispers now and then in Lisbon that the Portuguese are searching for a way around Africa by sea. What do you think of that?"

Caboto thought about it, vaguely disturbed. He knew that

no one was sure of the shape and size of Africa, or whether or not it was circumnavigable. Marco Polo had stated that a "large kingdom" lay to the south of Cathay and, according to Ptolemy, a vast *Terra Australis Incognita* filled a large part of the southern hemisphere and might join southern Africa to Asia. If it did, the Indian Ocean would be an inland sea and Africa definitely not circumnavigable. There were others, however, who dismissed as a myth the whole idea of an unknown southern continent.

But what difference did it make?

"If it were possible to go that way to the Spice Islands, it would be too far. Across the Western Sea would be shorter!"

"That depends, of course," warned Fra Andrea, who had dropped in during the discussion, "on who is right about the extent of Europe and Asia and also about the circumference of the earth!" And there it always ended.

After Gabriel had gone back to his ship and Fra Andrea had been rowed back to the monastery, Caboto would sometimes sit outside and look at the stars, and dream a little. And often he felt a vague restlessness, a sense of frustration. Then it was time to go in, and next day the ordinary affairs of life recaptured his attention.

So Giovanni Caboto changed inevitably from a happy-go-lucky seaman full of ambition and imagination to a sober, settled merchant and family man. The old dream of a voyage to the Indies was almost dead.

He might have gone on in this way, growing older and more settled and in time forgotten completely, but in 1480 he fell seriously ill.

XVI

Off Course

The disease, which afflicted him suddenly, was a sharp lung disorder and it threatened his life for several months, then required a long slow convalescence. A sea voyage was prescribed by his physician, Fra Andrea, when Caboto was on his feet again and, too weak to care much one way or the other, he went that spring as passenger on Gabriel's ship to Portugal.

The ship was small but weatherly, an ancient *cog* modified and improved by the addition of a mizzen mast fitted with a lateen sail. By the time they reached the Straits, Caboto had regained much of his old delight in the sea and felt, indeed, a kind of heightened appreciation of the world and the fact that he was still alive in it.

Sailing up the Tagus on a full tide, he saw the city of Lisbon for the first time and was surprised and impressed. Gabriel had told him often enough, of course, that Portugal had forged ahead as a maritime power in recent years and would doubtless outstrip Venice in time. Her rejuvenation had begun forty years earlier under the leadership of Prince Henry the Navigator who, besides establishing a center of

cartography and navigational science at Sagres, had spon-
sored voyages south along the coast of Africa to open up new
trading areas and, if possible, to make contact with the
elusive Prester John, who was now supposed to dwell in
central Africa. A profitable trade in slaves and gold had resulted, which in turn had led to further expansion of Portugal's merchant fleet.

Hearing about it from Gabriel, Caboto realized now that
he had not really taken it in. To see it all at firsthand like
this—the teeming harbor, the busy fishing fleet, the ware-
houses, wharves, and supply carts thick along the water front
—was a revelation. His attention was caught particularly, of
course, by the dozens of handy little caravels at anchor in
the stream, as well as those building in the boatyards. He
had seen this ship design develop over the years, combining
the stout hull and square sail of the North with the shallow
draft and lateen sail of the South. Now he saw that Portugal
had brought the design to perfection. Such ships, he suddenly realized, were the answer to Gabriel's, "Where will
you find the ships for such a voyage?" He said so as they
waited for the port officials to come aboard.

"Yes, that is true. You can sail both to windward and before the wind, as the need arises." Gabriel pointed out all the
caravel's attractive features. "They can sail within seven, or
even six, points of the wind, and many of them have been
known to do as much as ten knots in a gale! Their hulls are
shallow enough to pass over sand bars at river mouths and
coast unknown shores, yet quite weatherly enough for Ocean
storms."

Caboto's heart beat faster suddenly.

"So now we have a ship which could sail to the Indies and
back again."

"It does seem possible, *mon ami*, though I for one will still
be content merely to discover one small island off the Iberian

shore. When I find it, I shall turn around very quickly and come back to claim my reward!" So Gabriel still secretly cherished his old ambition. "I did not tell you, Caboto, that I have found a man close to the Court who may be able to help me. He has promised to mention my name in the right circles and swear that I am a famous island-finder. I shall take you to meet him tomorrow. He is a compatriot of yours, an old man now, but in his day he was one of the Navigator's men."

"Not Cadamosto?" He had heard of Cadamosto for the first time quite recently.

"The same."

Caboto recalled that Cadamosto had been in command of the expedition that had discovered the Senegal River.

"I was just born when Cadamosto left Venice," he said, groaning a little over lost opportunities. "Since then, men have reached the Equator and proved the Torrid Zone habitable, while I—I have been doing nothing at all!"

"It might have been wise to try your scheme in Portugal," said Gabriel.

But would the Portuguese have listened to young Giovanni Caboto, Venetian, in those days? He thought not. He had been too young then, too ignorant. Now he was too old! Middle-aged at any rate, with a wife and family, tied to business. He must blanket such foolish ambitions now. Such adventures were for young men, single men like Gabriel.

Meeting Cadamosto the next day, however, made Caboto realize how thin was the blanket between his reason and his ambition. As the old man talked of what Portuguese seamen had done on the African coast and how they were reaching far south of the river he had himself discovered, Caboto thought of the years he had wasted in humdrum living.

"Yes, you have the look of a Venetian," Cadamosto was peering at him sardonically. "Most of my compatriots these days are grave-faced men, cautious, cold-blooded. Once they had vigor and enthusiasm. Your day is over." He meant Venice and Venetians of course, but Caboto took it personally.

"I am Genoese by birth, and I do not agree that—"

"Genoese, eh?" The old man was a little deaf and seldom allowed anyone to finish a sentence. "Then you must know that crazy fellow, Colombo."

Caboto remembered the boy he had seen in the Genoa harbor so long ago, and his anger was lost in curiosity.

"I never met him, but I know whom you mean. Why do you call him crazy?"

"I should not, I suppose,'" Cadamosto admitted. "He's sane enough as a seaman and cartographer. I knew him first when he came to work in his brother's chart shop here in Lisbon. But he's an obstinate, impatient man, with his head full of strange ideas and his mouth ever full of Scripture. For a while he talked of finding islands in the Western Sea, but now I hear he has married a rich widow and gone to live in Porto Santo, so perhaps we shall hear no more of him." So Colombo too had had dreams of islands! "It takes the Portuguese these days to get anywhere."

"And Burgundians?" insinuated Gabriel.

"Ah yes, you've come to the right place, Messer Duchesne. Lisbon is the one place in the world where scholars and practical seamen can get together. Here, initiative is given encouragement." That was all very well, thought Gabriel, but it doesn't get me any farther at the moment. "It will be a sad day," went on Cadamosto, "for Venice when the Portuguese get around Africa. They will be halfway to the Indies then. Oh yes, Signore Caboto, don't look so surprised. You must have heard that the caravels of Portugal are not looking simply for gold and slaves, not even for the priest Prester John, but a new route to the spice market."

Caboto had discussed this with Gabriel, of course, as a

remote possibility. To hear Cadamosto say it so calmly, as a certain and settled thing, made him feel as though a ewer of cold water had been thrown over him. He was given no opportunity to comment, however, for Cadamosto in the fashion of old people allowed his mind to slip suddenly into the past.

"Did I ever tell you, Duchesne, that I once ate elephant meat?" He had, but Gabriel refrained from saying so. "Yes, by San Pietro, I was the first white man to cook and eat elephant!"

"And how did you find it?" asked Gabriel patiently. It was necessary to keep the old man cheerful.

"Very tough and stringy!" Cadamosto laughed gleefully. "But I was young then and had good teeth." He went on to tell them of the Green Walls of Gambia and of Budomel the Moslem Chief, but at last, promising to come for another visit, they got out of the house.

"I wonder if I'm wasting my time," said Gabriel gloomily, as they walked down the hill to the harbor. "The old man is obviously failing, and he may not have the influence he pretends to have. I am afraid the Portuguese want no outside navigators any more—they have enough of their own now."

"One thing is certain," Caboto said, "there is money in Portugal today. It must cost enormous sums to send captains around Africa and at the same time pay out rewards for islands discovered in the Western Sea."

"They haven't paid out for many so far!" said Gabriel.

They walked down through the spectacular town with its jumble of colored houses, its great hill surmounted by the Moorish castle, and down again through narrow streets to the water front beyond the walls. There was a cafe near the foreign wharves which they knew served excellent fish soup and, having walked some time in silence, they turned into the place without discussion. It was full of men, noisy with the clatter of foreign tongues. They found a table off to one side and gave their order.

"Sometimes I think I shall just set off in my little *Sainte Marie* alone," said Gabriel, "and see what I can find."

Caboto smiled wryly.

"Times have changed since we were boys, Gabriel. Today one needs a King or a merchant syndicate behind one to provide ship, supplies, and crew. Men won't sail without having their wages guaranteed by government, and governments can't afford to leave exploration to individuals, not with gold deposits low and even the silver mines of Germany unable to cope with the demand for coinage. They know there will be no real expansion of commerce until someone finds a place where gold is mined in greater quantities than that found in Africa. Be patient, Gabriel. Perhaps Cadamosto will be able to do something."

"I doubt it, *mon ami*. I believe the Portuguese have enough trained captains of their own for such schemes. It is Portuguese voyages they generally sponsor, even the few that venture west into the Ocean Sea."

"Do you know of any that have sailed recently?"

"There was one—a ship of Fayal. She sailed to the north or northwest in search of an island or mainland thought to be the site of the Seven Cities. She returned, unsuccessful."

Caboto's eyes gleamed.

"The King did not send that ship out without being fairly sure there was something there! He must have had reports of such a land being seen. North or northwest—Gabriel, it may have been Thule!"

"Thule is Iceland," protested Gabriel. "And Iceland has been known to the Portuguese fishermen for as many years as it has been known to the Danes who rule it."

"I don't mean the Thule of Pytheas, but the Thule which

means 'the land farthest north.' Tartary, Gabriel, is the land farthest north of Cathay!"

"And so?"

"What if the land that ship of Fayal went to find was a projection of Tartary in the west?"

Gabriel, seeing Caboto grow excited, was typically ready to put a damper on things.

"You yourself, *mon ami*, have told me Cathay is at least five thousand miles from Europe."

"At the Equator, yes. But the earth is round, Gabriel, and narrows toward each of the poles!"

"Even so, one would still be a very long way from the Spice Islands."

"Once the coast was reached, one would only have to follow the shore south and southwest to where they lie in the equinoctial regions. Less than twenty-five hundred miles of open water in the north, then a coastal voyage of the same distance!"

Caboto's blood was leaping now. Gabriel, however, remained cold.

"Twenty-five hundred miles is still a long way. And on sheer speculation!" He was about to remind Caboto of the cold in the North, the icy winds, and the variable winds when he saw his friend's face light up, his eyes focusing on someone behind Gabriel.

"Master Thorne!" Caboto jumped to his feet, smiling.

Gabriel turned and saw a burly man in seaman's clothes staring with pleased recognition. He grasped both of Caboto's hands.

"By all the saints, Master Cabot, this is wonderful!" the Englishman cried, dropping the final "o" from the name in the usual English fashion. Standing back, he stared at the Venetian in sudden concern. "You're as thin as a strake, man! What's happened to you?"

"I've been ill, but I'm now fast recovering. Let me present you to my comrade, Master Duchesne. Gabriel, this is the English friend I told you about—Master Robert Thorne of Bristol."

The two shook hands and Caboto invited Thorne to sit with them. Over the fish soup and good local wine, the three men got better acquainted. Robert Thorne, a smaller, more muscular version of his cousin Sir William, was in Lisbon unloading a cargo of English wool and taking on a load of spices and wine for return to England. He was red-faced, forthright, as much fisherman as merchant, and Gabriel put him down as shrewd and unpolished, but bluffly honest. They spoke in English, Caboto having picked up a good deal of that language on his visit to Bristol, and Gabriel, the sea-man, a constant visitor to foreign ports, was used to un-raveling foreign tongues.

"England!" cried Caboto extravagantly. "You remind me of England, Master Thorne—England in the spring!" Gabriel stared at his friend in astonishment. "How I remember the green of the meadows! Nowhere in the Mediterranean, Gabriel, is it so green as in England."

This was the first time Caboto had shown signs of being either a nature-lover or, indeed, a lover of England.

Master Thorne beamed at Caboto paternally.

"Well then! Why not return with me on the *Griffin* to Bristol? I leave Saturday if the weather is fair. A visit to England will complete your cure."

"By San Giorgio!" cried Caboto. "Why not?" He glanced at Gabriel, who suddenly saw the light. Caboto had been angling deliberately for the invitation. Now, seeing what was required of him, he hastened to say—

"Why not, *mon ami*! There are ships returning to Lisbon every week or so. I can pick you up here at your convenience."

"Thank you, Gabriel," said Caboto happily, "That's all I wanted to know. Thanks, Master Thorne, I shall be delighted to accept your kind invitation. It is an opportunity which may not occur soon again."

And so it was arranged.

XVII

Return to Course

It was April of 1481 when Giovanni Caboto sailed with
Thorne on the *Griffin*. On the voyage to England—a fast trip,
lasting less than four weeks—the Venetian studied with close
attention the ship's behavior off the coasts of France and
vastly improved his knowledge of Ocean weather conditions,
as well as the sailing habits of a fore-and-aft type of vessel.
He was confirmed in what he remembered of this coast from
his previous voyage on the galley. How different from the
Mediterranean—with her bright warm days and starry nights,
her steep dropping off of the land from her coasts and her
almost tideless water! Here, off sloping treacherous shores,
the *Griffin* had to maneuver through days of fog and rain,
feel her way at night when no star was visible, and enter
no harbor without her officers' careful examination of tide
tables.

Caboto was allowed to handle the ship part of the time
and liked her sailing qualities. It would not be true to say
that on this voyage he learned all there was to learn of
pilotage along the western coast of Europe, but he made a
good start.

The two men became closer friends on the voyage. Now it was "John" and "Robert" and frank discussions of commerce and the state of the world. One night, Caboto spoke of Thule and his early hero worship of Pytheas who, after the Phoenicians, was probably the first Mediterranean man to land in Britain.

"I keep thinking of him on this voyage, imagining his dismay at the weather conditions. I wonder where he first met with fog. Surely he had had experience of it before he reached the 'sea-lung.'" Caboto stared through a mist in which the bow of the ship could barely be seen. They were only just moving, and lookouts were sharply alert. Everything one touched was wet, and all sounds were dulled by the atmosphere.

"Thule must have been Iceland," Thorn decided, "though I have never heard of mead being made there. Perhaps bees lived farther north in those days. The climate has certainly changed, even in my time. I can remember when the old men talked of voyages to Greenland, but that colony's probably died out altogether by now—too cold up there!"

"Greenland?" Caboto frowned, wondering where he'd heard a name like that before.

"Aye, Greenland's an island somewhere up northwest of Iceland, or so they tell me—I've never been there myself. Tales are told, I don't know how true they are, that the old Vikings discovered it long ago and set up colonies. If they did, they must have all died by now. Nobody nowadays seems to know for sure where the place was. 'Tisn't on any map that I know of."

Map! Suddenly Caboto remembered the map he had found in Alexandria, the one showing three islands off Europe. Yes, one was Groneland! And what was the one farthest west? He would have to look it up when he returned to Venice. Giovanni Caboto felt a familiar stir of excitement, some of the old thrill he had felt that day in Fra Andrea's library when the idea had first come to him of sailing west to find Cathay. "Perhaps *that* was where Pytheas went!"

"Unlikely, John. Didn't you say that old Greek's Thule was six days' sail from England? Well, Greenland's more like three weeks away, I'd judge."

"Another lost island," sighed Caboto. "A fairy tale, like the Isle of Brasil and the Seven Cities."

Thorne's face grew solemn.

"I wouldn't say that."

Caboto looked at his English companion questioningly. "You don't believe it's a fairy tale?"

"There may be something in it—but who can tell?"

Caboto sensed evasion.

"I've heard of St. Brandan's and Brasil and the Seven Cities so often, and now I'm growing cynical, Robert. I wonder if they aren't the product of sailors' imaginations, induced by seeing a cloud on the horizon. It seems strange that so many are sighted, yet nobody seems able to land on one and fix its position so it can be found again."

The Bristol man refused to be drawn.

"It's hard to say," he remarked. Provoked, Caboto found himself wondering all sorts of things. Thorne knew something about lost islands, something besides the half-real stories of Greenland, something—

"Sail to larboard!" came a sudden cry.

All saw her at the same moment—a ship looming up out of the fog. For the length of an Ave, the startled men on both ships regarded each other from their respective decks, realizing how close they had come to collision. Then a chatter of voices came from the other vessel, a shout rising above it—

"English, by damn! Man the guns!"

Caboto did not understand the words, but seeing the crew

of the stranger scurry to the guns he guessed what they meant.

"Danes!" muttered Thorne. "Bettter armed—better manned."

"Will they attack?" The ship was fading into the mist.

Thorne looked up at his sails hanging limp, except for a flutter or two in the topsails. The *Griffin* drifted, making only the faintest headway.

"Aye, if they can get back. And they're rigged high enough to take advantage of that breeze aloft."

No time for Caboto to wonder why the two ships should fight. He accepted Thorne's word for it and his mind jumped ahead to possible action. First, was it really possible for the foreigner to return on such a light breeze? She might, with her more efficient sail-plan, by tacking slightly. If she succeeded in intercepting the smaller, almost stationary English ship, they would be at her mercy, that at least was certain. Even in that quick glimpse he had seen that the armament of the Danish ship was far superior to their own. One small cannon was fastened to the *Griffin's* poop deck, and that was all. It was chiefly for signalling purposes and was probably fitted with a very small charge and low muzzle velocity. It would have little penetrating power, even fired at point-blank range. Any real defensive strength lay in the personal arms of the ship's company—sword, crossbow, and arquebus—but would they have any chance to use them at close quarters? The other ship had long-range, heavy-shotted guns, large enough to sink the *Griffin* from a distance. If, however, the Danes hoped to capture the English ship without damaging her, they might try to board and if this happened—

"We can only wait," growled Thorne, "and hope they lose us in the fog."

Caboto hesitated, but this was no time for considering the feelings of his English friend.

"Not necessarily. I have an idea."

"Well?" No harm in listening, Thorne's face said.

"Part of your cargo is oil, isn't it?"

"Aye, stored in casks."

"Bring up a dozen casks and keep them ready in the highest parts of the ship. If the Dane shoots from a distance to sink us, there is nothing to be done, but it is possible they'll try to board and capture us. If they do, that's our chance. You've heard, I suppose, of Greek fire?"

Thorne's eyes began to gleam.

"This will be the nearest thing to it we can manage," said Caboto grimly. "When they are nearly close enough to grapple, we must hurl those casks, burning, into their ship."

"Right!"

Master Thorne began to shout orders while Caboto, seized with another idea, set the ship's boys to work wrapping and tying cloths around the bolts of the crossbows. Meanwhile casks, flints, tinder, and wood shavings were gathered in the forepeak.

"Fill those fire buckets with water," ordered Thorne "and keep the sand handy. We don't want to set *ourselves* on fire!"

"There she is!" somebody shouted, and the Danish vessel appeared on the larboard quarter, a looming menace. But Caboto felt a surge of joy seeing the Dane's topsails all set, knowing she meant definitely to come right down on them. He saw grappling gear being readied, besides.

"Smartly now!" he cried to the boys, and Thorne gave the order to light torches. A whistling sound overhead announced a cannon shot from the Dane, but it passed the *Griffin* wide.

"Light up!" shouted Thorne again, and himself smashed the top of an oil cask with his axe, while the nearest sailor applied a lighted torch to the oil. "Steady! Up shoulder high! Now!"

From the height of the peak, two flaming casks were slung into the waist of the other vessel, where they burned harmlessly for the moment. An arrow whizzed past Caboto's ear, making him jump.

"Into her cargo now, lads!"

Caboto set the example by lighting his oil-soaked bolt from a burning torch. As he fitted it to his crossbow, a sailor standing beside him screamed and fell back with stone-shot in his chest. Caboto's arrow steadied, then flew straight to its target, the open hatch of the Danish vessel, and disappeared below. Already the other ship was in panic, for fire is the thing most feared in wooden ships. Now, seeing smoke issue from the hatch, they forgot all about the English and rushed to fight the fire below decks.

"Keep it up!" cried Thorne exultantly. Then, his heart in his mouth, he leaped to stamp out a flame that had spread from a cask to some gear on his own deck. "Take care, you fools! Do you want to burn us up as well?"

Caboto saw another danger. The burning, frantic Dane was drifting down on them, her helm deserted for the moment.

"Fend off!" The mate saw the danger at the same time and screamed to his men to leave the casks, to use oars, pikes, anything handy, to keep the Danish craft from drifting into them.

The Dane, her foresail alight now, her deck a hurly-burly of fire fighters, missed them by inches. She slid by and disappeared into the gloom, even the flare of her burning sails at last blotted from sight.

"Douse the fire!" cried Thorne, exhausted but jubilant, and the crew ran for the fire buckets. When the last flame was safely extinguished, Thorne and Caboto looked around them. One man, the bosun, lay still on the deck, an arrow through his throat. Another, the man beside Caboto earlier, sobbed to himself, his arms tightly hugging his chest. One or two mopped at bloody heads.

Thorne sent the ship's boy below for bandages while he himself did his best to staunch the blood of the wounded man with a neckcloth pressed against the wound.

Part of the *Griffin's* gunwale was swept away by gunshot, one of the sails was torn, but otherwise they had come off well—very well, considering the odds. They might all have been dead by now.

The English saw no more of the Dane. By morning the fog had cleared and they sighted Avonmouth. There they had to wait for the tide, so the *Griffin* anchored for the night—a calm night in the shelter of the land. The two men strolled the deck and the usually loquacious Thorne was quiet, listening apparently to the remarks dropped by Caboto but saying little himself. Suddenly he broke into something the Venetian was saying about wine tunnage—

"John, you did me a good turn yesterday."

Caboto smiled in the darkness.

"It benefited me as much as you, my friend."

Thorne brushed this aside.

"I dare say you're wondering what it was all about."

"You told me England and Denmark have been at war, sporadically, on the sea at least, since 1477 when the Governor of Iceland was killed by English sailors in a riot. I gather it really stems, however, from rivalry over the Iceland fisheries?"

"That's the basis of it, yes. We used to do a lot of business with Iceland, especially in fish, and we miss it. The Hanseatic League is bent on dominating Iceland and its fisheries, and there's been more than one armed clash between us in neutral waters. Also our ships are seized if they enter Danish ports. It's getting so the whole game isn't worth the candle. Nevertheless we must have fish!"

That was true enough. Fish commanded a sale anywhere in Europe at good prices. Salt fish especially was a staple item of diet in all Catholic countries. The power of Portugal had grown from her fisheries and fishing was still one of her most important industries.

"Now what I have to tell you is in confidence, John." Caboto nodded. "We've been looking for new fishing grounds." Natural enough. But now Robert Thorne lowered his voice still more. "A few years ago, a Bristol ship was blown west on a freak wind that lasted off and on for five weeks and at one point, when they were completely lost and in fear of their lives, they saw a rocky land loom up to the west." Caboto's heart gave a leap. "Remember now, they were over a month out from Ireland at that time and as far as they could tell they'd been blown steadily west and north-west. At the time, their one concern was to claw off that lee shore. Even if they'd thought to mark their position, they couldn't, having long since lost track of their dead reckoning. But—and mark this, John—this is the meat of the matter. Three days later they came upon an incredibly rich fishing ground. They say—I know the men and can vouch for their honesty—that the fish were so thick they could be hauled up in baskets! Cod and stockfish—more than they'd ever seen in their lives. I saw the cargo myself when the ship docked— oh yes, she got back eventually—a miracle to my way of thinking. But here's the tragedy—no way of finding those fishing grounds again! They're lost! We want to find them— and we can't!"

It was not the fisheries of course, but the mention of land which excited Giovanni Caboto. What land was it? Tartary? A projection of Cathay to the north? One of the lost islands? He had to force his mind to follow what Thorne was saying.

"And since such a fishing resource could be taken up entirely free from armed conflict with Denmark, we *must* find it again. They could have our habitual fishing grounds and welcome, if we had Brasil."

"Brasil?"

"That's the name we give it among ourselves, John. Of course, the land they saw might be St. Brandan's lost isle or another. The name doesn't matter. It's the fact that it points to those lost fisheries that interests us. Only we're keeping very quiet about it, because it's not only the Icelanders who'd be happy to hear about that landfall. The Portuguese are always on the lookout for newer and richer fishing grounds. So—quietly—last year we sent out a ship to look for it." Caboto held his breath. "We got the best mariner in all England—Captain John Lloyd—but he never found a thing. Still we're not giving up. This year we're sending two more ships. We feel, you see, it's worth almost any amount of money and effort to find that cod again!"

Caboto's heart swelled with desire. Two ships going out across the Ocean Sea to look for land in the west! An island possibly. Perhaps even mainland. The mainland of Cathay, of Asia! Why not? By San Giorgio—if only he could sail with them! But of course it was impossible. He was a stranger, a foreigner. It was a local affair and highly secret.

". . . and they're the *George* and the *Trinity*."

Caboto jerked his mind back. Thorne was talking about the ships that would make the quest.

"Good stout little ships. They'll sail the latter part of June most likely. I don't suppose—" Thorne paused, shot Caboto a look under shaggy brows. "I don't suppose now you'd like to go along?"

"Santa Maria! How did you know I wanted—"

Thorne chuckled, suddenly full of good humor.

"Didn't anyone ever tell you, John, you've a speaking

countenance? Aye, the longing was in your face, but that wasn't why I asked you."

"Would it be permitted?" Caboto's anxious gaze sought Thorne's. "I'm a Venetian, a foreigner. Would they trust me?"

"I trust you," said Thorne simply. "Besides, frankly, I think you could be useful to us. You're not only an experienced mariner, you're an educated man. You're up on matters to do with navigation—all these new tricks we only hear about. Our seamen depend on rhumb lines to follow, with a bit of help from the stars. Now it seems to me that's not enough for our purpose. We need someone who can handle these new-fangled instruments, like the Portuguese have, so we don't have to depend altogether on dead reckoning. Mind you, John, so far this is my own idea. I'd have to take it up with my partners before I could give the word."

"Naturally! I understand that." But Caboto's heart surged with optimism. Was it to be as simple as this, then, after all? A project already accepted, plans made, a place open for him. It was true he knew something of the new navigation, could use both quadrant and sea astrolabe. Also, of course, he could take star sights and figure latitude, as well as navigate by dead reckoning. None of the instrument reckonings could be made with much accuracy on a plunging deck, but if he could get ashore he knew with certainty he could fix his position so as to find it again.

"We English can find our way well enough around Britain and Iceland and down to the Azores by figuring so many rhumbs north, so many west, and so on—but charting a way across that big Ocean and marking the fishing grounds so we can find them again, that's the hard part. That's where you come in."

Caboto felt like shouting. He also felt like admitting to Fra Andrea at last that he was right. Learning was now paying dividends! He forced himself to be calm, however, knowing the English thought the Southerner much too emotional. Huggings and cryings simply embarrassed them. They didn't, themselves, go in much for displays of emotion. So he contented himself with a broad smile and a grip on Thorne's shoulder which must have hurt him.

The idea crossed his mind that he ought to tell Thorne his own secret, but he hesitated. He felt sure he could trust the man, but Thorne was only one of a group, and he did not care to entrust his secret to all Bristol, not at this stage of the game, when he himself was still unsure of what lay across that vast expanse of water. As far as he could see, it had never occurred to Thorne or his colleagues that land in the west might form part of the continent of Asia. If they had read the works of their own scholars—Roger Bacon, for example, or Sacrobosco—the English might easily have jumped to this conclusion themselves!

"Have you ever read the book of Marco Polo, Robert?" he asked tentatively.

"Marco who?" asked the merchant. "Can't say I read much. I'm not much of a Latinist. I don't suppose the fellow wrote in English?"

"No." Not Marco Polo, or Bacon, or Cardinal d'Ailly, nor any of the academic geographers. Thorne did not continue the subject and Caboto decided it was a sign he should keep his knowledge to himself for the time being.

Again the enormity of what was happening swept over him. His great moment seemed to have arrived without plan or preparation. It was almost too easy. Then he reminded himself that such a voyage, even if they found what they were looking for, could be no more than a reconnaissance. There would be no gold, no spices, in Northern Asia. Perhaps no cities either. If he found the continent of Asia over there, his work would only be half done. Still, the first step would

have been taken. He thought of Pytheas with a glow of fel-
low-feeling!

Mattea received word from her wandering husband that
he intended to wander a little farther before returning to
Venice. He would, in fact, not return until the following
year.

"There is plenty of money in the bank," he wrote, "to take
care of the boys and yourself. And of course there is always
Uncle Luigi to call upon in an emergency. Perhaps you had
better show him this letter. I kiss your hands, my darling,
and the year will be long without seeing you . . ."

Mattea had to gather her courage in both hands to take
the letter to Uncle Luigi whom, if the truth must be told, she
feared. She was certain he would be angry even if, as usual,
he did not show his feelings openly. She tried to read his face
as he perused the letter.

"So he remains in England for the winter, and most of the
summer as well." The cold eyes were expressionless as he
handed back the letter. "I thought Zuan had got over these
fits of irresponsibility, but it seems not. He has always had
this romantic vein. One can only hope that when he returns
he will have finally got the wanderlust out of his system.
Then he can settle down in his proper sphere of life. That,
my dear," he added meaningly, "will be largely up to you. I
trust you will remember, if Zuan does not, all he owes to me,
and all he will have in the future if my generosity and affection is properly repaid." That was all he said, but Mattea
fully understood the underlying threat. No more romantic
nonsense, or away goes the inheritance!

From Bristol's standpoint, the voyage was a failure. From
Caboto's too, it was disappointing. If he had not fully real-
ized before the magnitude of the task set the captains of the
George and the *Trinity*—to find a particular uncharted desti-

nation on that great waste of waters—he knew it by the end
of the voyage. Caboto himself had had no official position on
board the *George*. He was down on the ship's papers as
bosun, was expected to keep a dead reckoning of his own,
and if land was found, to fix its position by instrument. But
no land was found. Moreover, the captain, a silent and dour
Yorkshireman, was unwilling to admit that a second navigator was necessary. He withheld from the Venetian interloper
certain vital information on the course and generally made
things as difficult as possible. In storm and fog, unable to
keep track of changes in direction and able only to guess at
speed, Caboto was soon distrustful of the deduced figures
in his reckoning. Nevertheless, he put the voyage down to
useful experience. If he were ever to cross the Western Sea as
master, he would know better what he was about. He was
given an urgent invitation from Robert Thorne and his partners to have another try with them next year.

Caboto went home to Venice in the autumn, looking fitter
and happier than Mattea had seen him look in years. She
dreaded to tell him the news. Uncle Luigi had suffered a
heart attack in his absence and would be laid up for an indefinite period. The whole burden of his business and private
affairs, therefore, would fall on his nephew, and Zuan would
have no spare time for exploring adventures. Ah well. He
owed Uncle Luigi something. It was good to be back with
Mattea and the boys. It wouldn't be long before Uncle
Luigi recovered and he, Caboto, would be free again.

But Uncle Luigi was ill for a long time, and convalescent
over an even longer period. Soon after Caboto's return
from England, he was sent on a voyage to the Levant to
straighten out the Arab end of Uncle Luigi's business. In the
next summer a third son, Soncio, was born to the Cabotos,
and Caboto had to write to Thorne to explain that he would

not be able to accompany him on any voyages to Brasil for a while. Perhaps next year—

Shortly after his voyage and return, he had visited Fra Andrea who was delighted to hear about the experiment in England. He himself was laboring under some secret excitement, though he managed to contain it for the moment.

"So you believe," he said, "that what the Bristol men are looking for is what you too wish to find."

"I do! I believe we only call the same thing by two names. Their Brasil is my Asia—Asia, or one of its outlying islands. As far as I can judge from their description and the amount of time they spent on that first accidental voyage of discovery, the land cannot lie much more than two thousand miles away."

"So little?"

"We know the globe narrows in the north and that makes the distance shorter. It seems to me that this proves the circumference cannot be as great as Eratosthenes estimated. Even around the Equator, the Spice Islands should not lie much more than six or seven thousand miles from Europe."

"Toscanelli says five thousand!" cried Fra Andrea, unable to contain his news a moment longer. He smiled excitedly as Caboto gave him his full attention. "Yes, I have met and talked with the great Dr. Toscanelli."

Caboto had naturally heard of the great Florentine physician whose hobby was mathematics, who was an amateur geographer and a devoted reader of *The Travels of Marco Polo*.

"He has studied Marco Polo's itinerary and has come to certain conclusions about the possibility of sailing west to reach the eastern shore of Asia. He has even drawn a map of Asia according to Polo's descriptions."

"San Giorgio! If I could only see it!"

"I have a copy, you may be sure," said the friar smugly, and laid it out for him to see. Caboto studied it.

"What do the lines mean? What sort of co-ordinates are they? They're not Ptolemy's kind."

"Toscanelli has used his own system. The lines running lengthwise indicate the distance from east to west, and those from top to bottom the distance north and south."

"How many miles in each square?"

"Two hundred and fifty."

"Then—" Caboto calculated swiftly, "from the city of Lisbon due west to the city of Kinsai in the province of Manjii—twenty spaces, five thousand miles!"

"And look, Vanni, the map shows steppingstones along the way—first, the Canaries, then Antillia, or lower down, the Cape Verdes and St. Brandan, finally Cipango! Which leaves virtually only two thousand miles of open water!"

"It sounds," said Caboto slowly, "too good. Five thousand miles across the sea at almost its widest part. It can't be." Fra Andrea's face fell. "Yes, I know Dr. Toscanelli bases his figures on what Marco Polo said, but Polo was pretty indefinite about actual latitudes and mileage. Then Antillia is still an unknown quantity. If one missed it, the sea voyage would be nearer five thousand than three, and still a good way down to the Spice Islands."

"Dr. Toscanelli is a scholar of the greatest probity and renown, but of course he is human. He could be wrong."

Caboto smiled.

"I'm glad to see you putting your precepts to work, Padre!" His eyes went to the top of the map. The North did not project in the way he had hoped. Still, the chart of Toscanelli was a fascinating piece of evidence. He told the friar so, and thanked him.

"But you're quite right," admitted Fra Andrea. "We must not allow ourselves to be carried away by a piece of paper,

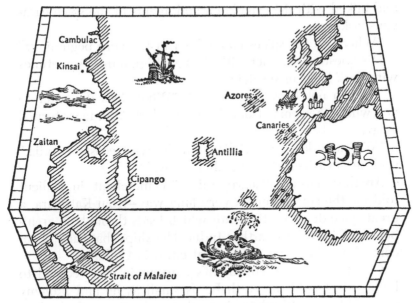

Reconstruction of Toscanelli's chart

even though I understand he sent a similar map to the Court of Portugal—and also to a Genoese seaman interested in discovering Ocean islands."

"Genoese?" Caboto felt a foreboding. "Wouldn't you say it's my old compatriot Colombo again? How that man keeps crossing my path!" So Colombo was another island-hunter. As long as he only hunted islands, Caboto did not fear competition.

It was exasperating to go back to the old routine of buying and selling, but he was growing more cautious. Promising himself a visit to England as soon as Uncle Luigi was on his feet, Caboto settled down to business. However when, the following year, he was obliged to make a business trip to Alexandria, he seized the chance to follow out another line of inquiry. He made a brief trip to Mecca and there he met and talked with the camelmen and agents of the spice caravans, asking—

"Where do the spices come from in the very beginning?"

His question was met with shrugs of ignorance, sometimes with dark looks of suspicion.

"We do not know," most said. "What does it matter to you where they come from?" And the dark Arab faces turned away.

"We came last from Calicut on the west coast of India," said one evasively. "That's all I know."

Another, more talkative, said, "A merchant in Calicut told me the spices came a very long way—from Kattigara, a great spice depot on the strait which leads through an archipelago of islands to Farther India. The ships that carry them come from the north, from great cities in Cathay."

Caboto looked at Toscanelli's map again and yearned to believe it. Could the earth be as small as he and Ptolemy argued? He went back to Eratosthenes, hoping to find a flaw in that Greek's measurements. He even hired an Alexandrian mathematician to go and make the calculations himself. Caboto was delighted with the results. It seemed that Eratosthenes might have been mistaken. The sun, his agent told him, did not shine directly down any well in Syene. Neither was Alexandria directly north of Syene as the old Greek had claimed. Moreover, Eratosthenes was said to have made his calculations by camel arithmetic! Assuming the fairly constant speed of a camel to be one hundred *stadia* a day (and who knew today what the length of a Greek *stadia* was in miles?) Eratosthenes had measured the distance between Syene and Alexandria by that method, and had got twenty-five thousand miles. Posidonius' method could not be discovered, but his figure of seventeen thousand was backed by the opinion of the great Ptolemy. Perhaps Toscanelli was right after all! Gradually, he returned to his original idea of a voyage straight west from the Canaries, direct to the Spice Islands.

Slowly Uncle Luigi regained his health and strength and Caboto dreamed of putting his conclusions to the ultimate test. Tentatively he mentioned his ideas to Mattea. She was apprehensive at once.

"You mean you would sail on this voyage yourself?"

"Of course. I wouldn't want anyone else to try it. It is my idea! You think I am too old, is that it?"

"No, no, of course not!" Mattea was quick to reassure him on that score. "You are not old, *caro*, but the voyage might be dangerous. You don't know what might happen!"

"I've made plenty of dangerous voyages in my day. I don't see that this one would be any worse than the others. And the rewards, my dear, would be enormous. Think of the riches I could bring to you—pearls, gold—"

"I am content as I am, Zuan, so long as I have you and the children. Why can you not be content too?" she pleaded.

"Mattea, a man with a dream is never content until he has put the dream to the test."

She looked at him forlornly.

"When—when will you leave?"

He embraced her with gratitude.

"As soon as I can find a sponsor."

"But didn't you say Venice would never allow—"

"Not in Venice. We will go to Spain."

She broke away in horror.

"To Spain? You mean leave Venice—all of us?"

"Of course. It will be a long business—"

"But what about Uncle Luigi?" she asked urgently.

"He's better now—"

"I don't mean that! I mean what will he do? He will never forgive us, Zuan. The money—the inheritance—"

Caboto set his jaw.

"Uncle Luigi must do as he thinks best about that."
Mattea threw her arms around him, tearfully.

"No, no! You can't, Zuan—you can't leave Venice, give up everything, our whole future—all you've worked for—just for a dream! The boys, Zuan—what about the boys? Their future! You can't throw it all aside for nothing!"

"For nothing?" he cried. "My dear Mattea, if I am successful, you and the boys will be richer than Uncle Luigi ever dreamed of being!" But it was no use. For Mattea the present and immediate substance were real, a dream was a dream and no more.

The argument went on, not for hours, but for days. He could see her side, of course, which made it difficult to hold out. Mattea was Venetian-born, the mother of three boys, confidently looking forward to the day when she and her husband would be well off, the boys' futures assured. Now she was being asked to step out into the unknown in a project which for her held neither reason nor attraction. She was an Italian woman, she loved her husband, and in the end she would go, uncomplaining, where he led. He knew that—but also he knew she would fight to the last breath before giving in. She brought in his brother Piero as a supporter.

"She's right, Vanni." Piero was on the side of his sister-in-law, on the side of common sense. "You'd be crazy to leave now. Uncle Luigi is getting old. It can't be long now before you come into everything and then you can do as you please."

"It will be too late."

"What's a few years? You must think of Mattea and your children."

According to all common sense and reason, they were right. Was it fair of him to make his family suffer for what he alone wanted?

"Take more time, Vanni," Piero advised him. "Think it over."

"A year! Only a year," pleaded Mattea, "for my sake? For the sake of your sons! Please, Zuan!"

In the end of course, he agreed. A year wasn't long. He could spend it in building up his savings, so as to be ready when the time came. He owed his family that much. Yet even as he told himself this, he had the secret fear in him that perhaps it was his own cowardice that had made him give in—his own voiceless doubts. At any rate, it would not hurt to wait a year, and see . . .

At the end of that year, baby Soncio was ill and the time was not ripe. The boy got better, the months went by, and another year had slipped away before Caboto knew it.

He heard news through Gabriel of what was happening in other parts of the world. The Portuguese continued to forge ahead. Their man Cão had planted stone pillars as far south as the Congo. Spain was increasing her pressure on the Moors in a final effort to drive them from Spain. She would soon have time to put her growing energy to work rivaling Portugal's maritime progress. Colombo, that ubiquitous fellow, had put before the Portuguese King some scheme for a voyage to find lost islands and had been turned down. In his despair, rumor said, he had gone into a monastery in Spain.

There was no word from Bristol. The Thornes were not letter-writers. Caboto, moreover, swayed by Toscanelli and by his own researches in Mecca, was now all for a voyage across the Ocean in lower latitudes—direct from the Cape Verdes to the Spice Islands. He even constructed a globe on which he traced his route. Yet more and more, it all began to have a dream quality . . .

He told himself that in one more year he would have enough put by to be independent of Uncle Luigi. Along with his factor's work for Signore Romano, he was dealing in real estate—buying, improving, and selling at a profit. Soon he would have enough to provide for his family without working—for a while at least. He would take a sabbatical year, investigate his project seriously before taking definite action.

Sometimes for months at a time, he forgot all about the Spice Islands.

He was forty now, settled, successful. Why take a chance? His father had been dead for some years. Emilio had gone to his rest at last. Piero was married, with a large family, doing well in the family business. He sometimes visited Venice and took a share in some of his brother's real estate deals. Family affection between them was strong. Piero was right. Why grasp after a will-o'-the-wisp? Be thankful for what you have.

Yet now and then, at night usually, when sleep would not come, Caboto was abruptly appalled at how time was passing. He had waited too long, wasted too much time! Each year would make it harder to break away. Then he would toss and turn in his comfortable bed until he could stand it no longer, would fling back the covers and go out on the balcony to stare up at the stars. They were as familiar, but as far away, as always. One might as well speculate about them as about the Indies! They were certainly no farther off as far as his own hopes and plans were concerned. He tasted the bile of bitterness and failure. Mattea, inside, lying awake, was afraid.

To Fra Andrea, who had grown visibly old of late, Caboto expressed himself in the plainest way—

"Aristotle says we are engaged in becoming. I, Padre, am engaged merely in dying! I am middle-aged! Forty-one on my next birthday, and I have done nothing."

Fra Andrea, a little tired, a little resigned too, tried to reassure him.

"Nothing, my son? You have done much—lived uprightly, raised a good family. Perhaps that is all God means you to do. If it is His will that you should do more, you will know when the time comes. Slowly, slowly." But with the usual familiar two-word advisement, Fra Andrea's eyes grew wistful. He admitted to himself that he would like to have participated in a dream before he died, if only by proxy.

These times of indecision were the worst.

Then, over the short period of a year, three things happened in quick succession.

The Cabotos had a visit from Mattea's old friend, Ari Olafsson who, during an evening of talk, mentioned that he was writing a poem adapted from the Sagas. Then, for the first time, Caboto heard the story of the crossing of the Ocean Sea four hundred years before he was born. It shook him to the core.

This thing had already been done! Eric the Red and his son Leif, and Thorvald and Karsefni had found and settled a portion of the land west of Iceland—not onl·· Groneland but the island called Vinlandia on his Alexandrian map! Vinlandia could be the Brasil of the Bristol men, the Cathay of Marco Polo! Caboto badgered Ari for information. How did they go—what sort of ships did they have? How long did it take them? What weather did they encounter? How long did they stay—and why did they leave? Ari did his best to answer. The Vikings had sailed in open vessels called *knorr*, they found their way by observing the shadows of the gunwale on the thwarts at noon, they even understood some practical astronomy. Sometimes they followed birds to find land. They generally sailed from island to island but there was no certain record of distances or days traveled, in most cases. They encountered fog and ice and storms and cold in most of their voyages. Over a period of years—how many was not known for sure—they established colonies on the shores of Groneland and Vinlandia, also Markland and Helluland.

"But the natives of the country made things too hot for them and eventually they gave up. Remember this is a mixture of poetic literature and a history of things that happened way back in the tenth century, so I cannot give you day and date."

"I should like to have seen their ships!" murmured Caboto. When Ari was gone, he got out his Alexandrian map and studied it again, willing it to tell him more—but all he saw were the three islands off the coast of Europe with no evidence as to their latitude or longitude. He turned again to Toscanelli's rigidly squared-off chart. Off Asia's east coast, above and below Cipango, were many islands—unnamed, unmarked. Could they be the same islands the Vikings had found? The maps showed so much—and so little!

Next he had a visit from Gabriel who told him that a man named Bartolomeu Diaz had returned the year before from a voyage out of Lisbon, claiming he had rounded the tip of Africa in the name of Portugal. Africa was circumnavigable! It was only a matter of time now before succeeding Portuguese captains would find their way up the other side to India, but what struck Caboto most forcibly was that Ptolemy—the great Ptolemy—had been wrong about the Indian Ocean! It was not an inland sea after all. Moreover, Africa was *not* joined to *Terra Australis Incognito*, which remained still unknown.

Finally, at the end of the year Caboto was called to the Franciscans' monastery where Fra Andrea lay dying. When he arrived, the Little Brother had just received the last rites and had disposed of the contents of his spice box, his only worldly possession, among the other Brothers. Now he was free of all cares.

Tense with grief and loss, Caboto sat beside his old teacher all that evening. The old man was conscious most of the time and they talked of the past, of mutual friends, of ancient scholars. Toward midnight, Michiele arrived and sat with them, and after giving Michiele his blessing, Fra Andrea drifted into sleep. The two friends sat in silence watching the beloved face grow ever more peaceful.

As the light of dawn crept through the narrow window, a nursing Brother came and took away the candle. The sick man murmured and sighed, then tried to lift himself. Caboto hurried to put an arm under the thin old shoulders, and saw the brown eyes fixed on him, wise and kindly as of old yet not really seeing him.

"Back—back to the past," whispered Fra Andrea. "Don't listen to—gondolier. Go and see—for yourself."

Caboto nodded wordlessly and the old man smiled, relaxed, grew heavy in Caboto's arms . . .

That was how, in the end, Giovanni Caboto reached his decision. He would go and see for himself!

Mattea was already half-resigned, expecting it. Telling Uncle Luigi was unexpectedly difficult. For the first time, Caboto felt sympathy for Signore Romano, who was old now and in recent years had come to depend on him. He acknowledged too how much he owed his Uncle.

"I'm sorry, Uncle. There comes a time, however, when everything must be sacrificed to one overpowering urge. This is something I have groped toward since childhood. I can deny it no longer."

The hooded old eyes filled with remembered coldness and Caboto was reminded sharply of that first day in Venice so long ago. The voice still clipped each phrase off short—

"You were always determined to go your own way. Very well. You have made your choice. I make mine. Piero and Piero's children will be my heirs."

It was a relief to be rid of the brief sympathy he had felt for a man with whom never in his life had he really felt at ease. Caboto bowed stiffly as if to a stranger, and left the *palazzo.*

Running down the steps to his boat, he knew he must waste no time. There was no knowing what a vindictive old man might do in a moment of angry disappointment. Fortunately all was in readiness. Gabriel's ship had been lying outside the Lagoon for days and already much of the Caboto goods was stored in the hold. Night came and the Caboto family embarked in a gondola for the last time. At the Arsenal wharf, Michiele was waiting with a *barca* to take them out to the ship. Caboto urged Michiele to leave the boat to him and go back, for safety's sake, but Michiele would not hear of it.

"You'll need help rowing," he whispered. "Besides, someone must bring the boat back."

So, with muffled oars, with Mattea and the children huddled in the bow, the two rowed silently across the Lagoon and out through the passage. Caboto was reminded of his smuggling days. Guido and his brother had long ago been caught by "the Lords of the Night," ending up in the dungeons of the prison and finally the grave. Captain Fontana had never returned from one of his illicit voyages. Yet here was he, Giovanni Caboto, nearly thirty years later, taking out of Venice a secret far more valuable than a formula for making glass, or all the smuggling the Pestrelli brothers had done in a lifetime!

Now they were alongside Gabriel's little *Sainte Marie* and Mattea was being helped up the side. Michiele groped for Caboto in the dark and they embraced wordlessly.

"Remember, when you're ready to go, send me word and I'll be there!"

Caboto nodded and sprang for the bulwark, leaning down afterwards to seize the bags Michiele passed up.

Heart full, Caboto leaned into the darkness over the rail watching the little boat turn and head back to the Lagoon. Would he ever see Michiele again? One thing was certain, he would never see Venice . . .

Presently the night wind filled the sails and the ship set her head toward Spain where at last he could put his project before King Ferdinand and Queen Isabella.

It was early spring of the year 1492.

XVIII

Valencia

On the voyage to Seville, Caboto clarified his geographical concepts once and for all, marshaling has arguments for presentation to the Spanish sovereigns.

First, he rejected Eratosthenes' seventy-mile degree of longitude on the grounds that that long-ago mathematician had made inexact measurements under dubious conditions, and, subconsciously perhaps, because if Eratosthenes was right his whole design of a voyage west to the Indies was unrealistic! Instead, he accepted the measurement of Posidonius, which gave him a degree of only fifty miles. In this selection, he was supported by Ptolemy.

Next, in deciding the length of the Europe-Asia land mass, he made his own calculations, beginning with Ptolemy's estimate of a land area covering 180 degrees of longitude. However, since Ptolemy's world map showed unknown land stretching to the very edge of the paper and did not include China, he added Marco Polo's twenty-eight degrees for that country, arriving at 208 degrees altogether. Subtracting this from the full circle, he was left with 152 degrees of water, or 7,600 miles.

If he began his voyage across open sea from the Canaries, he would cut fifteen hundred miles from this figure to start with. Moreover, he could hope to find Antillia on the way, where he would be able to rest his ship and crew and take on fresh supplies. He could not, however, count absolutely on finding this island. It might not even exist. He did count though, and heavily, on arriving at Cipango on the way—or if not Cipango, one of the many islands near it. From Marco Polo's description, he visualized hundreds of islands in a long line off the coast of Asia, from the latitude of Madeira to that of the Congo in Africa—and they were so pictured on Toscanelli's map. One could hardly miss them!

Here or on Cipango he would land and question the inhabitants before completing the voyage to Kinsai. He would need to know more about those two great cities of Cathay—Kinsai and Zaitan. Marco Polo had given no latitudes for them.

He therefore deduced another fifteen hundred miles and was left with an open-sea voyage of only about four thousand miles. Still a long way. Still a very long way. Yet not impossibly far. Had he not had experience in the North of a voyage something like two thousand miles long—and in seas much rougher than the ones he planned to sail in next? Northerly winds would take him down to the Canaries, and he knew from Gabriel and other seamen he had talked with that in winter the winds blew due west from these islands through a warm sea and a mild climate, though how far west they blew no one knew. He saw no reason, therefore, why a well-found ship—a caravel for preference—could not cover that distance in something under three months. It would simply call for courage, persistence, endurance, and the help of Heaven.

He must not, however, blind himself to the difficulties. Water. How much could be carried? How long would it last?

Fresh supplies might be got at islands along the way, provided they encountered any, but he must carry the maximum to be safe. To cut down the crew as much as possible was also important, so that fewer supplies would have to be carried. Crew. That was the most difficult. Where would he find a loyal and devoted group of seamen who would have enough faith in him to sail for three months or more through strange waters to an unknown destination. He would be a stranger in Spain and also in Portugal. Would his own personality and force of character be sufficient to secure such men and then keep them so content on the voyage that they would not mutiny? Two things were on his side. On such voyages it was customary to pay higher wages and the crew were assured of prompt payment when a government was the sponsor. Also, he remembered, Italian navigators were still well received in other maritime centers on account of their superior academic knowledge. It might be done!

He made himself look on the wholly dark side too. If he found no islands on the way, if he passed inadvertently through the archipelago of islands and even past Cipango, then he and his men would be obliged to sail across *six* thousand miles of open water at the very least. That would be too much. Water and food would give out long before they reached Cathay. If, moreover, by some dreadful chance, Eratosthenes was right after all in his estimate of the world's size, then Asia was twice as far away as the greatest distance he had calculated. They would never reach land at all, nor would they be able to come back.

He had calculated to the best of his ability. No one, he thought, could have been more careful to take everything into consideration. Yet in the nature of the business, he would never know for sure until he had tried. He must not let any doubt show when he presented the matter to their Majesties.

On his first day in Seville, he ran into an old friend. Gaspar Rull was a Spaniard whom he had met in Barcelona and with whom he had subsequently done a good deal of business. A lucky meeting, for Señor Rull was a courtier in the train of Ferdinand and Isabella. Having carried Rull off to Gabriel's ship for a glass of wine, he put the question bluntly. Could he get Caboto a hearing at the Spanish Court? Rull gave a mystified but not unreceptive smile as Caboto plunged into explanations. He told Rull exactly why he had come to Spain and what was in his mind, and as he spoke the Spaniard's smile faded. A look of acute embarrassment took its place. Caboto stopped anxiously in mid-sentence—

"You think my plan impracticable?"

"My dear Señor Caboto, it is not that—" Rull paused, saw there was no help for it. "Had you not heard? You are too late! Another man is about to start on a similar expedition. It is Cristóbal Colón. He has got his way at last."

"Colón?" For a moment, Caboto failed to recognize the Spanish form of the name. Then— "Colombo! The Genoese who tried to get King Manuel of Portugal to sponsor the discovery of ocean islands? But he was turned down, wasn't he?"

"More than once, not only by King Manuel but by our Spanish sovereigns. Nevertheless, he would not take no for an answer. Recently he went to Santa Fe to hear the findings of a new commission appointed by the Queen to consider his case. Because of his exorbitant demands, his proposal was turned down once more. He made it known then that this time he was giving up and would look for support elsewhere. Then the Queen, urged by Luis de Santagel, Keeper of the Privy Purse, changed her mind at the last minute and decided to meet his price. So in the end this Cristóbal Colón, as he now calls himself, came away triumphant. The contracts were drawn up and signed, and he will sail from Palos as soon as his ships are ready. In a matter of days now, probably."

Caboto rose so suddenly he struck his head against the deckhead and never felt the pain.

"But Colombo looks for islands! My project is different."

Rull shook his head sympathetically.

"No, *mi amigo*, it is the same. He has said quite openly in Court that he hopes to reach the shores of Asia and find the islands from which come all the gold and spices. Naturally this goal was not actually mentioned in the articles drawn up."

The blow was a heavy one. A complete and utter setback, just when he himself was ready to act. The inspiration of a western route to Asia, he had thought, was his own unique idea—and he had been wrong. Colombo too had worked it out, and Colombo had wasted no time.

"How many ships?" he asked dully.

"Three."

"Why Palos?"

"The Queen has ordered the inhabitants there to provide ships and crews as punishment for some recent misdeed the town committed." The Spaniard searched for comforting words. "The man may fail, of course. Indeed, many people feel he is both a fool and a fanatic and will be lost on the voyage. Then you will have your chance perhaps."

Caboto shook his head.

"If he fails—" Caboto faced it without illusion. "Their Catholic Majesties are not likely to hand out funds for a second attempt!" He wished Rull would leave. He wanted to be alone, to measure the magnitude of his defeat and come to some plateau of understanding—see if it was possible perhaps to reconstruct his life and his plans. Rull, a perceptive man, must have understood, for he gave up the effort at consolation and rose to leave.

"Keep in touch, *mi amigo.* I may be able to help at some later time. When I follow the Court to Barcelona in the spring, I shall leave word so you will know where to find me."

Caboto thanked him with all the warmth he could muster and showed Rull off the ship. Then, instead of going to his cabin, he dropped over the side into a skiff tied at the stern, calling to the ship's boy that he would return before dark. He cast loose and rowed slowly up the river. After a half mile or so, he found a small cove overgrown with reeds and, shipping his oars, he let the craft drift ashore with the current.

How was he to break the news to Mattea? Against her advice, he had thrown overboard all their substance, all their hopes of future security—for nothing! What would his family live on when the money he had was gone? At his age, in a foreign land, he would be fortunate to secure a sea-man's berth. Anguished, he looked at his prospects. They were as black as might be.

If only he had had the courage to leave Venice long ago. Even nine years back, on his return from Bristol, he could have taken the step he had now taken too late, and would have been nine years ahead of Colombo. How Uncle Luigi's cold lips would twist when he heard. How disappointed Michiele would be. Fra Andrea at least would never know how his own cowardice had ruined him.

In bitterness, Caboto asked himself what future was left to a man of forty-two with no influence, nothing to mark him out from other men. What hope, what dream now, would give him a straight back, a bold step? He ought to have known he was too old. He ought to have been content . . .

Yet Colombo was the same age.

If only he could see Colombo and talk with him!

Though that was out of the question, at least he could

find out what the man's plan was. Suddenly, urgently, Caboto wanted to know. What were Colombo's calculations, and on what did he base them? Which route did he intend to take? Where did he expect to land? At Cipango? On the mainland of Cathay—at Kinsai or Zaitan?

In the rush of questions, he saw that his own misery had been temporarily forgotten. He marveled a little to feel this urgency. What good would it do him to know? The gold and the glory would go to another man. Yet he still wanted answers! The quest itself gripped his imagination more than the reward that might come out of it. Still, there could be no answers until Colombo got back. Caboto must wait and face in the meantime his own immediate problems. Slowly, he pulled back to the ship, beginning faintly to feel that he might live through this disaster after all.

From somewhere he got courage to tell Mattea. Her stricken face cut him to the heart, but then she too seemed to reach out for some strength beyond herself, to comfort him.

"It was not your fault, *caro mio*," she said with her arms around him. "I shall not let you blame yourself. I have learned that a man must do what he thinks is right. You have lost this chance. Another will come."

"*Io t'amo*," he whispered gratefully. "But meanwhile?"

"Meanwhile, we can manage. Ludovico is old enough to earn his own living and he has been teaching Sebastiano to draw maps too. There is only Soncio to educate and then our sons will be able if necessary to take care of *us!*" She smiled when she said this, so he would know that she was not speaking seriously, would know she had faith in him still. "I suppose there is no hope of going back to Venice?" she asked tentatively.

He shook his head. That road was closed.

"There is always Genoa," he said. "Piero might find a

place for me in his business. Yet I will not ask him for help
unless all else fails. He has his own family to consider. No, I
must find something to do here, in Valencia." He found he
could plan now for the future. "Gabriel may be able to use a
partner. He hinted once that he could use additional capital, and my experience should be useful to him in selling. He
himself admits he is no businessman, which is why he is always on the edge of bankruptcy." But first he must get answers to some of the questions that were still racking his
brain.

Through Rull, he met and talked with men in both Seville
and Valencia who had heard Colombo argue his case in
Court, but there was one man in particular who had been
fairly intimate with the Genoese captain—an English merchant of Andalusia called Day—and Caboto managed to
meet him. He was a pleasant, cautious-looking man who
after some hesitation admitted he had been in Colombo's
confidence to some extent. What had drawn them together
was John Day's own interest in geographic discovery and
his personal familiarity with the book of Marco Polo.

"Since all is arranged now," said Day, "and he will soon
succeed or fail without help or hindrance from me, I shall
be giving away no secrets. What do you wish to know, Master Cabot?"

"What exactly is his plan?"

"Simply, it is this. He believes the earth is round and that,
therefore, he will reach Cipango and Kinsai on the east coast
of Asia by sailing west."

"How far west?" asked Caboto urgently.

"He believes Cataya to lie some five thousand miles from
Lisbon in roughly the same latitude."

Caboto nearly exclaimed aloud. Only *five* thousand miles
to Cathay?

"No more than that, perhaps less," said Day positively.

"He means to start his open-sea voyage from the Canaries."
Caboto's own plan. "The Canaries lie about a thousand miles
from northern Spain. From the Canaries, he will sail on a
winter wind which he says blows steadily west in those latitudes, until he reaches the island of Antillia where he will
land and refresh his crew. He will then go on to Cipango
where he hopes to get word from the inhabitants of the
quickest route to the Spice Islands." Fifteen hundred miles
from Cipango to the mainland. An open-sea voyage then of
only twenty-five hundred miles! It was too short. Too short
by half!

"How did he arrive at these figures? What are his authorities?"

John Day smiled.

"He quotes more than one authority, Master Cabot, but
particularly the Bible. He also relies heavily on Ptolemy and
Marco Polo, but only so far as they agree with his own calculations. The famous Florentine astronomer, Dr. Paolo Toscanelli, supports most of his opinions."

Not even Toscanelli had suggested an open-sea voyage
between the Canaries and Cipango of little more than two
thousand miles. And as for Antillia, who had ever fixed its
position accurately? It was on maps, true, placed variously
from just off France to a more southerly position in mid-
Ocean. Map makers, however, as Caboto knew to his sorrow,
were not always reliable. They had even been known to
draw what was not there.

"You're certain he figured five thousand miles altogether?"

Master Day knitted his brows in thought.

"I'm sure I've got it right. Yes, let me see now. First, he
decided the proportion of land to water and, according to
the Bible and to Marinus of Tyre, that was 225 degrees of
land to 135 degrees of water." Caboto had heard of Marinus
of course, but only as the author of works which Ptolemy had

set out to correct in his *Geography*. Ptolemy's 180 degrees each was surely more reliable? Colombo, like himself, would have added on Marco Polo's China, twenty-eight degrees, getting 253 degrees of land altogether—leaving, therefore, only 107 degrees of ocean. Well this accounted for some of the discrepancy, but not all.

"What was his estimate of the earth's circumference?"

"I'm afraid I don't recall—"

"The length of a degree of longitude, I mean."

"Oh yes. Forty-five miles."

San Giorgio! A degree only forty-five miles long? That meant a circumference of only 16,200 miles! No wonder Colombo had been able to reduce his ocean to a total of five thousand miles!

"Where in the name of Heaven did he get forty-five?"

"Out of some Arab manuscript, if I remember rightly."

And that was about all the Englishman could tell him. A degree only forty-five miles long, five less than he had himself reckoned after a search that had stretched over twenty years. Fifty degrees was Ptolemy's estimate too. Posidonius would agree with that, and so would Dr. Toscanelli. What Arab had found forty-five? Not Alfragan, who put it at sixty-six, but wait— What if Colombo used Alfragan's figure but made a mistake in reducing an Arab mile to an Italian one—even made the mistake deliberately to bring the distance down to a reasonable figure and so help him gain support for his project? The man had obviously seized on everything he could possibly find to support his own optimistic beliefs, in which case—

"In which case," said Gabriel, when Caboto told him, "Master Colombo is building upon air and one knows what happens to structures without foundation! We may yet have the opportunity, *mon ami,* to prove your theories more correct."

Caboto stared at him, incredulous.

"You say *"we"*—for the first time! Now when there is so little hope of any opportunity to test them."

"I have changed my mind." Gabriel shrugged, smiled his cynical smile. "I suppose I have grown gradually converted without knowing it. And now—now that you increase my business 150 per cent, it is quite certain you can do anything this fellow Colombo can do!"

Ridiculous reasoning, yet the nonsense heartened Caboto. It was just faintly possible that if Colombo never came back or came back to admit he had not managed to reach Asia, he himself might win his chance. Yet it would not do to count on anything so uncertain. At any rate, he was now able to put aside his desperate disappointment and think constructively of the future.

Gabriel had not waited for Caboto to offer his services but had begged him at once to become his partner. The result had been as he said, that his business was now in a thriving condition. Caboto had time left, moreover, for other work. He met Gaspar Rull one day and was persuaded by that gentleman to go to Valencia to enter a bid for the construction of a harbor in that city.

"You must know well all the ports of the Mediterranean, Caboto, and can surely suggest a method of construction to His Majesty. This would not only provide you with an income for a year or two, but would put you in an excellent position at Court should the time ever come for you to discuss the other matter."

"It would not hurt, certainly, to look the situation over. I could draft a plan on paper—"

"Excellent. I had forgotten your ability in that line. After that, it will be a matter of preparing estimates and there I should be able to give you some useful advice . . ."

So in his spare time Giovanni Caboto applied his cartographical and sea experience to the preparation of a scheme for enlarging and improving the harbor of Valencia. Eventually he moved his family there. It made little difference to Gabriel whether he operated from Seville or Barcelona, his little ship plying regularly between ports on the Iberian peninsula and in the Mediterranean.

At present the harbor site was simply a beach. After making a careful inspection of the area, Caboto thought it would be possible to build moles and breakwaters after the fashion of Genoa and Barcelona and so turn the beach into a useful harbor for large ships. The scheme interested him and he was soon absorbed in making the plans—plans which went to Rull who put them into the hands of the Governor-General, Diego de Torres. Eventually they were presented to the King and the result was an order to Caboto and Rull to appear at Court and explain the plan in person.

"You understand, *mi amigo*, you cannot talk to His Majesty about anything else. It would not be allowed." Caboto nodded. "It will, however, be an opportunity for you to create an impression of reliability and efficiency against the day when you might go to the sovereigns for another sort of hearing!"

Caboto looked forward to the interview with considerable interest and was careful to study Spanish Court procedure and etiquette beforehand. In Spain he was using the name "Johan Caboto Montecalunya," hoping to mislead any Venetians in the city who might be tempted to report his activities to the Council of Ten. He had after all left the city without permission. Most Venetians living abroad, he knew, were automatically employed on the side as spies of the Venetian Senate. Though he thought his affairs at the moment essentially too unimportant to interest the Republic, it might be as well to take all precautions. He was therefore introduced to the Court as Johan Caboto Montecalunya.

The hearing was held in the open, in the courtyard of the Castle of Aragon in Barcelona, and the sovereigns sat high above the crowd on a dais at the head of a wide flight of stone stairs. He looked up from the foot of them at the completion of his bow and saw Their Catholic Majesties for the first time.

Isabella, the Castilian Queen, was fairer than he had expected, both in feature and coloring. He thought she looked both clever and gentle, though he knew she had a reputation for severity at times, particularly in matters of religion. The King—so he had heard—was a sly nonentity who deferred to his wife in public but preferred more pliant ladies in private. In the discussion of the harbor scheme, however, he showed real interest and asked most of the questions. Caboto was able to answer to his satisfaction and the hearing went off very well. Caboto was instructed at the end to receive the King's jurors on an inspection tour of the site.

"You have our permission to retire, Señor Montecalunya," said Ferdinand, and the Queen nodded, giving Caboto a little smile which he thought an encouraging sign for the future.

Now he threw himself into work again, inspecting the stone he planned to use and assuring himself that the scows he meant to hire could carry enough material during the summer months to complete the work. He had a second interview with the King while Gaspar Rull was working with the Governor to find ways of raising funds for the work.

Nearly a year later, the program was still at this stage when one day Rull came unexpectedly to the house. Mattea hurried out to the garden where her husband was writing letters.

"He never comes on Sunday!" Mattea's face was anxious. "What can he want?"

"He's coming to say the money is here at last," Cabot

soothed her, but as he gathered up his papers Mattea was still fretting.

"I think it's bad news, Zuan. He looked—embarrassed!"

Caboto found Rull in his study, pacing anxiously. One look at his face and Caboto said—

"The plan for the harbor has fallen through."

"Yes," Rull answered heavily. "The money cannot be found for it at the moment. But that is not all I have to tell you." He paused, sighed, and blurted it out. "He has done it, Caboto. Colón is back and he says he has found the Indies."

Something hard but invisible smote Caboto between the eyes, making Rull's figure seem to blur.

"You are sure?"

The Spaniard nodded.

Caboto turned away, unwilling for Rull to see his face.

Then this was the end. Two years wasted. Nearly all his money gone, and now hope as well.

After a moment, he mastered himself, turned back to Rull. It was necessary to face facts—and with dignity.

"Colombo has done well. I must be proud that it is a compatriot who has succeeded. The world will talk of this." The taste of defeat was bitter in Caboto's throat.

"He is commanded to Court." Rull tactfully avoided Caboto's eye. "He has sent a letter but is to read it in public when he comes. They say he will arrive early in April. Will you wish a place at the reception?"

Caboto's first instinct was to say no, but that was weakness! Besides, he wanted to know.

"If you can arrange it, yes. Thank you, Rull. I shall be there."

He made the journey to Barcelona by sea with Gabriel and Gaspar Rull. On the day that the hero was sighted approaching the city, they found their places inside the gate of the courtyard of the Castle of Aragon. The crowd had been gathering outside the Castle yard since before midday. One could hear the growing murmur of excitement rising suddenly to pandemonium.

"Viva Don Cristóbal Colón!"

"Viva the Admiral of the Ocean Sea!"

"Colombo! Colombo!"

"Discoverer of the Indies! Viva Colón!"

The words rang sourly in Caboto's ears.

Then the gates were drawn back and the procession appeared, led by a proud man on a white horse. The townspeople, mad with excitement, tried to press in after the group, but the soldiers pushed them back and the gates were closed. The King and Queen appeared through the curtained doorway at the top of the stairway and stood waiting as the Admiral of the Ocean Sea dismounted and bowed deeply at the foot of the steps.

There wasn't much to remind Caboto of the boy he had seen so long ago on the Gulf. The red hair was now heavily patched with gray, the face sunburned, the clothing rich and elegant. Colombo's whole appearance, as he made his sweeping bow to the Court, proclaimed his triumph and joy and was a taunting reminder, no doubt, to the many there who had once derided him and put obstacles in his way. Yes, this was Colombo's day!

Behind him were grouped his officers and hired servants, as well as the ordinary crew members, swaggering and displaying their barbaric bracelets and earrings of gold. In their midst stood a small disconsolate group of brown-skinned men. They were attired in feathers and ornaments of fishbone and gold, and carried parrots whose raucous cries mingled strangely with the applause of the crowd. To Caboto's eyes, the natives looked beaten and bewildered, as well they might after the long voyage on the stormy ocean, and then the long march through a strange land.

The Queen raised her hand and in a gracious voice commanded Colombo to come up. Flushing with pride, the Admiral mounted the stairs and stood face to face with his rulers. He was given a chair on the right hand of the King, and the Court thundered approval.

Over the noise of the crowd, at such a distance, Caboto and his friends could not hear what was said, but they could see the officers and men parading before the dais, bowing to the King and Queen. Then the native men prostrated themselves and finally Colombo rose and began to read aloud from a roll of manuscript.

"There's the famous letter," Gabriel said gloomily, "and we can't hear a word of it."

"Copies are to be printed," Rull assured him. "I shall see that you get one."

"Meanwhile," said Caboto with a certain grimness, "if I know sailors, we ought to be able to get quite accurate information in the taverns tonight, provided of course they are allowed the freedom of the town."

Allowed or not, most of the seamen and officers found their way after dark to the bars of Barcelona and the two men from Valencia soon marked down their man—a petty officer from the *Niña*, a little the worse for drink but still able to talk.

"We sailed south from Palos on August 3 with three vessels." The man was only too happy to be of service. Besides having his glass filled regularly, he was full of pride at having had a part in the glorious exploit. "I will tell you all about it, Señores. There was the flagship *Santa María*, a *nao*, and two caravels, the *Pinta* and the *Niña*. I am mate on the *Niña*! We were about ninety all told, nearly all of us Spaniards. We stopped at Las Palmas and Gomera to repair *Pinta* and re-rig *Niña*, then on September 9 we left the Canaries and sailed west. There were some frightened ones, of course, who wished to turn back even then, but the Captain-General would not hear of it. Winds and currents were favorable and after thirty-four days on the open sea we found land again on October 12."

Only thirty-four days at sea! Little more than a month! "What winds did you have?" Caboto asked, incredulous.

"A steady northeast wind blew us westward for twenty-nine days," the man replied. "Truth to tell, we feared we'd never find a wind to take us back to Spain! But the Captain-General urged us to have courage and sure enough the wind veered at last. Finally we sighted the island which Señor Colón named San Salvador. We took possession of it in the name of our King and Queen." He laughed and drank deeply. "The natives were afraid of us at first. They thought we had dropped down from Heaven, that we were gods! Afterward we made friends with them and they guided us to other islands and even to the mainland—"

"How do you know it was mainland?" asked Gabriel.

"The Captain-General knew because his dead reckoning told him we had made ninety degrees of westing, which he says is where Asia begins—the province of Manjii he called it."

"In what latitude?"

The seaman glanced around the noisy room and seemed to make up his mind that no one was observing them. Gabriel shoved a fresh mug of wine in front of the officer.

"I know we sailed across mostly on 28 North," said the officer, "and allowing for the change of course southwest near the end of the voyage, I'd say we found the mainland in about 22 or 23 North."

"Did you explore this mainland?"

"Some of it. The natives told us it was called Colba and that inland there was plenty of gold. Trading was good there, they said, especially at 'the place of the Grand Khan' or that's how it sounded. The Captain-General—the Admiral I ought to say, as he is now—the Admiral was pleased, for he thought they meant Kinsai, one of the cities of the Khan."

"And was it?"

"No, the Devil take them!" The dark face betrayed remembered disappointment. "We found only palm-thatched huts and natives who could not understand de Torres, the interpreter, any better than the Indians on the coast. We saw a queer thing though—natives drinking smoke from a firebrand made of herbs, *tobacos* they called it."

"So you hadn't found mainland after all."

"Who says so?" The officer's voice was thick now, growing belligerent. "You think we had time to explore the whole damn country? We only got to the edge of Asia, remember, only to the edge! But we're going back—back with a dozen ships—see it properly, find the gold mines!"

"You did find some gold?"

"Only belts, bracelets, and that," said the man disgustedly, "no mines. Only a few cheap spices." His head began to nod. Caboto shook him awake.

"Did the Admiral reckon his position with instruments?"

"Now and then," the man muttered sleepily. "Rest of the time he kept track on ship's slate—"

Caboto nodded across to Gabriel. Dead reckoning—still much the safest way to fix a ship's position. And that was all they could get out of the man. The rest they learned eventually from a copy of the printed letter of the Admiral.

"I followed the coast to the westward," Colombo had written, "and I found it to be so extensive that I thought it must be the mainland, the province of Catayo . . . There were neither towns nor villages on the seashore, but only small hamlets, with the people of which I could not have speech because they all fled immediately . . . The people of all the islands which I have found and seen all go naked . . . They are wonderfully timorous, they have no other arms than arms of cane, cut when they are in seed time . . . They know neither sect nor idolatry, with the exception that all believe that the source of all power and goodness is in the sky, and they believe very firmly that I, with these ships and people, came from the sky . . . Because they have never seen people clothed or ships like ours . . . Their Highnesses can see that I shall give them as much gold as they want . . . and slaves, as many as they shall order, who will be idolators . . . our Redeemer has given this victory to our most illustrious King and Queen and to their famous realms . . . and all Christendom ought to feel joyful and make great celebration . . ."

That was the gist of it. To Gabriel's surprise, Caboto made no comment on reading it, indeed refused to discuss it, striding off the ship with a preoccupied air. On making port again some weeks later, after a short voyage to the Balearics, Gabriel was met by a very different-looking Caboto, one both calm and elated.

"Colombo's report does not make sense," he said quietly. "In the past weeks I have studied it from every angle and talked to people wiser than myself, and I have come to certain conclusions. In the light of what Marco Polo tells us of the East and, combining the matter in this letter with what we learned from the *Niña's* officer, I have decided that Colombo did not reach the Indies!"

Gabriel gaped at his partner, taken for once off balance.

"All he has found," said Caboto calmly, "are some islands halfway across the Ocean. Antillia perhaps."

Gabriel pushed the wine bottle across the table, but it was ignored. In the close lantern-lit cabin, the two men leaning toward each other across the narrow chart table looked oddly like conspirators.

"He claims to have reached the mainland of Asia without passing any islands, without sighting Cipango. He has, he says, found a land very beautiful, but without any of the usual signs of civilization. Ask yourself, Gabriel, is this the mainland of Cathay with its great ports, cities, ships? If so, where are the palaces, the roads, the inns? Where are the rich merchants, the cultured rulers, the teeming millions of inhabitants?"

"Back from the coast a little, perhaps," suggested Gabriel with his usual caution.

"Let me make it clear to you, Gabriel. Marco Polo tells us, quite simply in passing, that the customs dues collected at one particular road junction in Yunnan added up to a thousand gold pieces a day. Just one road junction, remember, among many between the interior and the coastal towns. And on the coast are two of the greatest cities in the land—Kinsai and Zaitan. Kinsai, Gabriel, is in the province of Manjii. It is a city one hundred miles in circumference with houses, shops, restaurants, pleasure gardens, lakes and parks, hundreds of canals and bridges, carriages and public vehicles, ten principal market squares each capable of holding fifty thousand people. There must of course be dozens of outlying villages and miles of farmlands to provide food for this one city. Yet Colombo, who claims to have explored the coast and visited the interior of this province of Manjii, found only wilderness. Think of it! We are asked to believe that within comparatively few miles of a city, a city larger than any in Europe, there live these primitive people, men without religion or learning or arms or culture, having no contact at all with civilization, thinking the Spaniards gods from Heaven! You have seen them, Gabriel. Are these the subjects of the Khan? Are these the sophisticated inhabitants of Imperial Cathay?"

But Gabriel refused to be stampeded.

"Did not Marco Polo say he heard of primitive men who lived like beasts on certain islands off the coast?"

"The islands he spoke of, my friend, were far to the south where the Pole Star disappeared from view. That would be only a degree or two north of the Equator, and Cathay's coast according to Colombo is in 22 or 23 North! Moreover, we have Polo's word for it that although these were the lowest primitives he found, even they had gods, engaged in agriculture, and raised domestic animals. The only others he mentions are those of Tibet, a land taxed by the Khan's official, with post inns every twenty-five miles. Positively, he mentions no men as primitive as Colombo's 'Indians' anywhere." Caboto was growing excited, gesturing emphatically.

Gabriel, playing the role of devil's advocate, drew a breath and ventured with a cynical smile—

"All this, however—forgive me, *mon ami*—depends on the truth of what Marco Polo says. His book is, after all, only a piece of literature."

"I do not believe it!" cried the other passionately. "It does not read like literature. It reads like an information brochure. The more I read his book, Gabriel, the more I see that it is not one written to entertain or to glorify himself. He hardly mentions his own personal adventures. Most of the so-called tall tales—paper money, black stones that burn, and so on—have turned out to be true. No. Marco Polo may have made errors—he was only human—but not deliberate ones. His book is too factual, too meticulous, the antithesis of Sir John Mandeville's, which we now know to be fiction. When Polo does not know for sure, as in the case of Cipango, an island he had not personally visited, he says so."

Gabriel threw up his hands.

"All right, *mon Dieu*, I believe you! You are the expert. So. You do not believe Colombo. You think he is lying."

"Not lying necessarily—mistaken. Possibly self-deceived. He strikes me, from all I have heard of him, as a man who will believe exactly what he wants to believe. He has persuaded himself against all the evidence of Marco Polo, whose book he claims to have studied, that he is on the outskirts of the richest, most developed country in the world. Why? Because he said he would find Asia in approximately ninety degrees of westing, some thirty days' sail across open sea. He has found land in this place—ergo, it must be Asia! But you and I, Gabriel, know that Asia lies farther west, perhaps twice the distance."

"We do not actually know, *mon ami*," cautioned the other. "Like Colombo, we *believe* this. We too could be mistaken."

Caboto nodded.

"Very true." He paused, smiled. "So the only way to find out if we are—or not—is to go and see!"

The other man sat back, his eyes narrowing thoughtfully.

"Colombo just made it, they say. His crew would have turned back, I am told, if he had not found land within a few days. What makes you think we could sail twice as far?"

"We will not need to sail so far," said Caboto calmly. Taking a letter from his doublet, he laid it on the table. "Here is a letter from Robert Thorne, our English friend in Bristol, who tells me that he and his partners have still not found the lost fishing grounds. They want me to help look for them. I am convinced, as much as any man can be under the circumstances, that the land the Bristol men saw was a northeast projection of Asia."

"Do the English say so?"

"No! By San Marco, such a thought has not even occurred to them! They are not men who trouble themselves with obscure geographic matters. D'Ailly's *Imago Mundi* and the book of Marco Polo are barely known in England. Our Bristol merchants are fishermen and businessmen. They look for islands and fishing grounds somewhere about two thousand miles to the west, between 45 and 60 degrees of latitude, or

Cabot's later plan, revised after 1492

a. Iceland
b. Brasil and Seven Cities
   (Vinlandia)

c. Colombo's islands in mid-
   Ocean
d. Strait of Malaieu

as they put it, between a rhumb southwest and two rhumbs northwest of Bristol. I think the islands they call Brasil and the Seven Cities are the same the old Norsemen knew as Markland and Vinland the Good."

"Wait now—wait, *parbleu!*" Gabriel's usual calm was deserting him. "We know Colombo sailed nearly three thousand miles to find his islands, which *you* say are in mid-Ocean. You say also he has gone only half as far as he needs to go to find Asia—yet *you* expect to find land only *two* thousand miles off?"

Caboto's eyes gleamed by the light of the lantern.

"Have you forgotten that the earth is round? If I had my globe here, I could show you how Asia is brought nearer to us by the narrowing of each degree of longitude, as one moves toward the North. If Tartary projects eastwardly, it brings us nearer still!"

"Yes, yes, of course I see what you mean—but there are no spices in the frozen North!"

"Probably not!" Caboto laughed exultantly. "But what if one followed that coast southwest to the rich tropical regions of Cathay—where the spices *are*?"

Gabriel Duchesne stared at his friend with dawning understanding.

XIX

Bristol

From this moment, Giovanni Caboto did not look back. From this moment he moved steadily forward, overcoming obstacles as they arose, or going around them if that were the only way. No more doubts. No more hesitations. He was committed. There remained only the task of arousing others to an equal commitment.

"There is nothing to keep us in Spain now," he told the anxious Mattea. "Spain has Colombo and his islands. Portugal has her own experts on maritime affairs and is in any case committed to the African route to the Spice Islands. There is no place for me in either country. Besides," he added with a flash of insight, "I am not at my best here. The air of Ibernia is too heavy, too smothering. I shall thrive better, I think, in a colder brisker air!"

"But where, Zuan?"

"Our future now, *carissima*, lies in England."

His wife's face fell into such tragic lines he hastened to reassure her.

"England, my dear, is not the barbaric country you picture. True, her weather is unpleasant compared with ours and her people somewhat less sensitive, yet Britain is a good country for a man with an idea! She is ready for experiment —for expansion. That was evident to me fourteen years ago. Under this new monarch, Henry VII, I understand, there is an even greater surge of commercial vitality. Britain is as Venice once was but is no longer—a nation prepared to take risks for uncertain profits."

"What about schools?" his wife worried. "How will the boys be properly educated?"

"*Basta!* Our sons *are* well educated, Mattea, for their station in life! After all, they are not a patrician's sons."

"You were not always simply a seaman," she pouted, "but a scholar brought up in a *palazzo.*"

"Involuntarily, I assure you!" He smiled, remembering his first day in Venice and the pains Fra Andrea had taken to interest him in books. How violently he had at first resisted! He must sadly have disappointed Fra Andrea in never becoming a true scholar. Perhaps he would make up for it by becoming a successful explorer.

"Our families," insisted Mattea, "were cultured people."

"Yours was, my dear. My father was an ordinary Genoese storekeeper, a trader in a small way, like myself. In England I shall gain nothing by pretending to an aristocratic background. These Bristol merchants will have more respect for a man of the people, like themselves, who is above all an experienced seaman. Ludovico and Soncio take after me and will make good tradesmen, sailors or map makers. Sebastiano—" He shook his head. "I am not sure about Sebastiano. He has ambition, that much is certain. He can apply himself when he wants to, when the goal seems worth it, but he has no real love for the sea which is why I cannot understand—" He stopped, sorry he had gone so far.

"What, Zuan?" The strained look in Mattea's eyes told

him she had already guessed. "What can't you understand?"

"He wants to sail with me to the Indies."

"Zuan!" she wailed. "Isn't it bad enough for you to take such risks? I shall not draw an easy breath all the time you are gone. But Sebastiano too! He's so young!"

"He is nearly sixteen. Most lads of his class are on their own by now. He wants desperately to go. He says—" Caboto smiled indulgently. "He says he wishes to be a great man like Colombo! And so he must have experience in discovering new lands. He feels that with even one voyage behind him, he could demand an expedition of his own." Caboto shook his head ruefully, a little proudly too. "He has big ideas, that one. He reminds me of myself at his age, cocky, impulsive, but he is perhaps somewhat more practical. He should go far."

Seeing her mournful look, he added hastily—

"In any case, *carissima*, it may be years before our plans come to fruition. Don't worry ahead of time. Meanwhile we go to England."

Mattea sighed, thinking of the chores involved in packing and moving again.

"When?"

"We sail to Lisbon with Gabriel a week from tomorrow. In Lisbon we will take passage to Bristol on an English ship. Gabriel will join us there when he has settled up his affairs in Spain. In Bristol, I shall meet the Thornes and others I made contact with in 1481, and I think—yes Mattea, I am nearly certain that what I have to say will interest them!"

On a lovely spring day in 1495, they sailed up the Avon on a homing tide. Daffodils nodded from grassy banks on either side of the river and Mattea found she could look at the English shore with more equanimity than she had expected. Late that afternoon they passed between high gorge-

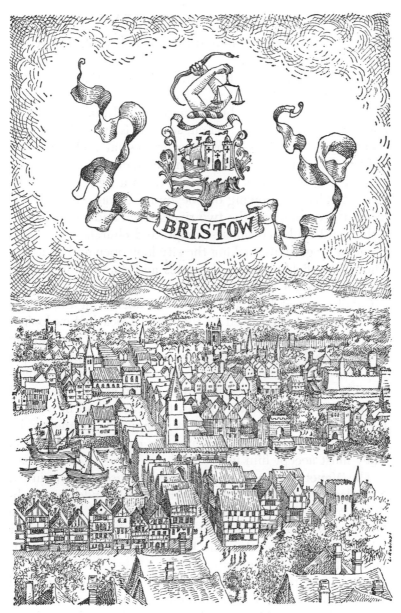

Bristol, circa *1500*

like walls, rounded a bend and there was Bristol, the second largest port in England.

"It's not much of a city, is it?" said Sebastiano in a disparaging voice.

"It's small, perhaps, but remarkably clean," his father noted with satisfaction. "Their sewage is carried away in underground channels." The boys grinned at each other, indulgent toward their father's familiar mania.

Mattea and her sons saw before them a tight little medieval city already growing out beyond the walls, but still lying in the embrace of the two rivers Avon and Frome. Over a thousand timbered houses, shops, and churches were surrounded by gardens, making the city look open and pleasant. There were fields beyond the gates and dominating all was a huge guardian Abbey.

Caboto saw at least a dozen ships docked at the King's Rode as they were towed to the quay. Dock loafers looked them over, recognized the ship as local, stared frankly at the little group by the rail. The knowing eyes appraised the southern clothing and made the correct deduction—foreigners. This, Caboto knew, was how the town as a whole would view him. It would not make his task easier and he wished he were more fluent in the English tongue. Nevertheless, he looked back at the townsmen with deliberate challenge. They must accept him in the end!

The Venetians found a convenient house to rent in St. Nicholas Street and Caboto was able to get Ludovico established as a journeyman map maker in a local shop, while Soncio was placed in the Abbey School to finish his grammar school studies. Sebastiano he kept with him to run errands and make himself generally useful.

Now it was time to see Thorne and explain how he wished to alter their plans a little. Caboto was of the opinion that the merchants' backing must be arranged before he made his appeal to the King. It would make his case much better if he did not have to beg for money. He hated in any case to be bothered with roundabout methods, with intermediaries, as in Spain. He would tell the merchants precisely what was in his mind, keeping nothing back. He could imagine what Uncle Luigi would say to such methods. "Trade and promotion should be approached with the utmost subtlety and calculation. One should lead up to the thing one wants slowly, never letting one's ears know what one's tongue is up to! One should always get the best terms and give back as little as possible." That was the Venetian way. It was not his way, however. The English, as Caboto had got to know them in the years of his friendship with Thorne, were not like Uncle Luigi. They may have been no more honest than other men when it came to business, but they would resent subtlety, which they would construe as suspicion. Shrewd bargainers, good at sizing up a customer, they could afford to rely on trust more than the people of his Uncle's city. A few words in Robert Thorne's ear was all that was needed. Two days later, a group of Thorne's friends and business associates met in the back room of his shop to hear the Venetian visitor present his case.

They sat there, sprawled comfortably on wooden benches, curious about this Lombard in their midst, willing to listen as long as there was something worth listening to. He must not bore them. He remembered what Thorne had said, that there was little interest among Englishmen in the discoveries made by Colombo. A few men at Court or those in contact with Spain on business may have heard vaguely of the voyage, but did not consider it of any particular account in their own lives. This was nothing new, they would say—men had been hunting for islands for years, even finding them sometimes. Look at the Azores, the Canaries. The revolutionary claim that Colombo had reached the shores of Asia would be known only to a handful of academics possibly, to Henry the King of course, and some of his advisers. But to the general public it was of merely passing interest that some Italian or Spaniard—a foreigner anyway—had discovered a formerly unknown island.

What Caboto had to say, therefore, must shock them out of their complacency. He felt calm, his only concern being whether or not he could make them understand with his limited English. Thorne, he knew, would help if he began to go wrong, but he wanted to keep the reins in his own hands if he could. He was first introduced to the company by Thorne.

"Master Cabot here, as some of you may remember, was our navigating expert on the *George* in 1481. His services then were of considerable value and he has continued to be interested in our efforts to rediscover the fishing grounds. I know we can trust him not to talk of what he's learned, though it is bound to be known soon in any case. The Portuguese are suspicious already if I am any judge. Anyway, you all agreed we should send for Master Cabot again and have him try once more to find Brasil and the Seven Cities, this time going in command of a ship. Now it seems he has a slightly altered proposition to put to us today. I know roughly what it is, but I'll just let him say it himself. Go ahead, John."

Caboto began by telling them exactly what Colombo had done and the claim he had made. He saw the start of surprise when he mentioned Asia, but when he gave it as his considered opinion that Colombo's claim was mistaken, they began to listen more closely. He spoke slowly, deliberately, about his belief that the land seen by the Bristol mariners ten or twelve years before, however, *was* actually a part of Asia. It might be an offshore island. It might be the mainland itself. A mutter of excitement went around. One with foresight burst out at once.

"A short way to the Indies, by Jove! But wait a minute, there aren't apt to be spices in the North!"

Caboto shook his head emphatically, relying on hands and facial expression to eke out his speech.

"No, no! One would only begin there, Signores. One would first mark the position of 'Brasil' and the fishing grounds, then follow the coast down south, or more likely southwest, to the tropical regions—along the shore line, you understand—a voyage of perhaps twice the length of the one across open sea." There were nods of understanding. The room buzzed with expectancy. "One would then always be in reach of water and wood, possibly with good harbors to shelter in, with all the necessities of life to be bought once one reached the civilized cities, as well as guides and interpreters. One would make contact with the officials of the Khan and so gain permission to open a trading factory. Then it would be possible to transfer the spices and gold coming in on Chinese ships from the Archipelago to ships which would carry them back to England. I believe the cost of spices would be cut in half and it would give this country a monopoly. Bristol would become a greater port than Southampton!"

"Zounds!"

"Or London! Spices! Gold too!"

"One in the eye for Southampton anyway!"

"It's worth thinking of, lads!"

"A trading factory, you say, Cabot?"

"It is done in other countries."

"You wouldn't expect to do all this in one voyage?"

"No, no," he assured them. "First I must find the land, make sure it fits the specifications—that it is continental and runs southwest. That should be sufficient for one season. The following spring, with ships full of trading goods, we would cross again and follow the coast to our ultimate goal. A short voyage across open sea, another more leisurely one along the shores of Tartary down to Cathay and the Indies, Signores! That is the matter in its utmost simplicity."

"The first voyage," said a man named Bradley with deliberation, "would be merely exploratory. One ship ought to do it."

"Two would be safer."

"Cost more!"

"One would do," interjected Caboto, having managed with a feeling of elation to follow the last rapid exchange. "I do not wish to be hampered by another ship, another pilot. Colombo, they say, had much difficulty on account of insubordination among his captains." Besides, he wanted to do it alone.

"That is a detail that can wait," said a man named Elyott. "I personally want more evidence from our friend here that Brasil—or Asia, if you prefer—is something more than a wilderness of trees and sand, which is all our men saw in their brief glimpse of it. How do you know there are ports, cities, people? I've never heard of any city in Asia east of Calicut!"

It was astonishing to realize that probably none of these men had ever heard of Marco Polo. Caboto gathered his forces and did his best to give them a quick resume, first of geographic knowledge to date, then of Polo's travels in the East. One man, as it turned out, had been to Oxford for several terms and had actually read Roger Bacon's thirteenth-century *Opus Majus* with its theory of a round earth and its arguments about the proportions of land and water, so could follow the geographic argument fairly well, interpreting when necessary for the others. It was hard work all the same and Caboto was exhausted when the meeting finally, reluctantly he thought, accepted his statements as to the breadth of the sea, the proportion of water to land, and the existence of a great civilization, one more advanced even than Europe's, on the other side of the Ocean Sea. He felt depressed now, his hopes falling in the face of the English-men's phlegmatic caution.

He could rest a little now while they talked money, exam-ining the project from different angles, occasionally asking a question. Slowly his tiredness left him as he realized with a throb of relief that they were interested after all. Some of them seemed positively enthusiastic. Thorne, after the meet-ing was over, confirmed this idea.

"They are satisfied, I think, that it is an acceptable propo-sition, at least from a financial standpoint. An exploratory voyage will be no more than we have been financing each year for the past seven years to look for the fishing grounds. And if you even succeed in finding those, the voyage will be worth every penny it costs. However, since it will be more than that in all probability, I think it will be necessary to get a charter from the King. With royal backing, we can take possession legally of anything we find."

"What is he like, this Henry VII?"

"Businesslike."

"Ah! Helpful then."

"Provided we don't ask him to put his hand in his own pocket."

"It should not be necessary. I can make my profit later in the ordinary way of trade. I do not want anything to hold up the business." It was true. Though wealth and fame were still shining goals, they were beginning to be secondary to the need to prove his theory. The voyage had become an end in itself, a thing he must do.

"There's one thing about the King," said Thorne, "he'll attend to the business himself. One can approach him di-rectly if the matter is of any importance to the realm."

However, the King was overworked that winter and for a time Caboto feared the project would be put ahead for an-other year. Then, suddenly, the King and his entourage descended in a visitation on Bristol itself and in the resultant bustle and flurry their chance came, the matter being broached by a chosen representative of the merchants. The King's reaction was noncommital. He would think about it.

Yet, almost on his arrival back in London, he sent for Caboto and Thorne.

"This looks promising!" cried Thorne.

"To get there in time, we must leave at once!"

The following day they set out on two horses, carrying little more than Caboto's maps, the small sphere he had made, and a change of clothing. They carried also a large salmon presented to them by their friends, to be cooked and eaten at inns along the way. The wayfarer's life in this England of 1495 was a hard and perilous one, but in spite of atrocious roads, bad inns, broken bridges, and the ever present danger of brigands, the two made the journey in just over three days.

Riding at last down the Dover Road, Caboto saw the city of London half-hidden in a pall of smoke, with the fine new Tower Bridge in the foreground. They did not cross the Thames at that point but, passing around the main part of the city, forded the river at Richmond where the King was then in residence. The old Richmond Palace was unimpressive as a structure but from the hill on which it stood, overlooking the whole Thames Valley, the view was magnificent.

They were received with businesslike promptitude and conducted to a reception room where a host of people were assembled, including many of the lords and prelates of the Kingdom, as well as the ambassadors of foreign states. Among them, Caboto recognized Gonzales de Puebla, the Spanish Ambassador, and also Lorenzo Pasqualigo, a Venetian merchant he had known for years, who stood in conversation with an elegant gentleman in russet silk—Italian, by the cut of his clothes. This gentleman, he learned, when he was presented by Lorenzo, bore the resounding name of Raimondo de Raimondi de Soncino and was the representative in London of the Duke of Milano. Soncino was a likeable sophisticate who confided to Caboto that his hardest chore in this barbarian country was to choke down eight to ten courses at each meal, and spend three hours at table twice a day!

Time passed slowly. Every so often, some member of the company was called from the room by a major-domo. At last their turn came and they were led to an adjacent chamber furnished with a long table and elegantly-cushioned benches. On the table, at its head, lay a large gilt sword. Beyond stood a magnificent screen of gold brocade. Presently, Puebla and his assistant came in, looking somewhat mystified—they had evidently been called to Court without learning the reason for it. One or two Court ministers also made their appearance through a side door.

The King was not announced. Suddenly, he was there. Caboto had an odd but certain feeling that Henry had been standing behind that screen most of the time peering through at them, taking stock of them all. Now he stood at the head of the table beside the gilt chair, dressed in a costly doublet of gold silk with a mantle of fur-trimmed purple velvet lined with white satin. On his head he wore a richly-jeweled cap. The individual inside the clothes seemed to Caboto at first singularly unimposing. Of middle height, thin and dark, he had the sharp-featured Welsh face. His manner as he came forward, however, was gracious. The aide, having made the introductions, stepped aside and Henry gave the two men his hand to kiss, then motioned to them to walk with him to a window beyond the hearing of the others.

"Welcome, Signore Caboto, to England." Henry spoke courteously in Latin, then asked Caboto if he understood English.

"Sufficiently, I think, your Highness."

"Very well. In a moment, Master Cabot, I shall ask you to set forth your proposition in the hearing of my ministers and other interested parties, but I must tell you now that one very serious objection will be raised by the Spanish ambassador." The thin face closed, the hard eyes were veiled. "You will want time to think of an answer, which must come from you, naturally, not from Us." A warning, in other words, not to depend on the King. Caboto's whole mind listened, intent on what this wily sovereign had to say. "You will be told that such a voyage would trespass on Spanish rights, since his Holiness Pope Alexander has confirmed these rights."

Caboto heard Thorne's indrawn breath, and himself felt a throb of anxiety.

"Or at any rate," went on the monarch dryly, "His Holiness has given his blessing to a treaty drawn last year by Spain and Portugal." A treaty. Caboto had heard of no treaty! "The Treaty of Tordesillas, it is called, and this is how it came to be drawn. Five years ago, the Pope issued a bull, *Aeterni Regis*, which approved the division of the Ocean Sea *latitudinally* between the two nations, the northern half going to Spain, the southern to Portugal. When, however, Columbus claimed the Indies for Spain, Ferdinand and Isabella asked for the line to be redrawn *longitudinally* through a line one hundred leagues west of the Cape Verdes. This gave Spain exclusive rights to the region west of the line, Portugal to the east of it. You understand so far?" The sharp eyes peered at him. Caboto nodded. "Portugal then claimed that this did not give her sufficient sea room for her African voyages and arranged a private meeting with Spain at Tordesillas last year, at which it was agreed that the line should be moved to a point 370 leagues west of the Cape

Verdes. It is probable such a change will be sanctioned by His Holiness." There was a pause.

Caboto glanced at Thorne who looked merely troubled and mystified. Something, clearly, was expected of them.

"Has His Holiness a *legal* right to sanction such a private treaty?" he asked tentatively. The thin mouth smiled.

"Let us say," said Henry, "that it has been customary hitherto to abide by the Pope's decision in such matters." He added piously, "I hope I am a good son of the Church and obedient to her degrees in any matter of—religion."

So the bulls were not legally binding. He knew now where he stood. Henry was telling him that he did not intend to be bound by treaties or papal restrictions, but that he did not wish to say so openly in court. Thorne must see it too now, for he was grinning with relief. What made Caboto's heart sing, however, was the implication of the whole conversation that the King was already favorable to his project!

"Now, gentlemen," said the King loudly, leading the two back to the table, "you must state your proposition openly before the Court. Nothing is hidden from my ministers, and the envoys of foreign courts are entitled to hear any applications which might have a bearing on their country's interests."

The group at the far end of the table bowed as the King took his place before the sword of state, then seated themselves according to precedence. Caboto was introduced to the gathering by the King's chief minister as "Master John Cabot, a citizen of Venice."

Caboto placed maps and globe on the table and, with Thorne beside him ready to interject an English word where necessary, he outlined his plan with care and brevity. There was no need to go into fine detail at this point. The King was obviously well informed, and if others were more ignorant, they would have a chance to ask questions later. He felt interest and expectation rise around him as he explained his plan to sail by the North and West to find a land which might actually be the coast of Cathay. The expected interjection came.

"Sire!" It was Puebla on his feet. "Your Highness, may I speak?"

Gravely the King inclined his head.

"But you must be brief, Señor Ambassador. This is not the time for argument—that will come later. You wish to register an objection, is that it?"

"Decidedly, sir! I have a very serious objection, Your Highness—the Treaty of Tordesillas! Since this treaty exists, Señor Caboto's voyage cannot be made without prejudice to Spain and Portugal! No such English undertaking could be without harm to both our powers. The original Papal Bull divides the sea between our two countries and the recent treaty defines the line of partition." He threw a glance at Caboto, bowed to the King, and reseated himself.

"What do you say to that, Master Cabot?" the King asked smoothly.

"A treaty is between two countries," Caboto said firmly, "and binds only its signatories. This treaty has nothing to do with England at all."

The Spanish Ambassador leaped to his feet again.

"For fifty years," he cried indignantly, "Portugal was allowed to trade in Africa unhindered, under the protection of a Papal Bull. Are we not now to be allowed the same privileges? The treaty was designed that we might trade with Asia without interference from other powers. Surely these bulls should restrict others as they restricted us in the past!"

Caboto looked questioningly at the King and, catching a glance of assent, turned to Puebla.

"Señor Ambassador, your interests and those of Portugal

lie in southern latitudes, extending only to the islands discovered by Colombo in mid-Ocean. *I* intend to cross in *English* latitudes far to the north of the Spanish islands. I shall
then follow the land I find to the south and southwest, to
the rich part of the Great Khan's empire which lies far
west of the Spanish Islands."

The Ambassador flushed angrily.

"Admiral Colón has found more than islands! He has
found the Khan's empire. He has planted the Spanish flag
in the actual province of Manjii!"

Caboto turned to the King.

"I shall give you reasons presently, Your Highness, why
this cannot be."

"You will agree at least," persisted Puebla, "that land
belongs to the one who first finds it?"

"Provided it is land hitherto unknown to Christians, yes,"
agreed Caboto, "but of course, Señor Ambassador, I intend
to be that one." (It was accepted as a fundamental law that
all Christians were in a state of war with all infidels and
therefore that all land belonging to them could justifiably be
conquered and occupied, if not by one Christian power then
by another.)

Puebla gave what was nearly a snort and looked plead-
ingly at Henry. Thorne was sure that the King put up a hand
at that point to hide a smile.

"Naturally," His Highness said with a peacemaking air,
"we must respect Spanish rights to what Spain has already
discovered, and even to a monopoly of the sea route which
leads to it." He paused deliberately. Henry did not need to
add that he would not, however, recognize in advance any
Spanish right to prospective discoveries not yet made. If the
English could get there first, in other words, the Spanish
must want! "Naturally, my good Señor Ambassador, there will
be a full and public hearing and the Court will listen to any

arguments for or against Master Cabot's plans at that time."
The Spaniard made one last effort.

"I must report this to my sovereigns, sire. I ask that the matter be held in abeyance until I have their instructions."

"There should be plenty of time for that. Drawing up the application for charter and all the other legal matters will take at least a month." In other words, the Spaniards had one month in which to make their protests, no longer—if it would do them any good! Caboto understood in a great wave of relief that for all practical purposes the charter was theirs from that moment. As Thorne said when they stepped on the Thames wherry that would take them to London town—

"His Highness had his mind made up before the audience took place!" He chuckled hugely. "Henry wants a piece of the cake the King of Spain has grabbed, and he means to get it one way or another, preferably with legality. Puebla knows as well as we do that the thing's as good as settled. First come, first served! In theory, the Pope's word is sacred. In actual fact, kings generally find ways to get around interference from the Vatican if it is anything which affects their political interests. It's the way it's always been and always will be. You must get there first, John, that's the important thing!"

"Why was it all so easy though? I expected the King to ask dozens of questions."

"He'll be on his toes sharp enough when it comes to financial matters. He's nothing to lose at this point and much to gain, that's all."

But it was more than that, as Caboto learned in a talk with Italian friends in Lombard Street the next day.

"You were fortunate, Caboto," said one of the Pasqualigo brothers who, in the interests of Venice, made it his business to know all that went on in English Court circles. "It is not generally known, but while Colombo was still pleading with

Spain to back his voyage, in London Colombo's brother Bartolomeo was sounding Henry on the subject! It is said, among those who should know, that the King was considering the matter when Spain decided to back Colombo after all. It must have been a blow to Henry to learn what an opportunity he had missed. He will take no chances of missing a second."

"So. I have Colombo to thank for my easy victory." It was a glum reflection. How the man's shadow fell across his path, always just a little ahead. *Basta!* This one time, he would be ahead of Colombo. He must be!

This curious piece of news confided to him by Pasqualigo told him something else. Venice was well aware of what was going on in English maritime affairs. The activities of their former citizen, Caboto, would be fully reported to the Senate now and in the future. He wondered if they would try to put obstacles in his way. Pasqualigo's friendly approach did not deceive him. That was the Venetian way. Caboto knew that even here in England he must be on his guard. He therefore went nowhere unaccompanied and was careful not to be caught out in a lonely spot after dark.

Back in Bristol, travel-weary but content, the two travelers visited their merchant-partners in Corn Street and told them of the interview with the King. Few signs of joy or excitement were shown, but the necessary proceedings were begun to put the plans into effect. These English! Admirable —and altogether aggravating. Caboto felt their power and appreciated their sense of responsibility, but sometimes he was repelled by them, lonely for his own kind. It made him realize how Mattea must be feeling, far from her own people, struggling to make a place for herself and her family in these strange, cold surroundings. He and Sebastiano met her one morning in the market. She was wrapped in a heavy wool cloak, but still she shivered a little as she picked over English vegetables with a discouraged air.

"Leeks and cabbages! Leeks and cabbages! No salad greens, no fruit, no *pasta*! No fish but cod!" She added despairingly, "And I think it's turning colder again!"

"Poor Mamma, never mind," said Sebastiano. "When I make my fortune in the Spice Islands, I will buy you rich furs to line your cloaks and dresses as the English do."

"Better still," said Caboto, "we will have a house in Italy for the winter as well as one here in summer."

"What summer?" asked Mattea with considerable bitterness.

Caboto took the basket from her and paid the farmer, then all walked together slowly toward St. Nicholas Street, Caboto occasionally doffing his hood with a bow to an acquaintance—

"Sir, God keep you."

"God speed, friend."

From Wine Street, they could see the masts and rigging of the seagoing ships outlined against the cold spring sky, and Caboto dreamed of the day when he could lay the treasures of the East at his wife's feet, while Mattea wondered if the fire on the hearth would have gone out in her absence! What Sebastiano dreamed of was himself in fine clothes and jewels, applauded by the multitude— "Bravo! Bravo! Sebastiano Caboto! Admiral of the Ocean Sea!"

They entered St. Nicholas Street and saw the figure on their doorstep, waiting, surrounded by luggage. A middle-aged man with dark, smiling eyes.

"Who in Heaven's name—" began Mattea.

"Michiele!" Caboto gave a great shout and broke into a run, causing the leeks to fall out of the basket and scatter far and wide. Sebastiano methodically picked them up as he came along, while his father and mother hugged and exclaimed over their old friend.

"I'm not too late then?" Michiele looked younger than Caboto remembered. Barbering evidently agreed with him! "They said you'd sailed."

"*Sciocchezza!*" cried Caboto. "Who said so?"

"Some Venetians I met in London. Anyway it is true, is it not, that we leave soon?"

"So you're coming with us!"

"If you'll take me."

"What a question! But are you sure, Michiele—"

"Do come inside," begged Mattea, conscious of staring eyes. "These English will think we are mad, capering about in the street. Come in, dear Michiele. Sebastiano, stir up the fire. Oh, it is good to see someone from home! You are the finest sight I have seen, Michiele, since I left Venice!"

"And you, Mattea," cried Michiele extravagantly, "are still lovelier than all the young signorinas of the Republic!"

"For that you get a fresh bottle of wine," laughed Mattea, departing in a glow of pleasure.

"Poor Mattea," Caboto looked after his wife with a deep consciousness of guilt. "She is not happy here."

"Ah, but wait until we come back from the Indies with our pockets full of diamonds and pearls!"

"Michiele, you are water in the desert! You have made Mattea smile for the first time in weeks. You really dare to come with us?"

"Why else am I here? How can I afford to miss an opportunity that comes to few men! And you need not think, *amico mio*, that I shall be excess baggage. I can make myself useful on your ship both as barber and surgeon. I can even haul on a rope when necessary!"

"It will be dangerous, you know."

Michiele crossed himself hastily.

"Fortunately, I am a bachelor!"

"It won't be comfortable. You may have to sleep on the floor of my cabin, or in the hold with the seamen."

Michiele cast his eyes to heaven, but did not weaken.

"You'll have hot food only in calm weather, and that won't occur often in the Ocean Sea. The water will be foul before we are halfway across, and there will be no fresh fruit or vegetables after the first week."

"Stop!" groaned Michiele. "No need to frighten me to death. If you can stand it, I can."

"On the other hand," said Caboto, looking at his friend with affection, "if I have you with me, Michiele, I feel that everything will be perfect. You will bring us luck. And half of all my profits will be yours—that is understood."

"I wish Fra Andrea could have known," said Michiele, and Caboto nodded.

"Ah well! Perhaps he does."

"Anyway," said Michiele with a satisfied smile, "there's no doubt now—we're on our way."

"Yes," said Caboto, "we're on our way!"

XX

The Crossing, 1497

After a day of calm and fog, the wind veered to south south-west and low, ragged clouds scudded overhead. The *Matthew* climbed a wave, shuddered, fell away to leeward, then slowly gathered way, only to be brought up short again by those frustrating head winds and choppy seas.

Caboto was three weeks out of Bristol on his second attempt to find the coast of Asia. He was well clear of the longitude of Iceland, more or less in latitude 50° North. In spite of aggravating weather, in spite of having wandered for days in the face of continual head winds, with bad water and rarely satisfying meals, he was a happy man. It was mid-June of the year 1497 and he was, if he was correct in his dead reckoning, already three-quarters of the way to Asia. This time he would make it!

By nightfall, he was not quite so happy. Blown by a full gale, he could no longer lay a westerly course but was forced north on a larboard tack under bare poles. Great smoking combers came out of the murk to windward, bursting against the *Matthew* from every direction. What with pitching and rolling, everyone aboard was wet and sick, or half-sick, and the pumps were working 'round the clock. The storm continued for three days and nights and then the wind veered again to the southwest, the huge waves breaking up into smaller spiky ones. The wind fell and in the morning they were becalmed in a gray wet mist.

It was not a bad voyage as voyages in the northern part of the Western Ocean could expect to be, but it was much worse than the momentous voyage of Columbus—on the way across, at least. He, fortunate man, had sailed before a steady wind with continual rosy dawns and sparkling days. Here in the north it was always wet, always changeable, and generally the wind was dead ahead!

Almost a year had elapsed since Caboto's first interview with Henry VII. There had been others, to grind out the legal and financial details. Months of hard work with lawyers and Crown ministers were needed to hack out the design and words of the charter alone, but at last it was a document as careful and unambiguous as human minds and hands could make it. The final version was sent to the King for approval, copied on the Rolls, and the great seal affixed on March 5, 1496.

The grantees were Caboto and his sons, their heirs and deputies, and authority was given him to use five ships of any tunnage "to sail to all parts of the eastern, western, and northern sea" (not the southern, where the Spaniards already were) at their own cost, to discover and investigate "whatsoever islands, countries, regions or provinces of heathens and infidels, in whatsoever part of the world placed, which before this time were unknown to all Christians." In other words, Caboto was allowed to cross the ocean in English latitudes only and, having done so and found new land, he could then follow its coast to any part of the world, provided it was land unknown to Christians—at least, to any Christians now living. This was the essence of the King's answer to the claims of Spain and Portugal, and it clearly implied to the world that Columbus had not reached Asia.

In the end, arguing that it was merely a reconnaissance voyage, Caboto was permitted to go with one ship only. She was a large converted trading vessel—he had no say in her selection—and the too-large, too-bulky vessel sailed from Bristol early in 1496. The voyage was doomed from the start. Running into bad weather in the Irish Sea, the ship began to leak and the pumps were inadequate to cope with the situation. It was late in the year for an Ocean crossing, and both water and food badly stowed. In a fortnight, therefore, they ran short of vital supplies and the crew began to clamor for a return to Bristol. Caboto himself was so unhappy with the ship and her behavior that he was only too pleased to accede to their demands. The experience had been useful, however, and on his return to Bristol he hardened his demands for a new vessel. In the end the shareholders agreed to build one.

All through the winter, under Caboto's devoted supervision, the hull took shape. Spring saw the small fore-and-after complete and lovely. She was small, much smaller than the first ship, but after she was rigged and fitted and he had made trials of her, Caboto felt she was a hundred times more seaworthy and better suited to his purpose than the earlier vessel. More willing too! The first ship had seemed to balk all the way and had run back to port as if fleeing the Devil.

This one was a little over sixty tons, seventy feet at the water line, with shallow bottom and the best of rigging and gear. She was as different in design from the *cogs* of the early part of the century as the round lumbering *cogs* were different from the first hollowed-out logs of ancient man. She was extremely capable when sailing with a following wind and could sail at least six points off the wind. Caboto

felt that he would be doing well though to get a steady
seven or eight. All sails were set from the yards. The fore
and main courses, with topsails, were square. The mizzen,
carrying a lateen on a tilted yard, were like those on the old
Santa Lucia but lighter and easier to handle. Forward under
the bowsprit she carried a sprit-sail yard and set a square of
sail sheeted home over the bows, which would be useful
when the wind was well abaft the beam. The foremast was
set well forward and the steering was by tiller. The bulwarks
were high and comparatively heavy, with a gun mounted
on each side of the main deck.

All the large square sails could be lowered to the deck to
be furled, reefed, and adjusted with comparative ease, while
the topsails were easily handled aloft, since they were small
and made of light canvas. Moreover, the lower part of the
large sails could be unlaced to reduce sail area and replaced
when more was needed. She was altogether a husky well-
balanced little ship, easy to steer, and amenable to command. Caboto loved her from the start. He named her "*Mattea*" but even before she was off the ways, the English
workmen had anglicized the name to "*Matthew*" and in time
that was the name she was called, even in the records.
Mattea did not mind. She was pleased to have received such
an original compliment, most of the ships of the time being
named after saints! She thought, however, that the ship was
far too small.

"She's so tiny, Zuan! It's frightening!" Mattea was perhaps
thinking especially of Sebastiano who had finally coaxed his
father into letting him go as grommet on this voyage.

"The important thing is not size, my dear, but seaworthi-
ness. She'll ride over the biggest seas rather than try to beat
a way through them."

"It sounds very uncomfortable."

Caboto admitted this was true, but that one couldn't have

The Matthew

everything. He pointed out that waves would seldom, if ever, sweep the deck and this was comforting. Mattea had been entertaining in her mind a vivid picture of husband and son being swept into that vast ocean with the first storm.

"Won't it be very cold and wet just the same? Will you get hot meals regularly? You have a stove, I hope."

"We have a stove, of course—come and see."

Mattea looked with dismay at the shallow metal tray filled with sand.

"It's not as large as it might be, perhaps," said Caboto cheerfully, "but with a charcoal fire we can have a hot meal every day." He did not add "if and when the weather allows."

"What sort of meal?" demanded Mattea. Her husband was accustomed to the hardships of life at sea. As Captain-General he had a cabin he would share with Gabriel, the master and pilot, and would sleep in a bunk. Sebastiano would have to sleep on the open deck or in the smothering hold. "What food will you take with you?"

"Anything," said Caboto, "that can be dried or pickled. Beef, pork, peas and beans, dried and salt fish." Mattea shuddered. "Now don't worry, my dear. Sebastiano will be doing most of the cooking, so he is sure to get enough to eat. The carpenter has already instructed him in the art of preparing a stew from dried beef, very tasty and nourishing I can assure you. Water and wine—beer for the English, of course—will be carried in proper wooden casks this time," he added grimly. "I shall see to that personally. I intend moreover to take on private stores of olive oil, almonds, raisins, garlic, rice, and honey as well as fruit and vegetables for the first week or so. And we will have bread in the form of bannocks or pancakes cooked in the ashes of the fire. So you see, *carissima*, we will eat like Kings!"

Mattea doubted it. She doubted it very much.

"I shall pack you a box of spices," was all she said. She

knew she could do no more for her menfolk now, except pray for their safe return.

Caboto hurried her ashore. There was still much to do, scores of things still to buy for the new vessel. New pumps, new hatch covers, additional anchors, flints and wicks to light fires, sandglasses to measure time; swords, pikes, crossbows, and gunpowder for possible hostilities; parchment, ink, quills, for map making; also wooden spoons, wooden plates, kettles, knives, candles and candle-sconces, saws, hammers, axes, and yes, beads and other simple ornaments which would be useful if they met with any primitive peoples willing to trade these articles for information. Cross-staff and astrolabe, several compasses as well as a piece of precious lodestone to remagnetize them, lead line and oars, ballast, calking materials, charts of coastal waters, a small boat, firewood and charcoal—all the necessities for a voyage which might take several months.

At last, on a morning in May, they were ready. The wind was fair and the tide was right, and it was time to go. The Captain-General and his crew of eighteen men, one officer and two merchant-shareholders, walked down from St. Mary Redcliffe after Mass. A crowd of friends, family, and townspeople followed to hear the priest bless the ship.

Caboto and his wife had said their real farewells at home and now Mattea was having all she could do to show the becoming fortitude displayed by Mistress Thorne and Mistress Elyott, whose husbands were sailing too. Though her heart and her eyes ached with holding back the tears, she was resolved not to disgrace herself and her men before these stolid English.

To Caboto's fond eye, the *Matthew* looked spruce and workmanlike, with all rigging set up, sails bent, and armaments stowed. The gilding on her figurehead and sterncastle gleamed in the early morning sun, and the great lantern

on the poop shone with fresh red and yellow paint. Masts
and yards glistened with oil, the rigging with tar. The smell
of it mixed with the smell of rope and brackish river water.
Even during the ceremony, Caboto's glance went to the
capstans to see that they were under proper stress and to the
seams to make sure the oakum was tight, the pitch thoroughly dried.

As the priest concluded his prayer, there was a pause and
then, as mothers turned to sons and husbands to wives for a
last embrace, Mattea was disillusioned. All the women began to weep and wail at once. With great relief, Mattea
joined them. She enveloped Sebastiano in her arms and let
the tears flow. When he could break away, he sprang quickly
on deck to hide his own watering eyes. Sebastiano waved
once to his envious brothers and set to work with the rest
of the crew unloading a last minute cargo hoisted up from
an oxcart. The bosun's whistle announced the Captain was
boarding, and a cheer went up from the dock as Caboto
turned for one last wave to Mattea. Then he gave orders to
cast off.

The windlass creaked, the lines dropped, and the topsails
unfurled. As the *Matthew* slipped into the stream and the
tide caught her, her Bristol pennant broke out and there was
shouting and waving back and forth over the widening
stretch of water. Hearing the soft whisper of the bow cutting
the water, Caboto was inexplicably reminded of his first sail
with Emilio, the memory all tangled up with this leave-tak-
ing on a foreign shore. He wiped his eyes with a quick brush
of his sleeve and waved at the diminishing figure of Mattea
and his two sons, then turned his back on Bristol town. This
time there must be no return before his aim was accomplished.

He assured himself that all immediate tasks were being
attended to, checked compass, chart, and sandglasses, then

as they moved at speed toward Avonmouth, he was free for the first time in months to look about him.

All seemed well. No overcrowding this voyage. A neat, tight crew of eighteen men. There was himself, the Captain-General; Gabriel Duchesne, master and pilot and his only officer; Thorne and Elyott, the merchant-shareholders; and Michiele, the ship's barber and surgeon. Sebastiano was to act both as steward and ship's boy. The rest were experienced Bristol seamen whom he hoped to weld into a close community on the voyage. So much depended on the men. The Captain's word was not always law. It sometimes needed a majority verdict to keep going. Caboto recognized the necessity of earning the men's respect, therefore, as well as their obedience. These were men who could turn their hands to almost anything aboard ship, from repairing a sail to making a rudder, from cooking a meal to forging metal parts for the gear. There were specialists, of course—Martin Brewer the bosun who also acted as sergeant-at-arms, for one. Smith the cooper looked after the casks, and Wills the calker ensured that the ship, a moving structure of separate wooden planks, both held together and kept out the water. Chips the carpenter and Gerrish the sailmaker would, like the rest, take their turn at the helm and pull on a line when necessary. Caboto had chosen all of them carefully.

He had seen, moreover, that they were warmly clad in shirts and breeches of wool with leather capes and a cap to shed the rain. Too often, left to themselves, seamen sold off their personal gear to buy drink and so came aboard ill-prepared for a voyage in northern waters. The clothes would come out of their earnings, of course, paid them at the return to port. Caboto meanwhile would do his best to keep them healthy, with Michiele there to take care of minor ails and accidents. Caboto was, with his now ingrained habit of fastidiousness, insistent on a clean ship, certain in his own mind that there was a connection between health and cleanliness. He was making it a strict rule, for instance, that the men use the boxes at the head of the ship for calls of nature, and not anywhere they happpened to be on board.

He wore the same sort of clothes as the men, except for the addition of leather boots and cloak. He had a best suit as well, safely stowed in his cabin for wear on special occasions. There might well be encounters with important inhabitants of Asia—even possibly the Great Khan himself—and then he must be seen to best advantage.

So the voyage began.

From the Severn Sea, they sailed north through the Irish Sea in freshening winds. The *Matthew* rode the waves well despite her burden of supplies, and Caboto relaxed.

"What if someone is ahead of us, Papa?" fretted Sebastiano. "Now that Columbus has shown the way, now that everyone knows about our own voyage, what is to prevent some other country's outlaw ship getting there first?"

"Lack of knowledge, lack of backing, lack of courage," said his father cheerfully, and hoped this was true. As for himself, he felt singularly lighthearted at this point about the whole thing. Here he was at last in action—grappling at first hand with the problems. What other men might do, did not for the moment matter. After all the long years of study and planning, he felt released at last from all fears and doubts. This was where he belonged! Above the wind and the noise of groaning timbers, he seemed to hear the music of the spheres!

Nevertheless Caboto did not take his job lightly. In particular, navigation kept him occupied a large part of every day and was a continual matter of anxiety. First, he had to find and run down his latitude—roughly on a fifty-degree parallel. He did this, not only by dead reckoning—deducing his course from Bristol where the latitude was known—but by checking with observations of the North Star when the pointers were in a certain position. For each degree marked on the scale of his quadrant, he counted sixteen leagues and two-thirds, or two miles roughly, reckoning three miles to a league. He then observed the star through both pinholes, like a crossbowman taking aim with his bow, and marked where the lead fell on the scale. He could get only an approximate position even so, for it was impossible to use such an instrument with any degree of accuracy on the unquiet deck of a ship. It would be more useful when he was able to take a fix on land.

Navigation on the *Matthew* was, therefore, almost entirely by dead reckoning. Besides compass, chart, sounding lead and vague directions from the Bristol pilots of a land "somewhere west, between 45 and 60 degrees of latitude, between a rhumb southwest and two rhumbs northwest from Bristol," he depended on a ruler, a pair of dividers, and the first four rules of arithmetic—adding, subtracting, multiplying, and dividing—to guide him over the Western Sea. And sandglasses, of course. With the sandglass, provided it was turned precisely on the half-hour, Sebastiano's job, Caboto could mark out the watches and get an approximate idea of the time.

The ship's speed could only be educated guesswork as to the length of time it took a chip of wood thrown from the bow to reach the stern, and it was easy to overestimate, though as long as the error was consistent it mattered very little. The main thing was to keep a strict account of his speed and direction in each watch. This meant eternal vigilance, never-ending calculation. And with all that, he could never know when the ship's speed and direction were affected by unknown currents. He was watchful too for the westward variation of the compass, reported by Colombo.

They experienced all the vicissitudes of the northern

Ocean and its weather at that time of year. There were exhausting days of working with wet canvas, days of fighting the tiller, days of lying becalmed in heavy mist, days of cold and continual wet, nights of sleeplessness when the ship was in violent motion from dusk to dawn—yet through it all, the crew remained in remarkably good spirits.

To Caboto afterward, it remained in his memory as weeks of violent motion, of ceaseless turmoil, with here and there a particular gale. He would always recall the sizzling sound of a wave before it struck, the sudden high-pitched scream of the wind in the rigging, the thrill of tearing through a black night at top speed, seeing only the bow wave foam white in the dim light of the binnacle. At those times he felt intoxicated, conscious of every sound, color, and emotion, twice as alive as he had ever felt in his life!

On May 20, the *Matthew* had left England. Now, after thirty-two days at sea, it was the twenty-first of June. The weather had grown perceptibly colder and he detected a chilly current flowing to the south. Soon after that, the *Matthew* bobbed her way into the main stream of this current and the crew awoke next morning to find the waters alive with fish! Caboto sent Sebastiano to wake Thorne with the news.

It was a pleasant awakening.

"At last!" Thorne cried thankfully, "the fishing grounds." And figuratively thumbed his nose at the Danes. But to Caboto it meant that land might not be far off.

Fish was not the seaman's favorite food, but Caboto ordered baskets weighted with stones and dropped over the side on lines, for the fish were so abundant it needed no nets to catch them. With ease, they drew up all the fish they needed before the wind began to freshen and bear the *Matthew* again toward the west.

Next day a flight of delicate black-winged birds with a

white stripe across their forked tails appeared from the west. The weather was still cool and the hot stew Sebastiano made that noon tasted good, though the ship's water was so thick with scum it could not be drunk by itself. Caboto listened that night to the wind playing in the shrouds and it seemed to him that the ship was singing. Water and air warmed again magically overnight and in the early morning, while it was still dark, Caboto was awakened by Michiele.

"Giovanni," he whispered, "I smell something strange!"

Caboto sniffed, hardly daring to believe what his senses told him.

"It smells—it smells—" said Michiele in utter bewilderment, "like a garden!"

"Land!" murmured Caboto. The smell of earth, of trees, sweet and strong after weeks of shipboard odors!

"But aren't we still a long way out?"

"A day's sail perhaps," said the Captain-General, keeping his voice steady with an effort. "But it's land, no mistaking it." There was no possibility of sleep now, so they put on their cloaks over their clothes and went on deck. There was nothing to be seen on the lightening horizon. Caboto looked up at the crow's nest and saw the watchman alert, staring toward the west.

The day broke finally with a clear sky—unclouded except for a line of rosy puff-clouds along the western horizon. Now half the crew were in the rigging whenever their duties allowed. There was also a man out on the leadsman's platform taking regular soundings. Weed passed by the ship and—at last—

"Land!" came the wild cry from the maintop. "Land!"

Land after thirty-five days!

Asia at last!

"The Isle of Brasil," cried Elyott.

There it was, a thin blue line appearing beneath the rosy

clouds and extending a long way in each direction. Sebastiano shrieked with excitement and most of the crew were shouting and dancing, but all gradually fell silent, awed, as the *Matthew* crept closer and closer to land. Now a cape, which Caboto named *Prima Terra Vista* (first land seen) took form against the paler blue of the sky.

Land over two thousand miles from home! Brasil? The Seven Cities? Or Cathay—the land of gold and spices!

Thorne shook hands with Caboto, his stolid English phlegm shaken for the moment at least. Michiele and Gabriel embraced Caboto with tears in their eyes. They, better than the Englishman, knew the long way Caboto had come. They had been with him.

"We'll anchor in that small bay," said Caboto out of a full heart. "We will land and take possession, in the name of England."

XXI

Discovery

The sun shone brilliantly as the small boat approached the beach.

"Bravo!" said Michiele softly in Caboto's ear. "Now at last you will walk where no man has walked before."

Caboto smiled.

"Hardly, *amico mio*. Cathay is a very old, very civilized land. Many have walked here before me, including Marco Polo. I'm afraid I shall never now realize that old ambition, Michiele. I was born too late. Anything important—except perhaps *Terra Australis*, the unknown southern land, if it exists—has been found long ago. Ah well! One's dreams grow more practical as one grows older. I must be content with being just a middle-aged merchant on a glorified business trip." Nevertheless, he found he was holding his breath as the small boat scraped her keel on the sandy beach.

The forest came almost down to the water's edge, a dark green tangle above, an army of tall straight trunks below, shot through with sunshine. Beyond, soft-humped hills of trees made a green background.

Caboto was the first to splash his way through the shallow

water to the shore of what some of his crew still thought of simply as an island near the fishing grounds. Robert Thorne and Michiele ranged on either side of the Captain-General and Sebastiano was close behind. Gabriel had stayed aboard ship with the rest, the cannon uncovered and ready. The dragging noises of the boat being hauled up on shore, the hollow rattle of the water casks bumping between the thwarts ceased, and for a moment it was terribly quiet.

"How strange," whispered Michiele, "after the eternal noise of the ship and the sea."

"I feel deaf," said Sebastiano.

But soon they could pick out sounds again—the quiet lap of waves, the gentle twitter of songbirds and, sharply, the raucous cry of a gull. The earth smell was now overlaid with the heavy tang of balsam and pine, and Caboto was reminded of Spain, though this scent was far stronger than that of the Spanish piñon. The trees themselves were four or five times as large too!

One felt strange, almost unsteady, with one's feet on solid ground again. Caboto heard Martin Brewer's slow voice behind him as they trudged up past tidemark.

"Grand trees for spars!" It was a fact, and Caboto saw now why the Norsemen had come all the way to Markland and Vinland for ship timber. This *must* be the land Leif Ericsson had found! He remembered then the savage Skraelings who had driven the Norse away in the end, and turned to make sure the crew had followed orders and were keeping weapons at the ready. He also made certain Chips the carpenter was bringing the flagpoles. Behind Chips plodded Elyott and Gerrish with their arms full of bunting, and Sebastiano carried the wooden cross. All was in order.

Caboto had noted the small knoll just beyond the line of loose stones. There they would erect their marker and flags. It was impossible to know at this time if the country was occupied or not, or if it was owned by Infidels or Christians. His instructions were to stake England's claim anyway, take no chances. The claim was in any case a gesture. To make it good would be another matter and perhaps none of his concern.

His boots rattled over the pebbles, then fell noiselessly on a carpet of peat moss and cranberry vine. Reaching the highest point of the knoll, he looked around. As far as he could see from this small eminence, there stretched hills of dark green woods running down to rocky points of land at either end of the beach. He heard the musical chatter of a brook nearby and thought he caught a gleam of silver falling through brush. They were all waiting for him now, expectantly.

"Martin, set your men to work gathering stones. We will put the cross right here, the flags on either side." He caught the eager pleading in Sebastiano's eye. "All right, Sebastiano, you and Gerrish may explore a little. Michiele, perhaps you had better go with them. See what you can find, but go no farther into the trees than a bowshot."

Like children, the three ran off along the edge of the wood, looking for an opening. While the seamen set up the cross and propped stones against it, Caboto took his quadrant and dividers and worked out a rough fix from the sun. His declination tables were meagre and unreliable but the ground was steady, and it was all good practice. Tonight on the ship in calm water he would take a star sight, and another in the early morning, to see how the results compared with his dead reckoning.

"What's all this?" asked the bosun, puzzled, unfolding a strange flag with a winged lion in its center.

"The lion of Venice!" said Caboto firmly, though he felt a trifle defiant. "I am a citizen of that city, you know, Brewer."

"Oh aye, sir!"

It was natural a man should wish to honor his city, but in this case it was more than that. Caboto knew that what he did here today might have far-reaching effects on Venice. He owed her something, if only a sentimental gesture. The contrast between that fabulous city and this little stretch of rocks and forest was wide, but the connection was there!

"The English Cross of St. George on the right, my city's flag on the left."

The two pennants streamed out proudly in the breeze, and the banner of the Holy Father was laid across the stones at the foot of the cross. Caboto read the words cut by Chips into the wood of the crosspiece—

"This land discovered by the Venetian, Giovanni Caboto, on behalf of Henry VII, King of England and France." The date had been added only that morning. "June 24, 1497."

There was a shout from the woods and Sebastiano appeared, waving a trophy of some kind, triumphantly. Behind him came Michiele and Gerrish. also smiling excitedly.

"Well?"

"We found a trail," said Sebastiano, out of breath, "and look! I am sure it's a snare!" He showed Caboto the pointed stick, the ties of braided sinews. "It could take a squirrel or a coney."

"This might be a needle, sir," said Gerrish. "I've seen somethin' like 'em in my village for mendin' nets." He too offered his find, a piece of bone obviously shaved and pierced by the human hand.

"There was a fire," said Michiele, "and dung, also felled trees, as if there might be domestic animals and people. The ashes were cold of course, and the trail went on into the woods."

"We wanted to go farther," said Sebastiano, "but Michiele said no!"

"Quite right," nodded Caboto. "There will be times better

suited than this, Sebastiano, for inland exploration. At the moment—" He raised his voice. "All of you, gather around!" He fell on his knees before the cross, and the company knelt one by one around him. He prayed briefly, silently, then said aloud, "In the name of Almighty God who has protected us and carried us safely across the Ocean Sea, I claim this land in the name of King Henry VII of England and France, now and for all time!"

"Amen!"

Then Caboto's inner ebullience got the better of him. He sprang to his feet, swept off his hat and waved it high, shouting—

"Three cheers for the *Matthew!*"

They cheered him then as well as the ship and themselves, capering and laughing until Gabriel on the ship must have wondered if they had lost their minds, dancing and shouting like savages on their mossy knoll. But then, as their voices died away, they were all suddenly conscious of how small were the sounds they made against that dark silence, and all at once they felt uneasy. Was the silence deliberate? What if hidden eyes were peering from somewhere behind those trees?

Caboto felt the eeriness too, and for a moment his vivid imagination conjured up a horde of savage men! Then he shook off the brief chill of alarm and addressed his little group cheerfully.

"Take the casks now, men, and get some of that good fresh water I hear trickling down the stones, but mind—no one is to go into the forest! I want every man of you back here when the bosun blows his whistle."

He was resolved not to linger any longer than necessary. His first duty was to get safely back to England and report what he had found.

One more thing he had to do before they left. Alone, he

went back to the knoll and knelt down, laid an old quill pen at the foot of the cross. It was one he had cherished for years, one given him by Fra Andrea. Perhaps the Little Brother would be happy to know how far his old pupil had traveled!

Back in England, the King awarded Caboto ten pounds, about the sum he would have paid a dancing girl who particularly pleased him, as a reward for finding Asia. However, he also promised a yearly pension of twenty pounds, and with that Caboto was content for the moment.

Now he was experiencing what Colombo had experienced. Triumph! Excitement! Popularity!

It went to his head a little. It affected all of them. Even Gabriel was lifted out of his usual dry calm when Caboto in his role of Admiral offered him an island. It was one of two they had seen on their way back from the discovery.

"*Merci! Merci mille, mon ami!*" At last Gabriel was a landowner!

"Of course, it will have to be ratified by the King," said Caboto grandly, "but don't worry. He will have to make the concession or go and find those islands himself! I've given the other one to Michiele. You can both go and colonize them some day and become lords over your domains."

"Count, please, Admiral! I will be no English milord!"

And so they lived a little above themselves for a while, dressing in silk, and basking in the plaudits of the crowd. The news spread over Bristol and with amazing speed to London, where a great fuss was made over them on arrival. People ran after Caboto in the street, calling him Excellency and Admiral and begging to be taken on his next voyage. Even quite grand people like Raimondo de Soncino, the Milanese ambassador, entertained him and his friends at dinner, begging to hear the whole story at firsthand. Son-

cino was a man of the world and well educated, yet he had
never heard of Marco Polo and the idea of sailing west to
reach the fabulous Spice Islands was quite new to him. He
was enthralled by the tale, and plied Caboto with questions.
"Is Brasil east of the Don? East of the Black Sea? In the
country of the Tanais perhaps! What is the land like? Are
there people? What is this you say about great quantities of
fish?"—and so on. In his mind's eye, Caboto could see Soncino already drafting a report of the business to his master,
the Duke of Milano. And Pasqualigo would be sure to send
a full report to Venice!

Later, with the King's approval, Caboto gave what
amounted to an illustrated public lecture, attended by all
sorts of people—scholars, gentlemen, courtiers, and no-non-
sense businessmen. With maps and globe, he described the
voyage and the country he had found.

"The land is good and the climate temperate. It seems to
me that brasil-wood might grow there and that the climate
would be suitable for the raising of silkworms. The tides are
slow and do not run as they do here. The sea nearby swarms
with fish! No, we saw no inhabitants, but my son found
felled trees in the forest and a snare spread to take game, so
there must be people living near. Once we saw from the sea
two forms running alongshore, but whether they were men
or animals we could not be certain. It was dangerous to sail
too close to land. We landed only once, in order to take possession—and, briefly, just before leaving, to refill the water
casks. For a month we coasted north and east from *Prima
Terra Vista* along the new found land to about the latitude
of southern Ireland and, from the easternmost cape of Tartary, set out again for England, having the wind behind us
most of the way. We made our landfall off the coast of Brittany in fifteen days." Caboto did not mention that had not
the Bristol men insisted he change course, certain he was

sailing too far north, he would not have passed by Britain and would have made the return voyage in even shorter time.

Questions came afterward.

"Was it island or mainland? How could you tell?"

"I coasted the land for a month and saw no channel, though naturally I did not follow all the twists and turns and gaps in the land. No seaman cares to go so close to an unknown shore. We stood off some leagues from the land as a rule, anchoring at night, and making sure storms did not catch us on a lee shore. We made soundings all the way and they are marked on my chart, also every cape and bay we saw along the route. We found no large body of fresh water emptying into the sea to indicate a river flowing out of a continent, yet I feel certain the land we found was the mainland of Asia, probably the eastern coast of Tartary. We are going back of course, as soon as a new expedition can be got ready, and will explore the land thoroughly, and for this purpose the King has promised us ships."

"But surely, Master Cabot, when you do go back, you will not expect to find spices and gold so far north?"

"Not in the North, Signore, no. I propose to sail south along the coast from the place at which I first touched, more and more toward the west, until I reach an island called Cipango, situated in the equinoctial region. Either there or farther south, I expect to find the place from which all the spices of the world have their origin, as well as the gold and jewels."

"But does anyone know for sure *where* these things originate?"

"I have been to Mecca on several occasions on business. Mecca, as no doubt you know, is a city in Arabia, a great trading and religious center of Islam where oriental and western goods are exchanged. When I asked those who brought the spices in caravans from the east what was the place of origin of these spices, they replied that they did not know, but that other caravans came with this merchandise to their homes from distant countries, and these again had told them the goods had been brought to them from other remote regions. I therefore reasoned that these things came from places very far away and so on from one to the other. Always assuming that the earth is round, then it follows as a matter of course that the last of all must take them in the most eastern point of Asia. Then, since these things grow only in warm countries, they must be found in the south. Now that we know where to go, a second voyage should not take much over a fortnight and then it is simply a matter of following the coast." Here was the youthful, over-confident Vanni speaking.

"Won't this conflict with the Spanish discoveries?" Caboto did not see exactly where the voice came from, but suspected that it emanated indirectly from the Spanish ambassador. He did not hesitate to answer. There was no need for secrecy. His Highness had already allowed the matter to be discussed in open Court before the new ambassador, Pedro de Ayala, as well as before Puebla.

"I have no intention of sailing in Spanish waters, or anywhere near them. I sail again in English latitudes and my destination is some two thousand miles to the west of Española." There was a brief murmur in the body of the audience. "It is my certain belief," added Caboto firmly, "that Signore Colombo has not gone far enough."

No more was said about the Spanish discoveries, but Caboto picked out the face and figure of John Day in the room and guessed that all he had said would be reported to Colombo. It gave him rather a strange, almost pleasant, feeling to think that now Colombo on his side would be curious about the English voyage. He would naturally approach

John Day who made regular trips between England and Spain, the man who had supplied Caboto with information about his friend Colombo. It did not matter that John Day would pass on this information. He was a perfectly loyal Englishman and would hand over nothing prejudicial to England. Moreover, it benefited Henry as well as Colombo and the Spanish sovereigns to have a go-between like Day who could provide reilable information outside the usual diplomatic channels.

There was pleasure in receiving adulation from the London crowds. It was delightful to see Michiele and Gabriel strutting with pride, waiting for the island grants he had got them to be approved by the King. Less satisfactory was Sebastiano's attitude, peacocking before the younger set in Bristol as if he and not his father had discovered land in the West! Yet it was natural. He was still hardly more than a boy. It was much more pleasing to see Mattea's pride both in himself and her son, and her pleasure as she walked beside him to the Mayor's dinner dressed in her new silk gown and fur cape. He often wished that others could be here to see their triumph—Fra Andrea, for example, Piero and his parents, Emilio—even Uncle Luigi!

Still, quite soon, popularity and excitement lost their charms and he was in a fever of anxiety to be off again.

The King had promised ten armed ships in the spring, but for months the whole business was left hanging, due to political upheavals, and there were times when Caboto feared the voyage would be put off indefinitely. While the *Matthew* had been away, the pretender Perkin Warbeck had conspired with James I of Scotland, and the people of Cornwall had risen in revolt. Now Warbeck was reported to have landed in the disaffected area and the King was obliged to leave London hurriedly with troops to deal with the rising. The King was not back in London until late November but then, having dealt successfully with the rebels, he was ready once more to discuss Caboto's affairs. There was again a public hearing, after which Caboto learned that the new charter would be approved in time for a voyage in the present year, 1498, but that due to the expense of the recent military campaign he could have only five ships, not ten. To him, this did not matter. He was confirmed in his position as leader of the expedition and his plan of operation was approved by His Highness—these were the important things.

"I intend, your Highness, to work along the coast from last year's landfall, after first making sure the land is continental, then head as directly as possible for Kinsai which I believe lies somewhere between ten and twenty degrees north of the equinoctial. The port of Zaitan will lie farther south and Cipango some fifteen hundred miles off that coast. In the cities I hope to get information on Cipango as well as directions on how to reach the Spice Islands. If this help is refused me, I shall go on without it. However, it is reasonable to suppose that the Khan's people will be willing to act as middlemen, since Marco Polo describes them as excellent businessmen, favorable to trade with other nations. Since they will have their own marketing organization already set up, that should be an advantage to us. They have hundreds of ships going to and from Cipango and the Spice Islands, and it may be more economical in the end to use them rather than our own vessels. We would then set up a halfway station or factory, like those in the Levant, somewhere on the coast, where the goods can be transshipped to England. Fishing stations and drying factories can also be set up and managed from that place."

The King listened and missed nothing, dryly noting the objections of Ayala and going straight on with the business. Later, he talked with Caboto privately.

"The trading arrangements, I think, can be safely left to

you for the moment. You will be better able to advise us on your return. Meanwhile I want you aware of the political situation."

Caboto waited with attention. They were alone in the anteroom of Henry's bedchamber. Beyond the door-hangings, Caboto could see the corner of a silken bedcover and a large writing desk piled high with books and papers. It was said that the penurious King wrote up all his household expenses personally to the last penny each night before retiring. Now the monarch, preoccupied, walked up and down with hands clasped behind him, his heavy satin dressing gown dragging behind him on the carpeted floor.

"I must tell you," said the King crisply, "that both Spain and France hope I will back them in a war against Italy. I have promised help to France, conditionally, but at the same time I do not care to lose the friendship of Ferdinand and Isabella." Caboto did not need to be told how much the King desired a marriage between his son Arthur and the Spanish princess, Catherine—it was matter for open gossip. "Fortunately, Spain is also anxious for peace, at least until she knows whether or not she will gain my support. So, though I do not fear Spanish disapproval of this project of yours, Master Cabot, I have no desire for an open break while certain negotiations are under way."

The Spanish, Caboto knew, already resented what they considered an intrusion into their Indies. Ayala had protested strongly that the land the English hoped to coast along was country already found by their servant, Cristóbal Colón, and had said in fact that the land called Colba was definitely the mainland of Cathay. When Caboto had showed his map in court, to prove that Colba was an island in mid-Ocean, Ayala had cried that it was false, and that he would so inform his royal masters.

"Therefore, Master Cabot," said the King, stopping short

to peer at Caboto in his crabwise way. "Try to reach your goal before the Spanish—or the Portuguese!"

"Sir?" he asked, startled. "The Portuguese?" His latest information was that the Portuguese were still trying to reach the Indies by circumnavigating Africa and sailing east, and he told the King so.

"That is the story they let out," admitted Henry, "but one is free to wonder. A Portuguese captain named Vasco da Gama left from Lisbon last July with four vessels, ostensibly to complete the work of Diaz in rounding Africa, and this may be true. We *know* only that he left the Cape Verdes and headed into the Western Sea."

Caboto was inclined to think at this point that the King's naturally suspicious nature was leading him astray. There was surely no reason to fear competition from the Portuguese in the West. The only fear was that they might reach the Spice Islands by the east before he himself got to them by the west!

"You wonder why I am suspicious," the King said shrewdly. "I will tell you. The late King John of Portugal was convinced that a large continent existed in the South—just below Southern Asia. A fourth part of the world, he called it, to balance Europe, Asia, and Africa!"

"*Terra Australis Incognita.*" Caboto nodded skeptically. "If it exists."

"I think it does exist," said the King, "and I think it possible the Portuguese mariners have fairly certain knowledge of it, as we have of land in the north. Certainly, Columbus is looking for it."

This was as new and startling a piece of information as the other.

"Colombo too is interested?"

"Colombo, as you call him, has, since his return from his second voyage been re-evaluating his geographic ideas. His last voyage was a great disappointment to everyone. He came back weak and ill, dressed as a monk, with his beard long and his hair gray, bringing nothing in the way of spices or precious metals, only dreary accounts of his first colony destroyed by the natives and of the hardships and dangers faced in establishing a new one. The whole Enterprise of the Indies was, I believe, for a while in danger of being dropped altogether. Master Columbus therefore is desperate to make this new voyage, and he knows it is imperative for him this time to attain some notable achievement or lose his credit with the Crown. There are plenty of Spanish *hidalgos* anxious for the chance to replace him! Now Columbus, it seems, has heard from his 'Indians' of a mysterious land to the south and he thinks it may be the Southern Continent, which is said to lie south of the spice lands of Asia. If he finds that Southern Continent, Cabot, he will doubtless follow its coast north to the true Indies!"

Caboto caught his breath at the coincidence of their plans. Colombo, and possibly da Gama, reaching to the south and turning north. He himself crossing by the north and reaching to the south! All with the goal of the Indies! It was a race, and one he must win.

"Now it is possible," said Henry in his paper-dry voice, "that you may meet one or both of your rivals at some point midway, perhaps very near the goal itself. If you do—"

Henry paused and fixed Caboto with a grim look.

"If you do, I want you to use every trick you are master of to outwit them if you can—short of outright warfare. Is that understood?"

"Yes, Your Highness."

"I depend on you, Master Cabot, you see, to exercise not only your navigator's ability but your diplomatic talents. I have discovered in a long and often difficult life that diplomacy, on the whole, pays better than fighting." The King added, "I want particularly no act of open hostility to upset the balance between my country and Spain. I would sooner you lost your—" he hesitated and Caboto wondered if Henry had been about to say "life," but the monarch added "—your race than your temper!"

All this simply made his job more difficult. He must not only cross two thousand miles of still-hazardous ocean, follow an unknown coast for twice that distance, and conclude a trade treaty on the way with the Chinese rulers, he must be ready at all times to deal with any Spanish or Portuguese ship he encountered in the area, and without open warfare! Henry of England expected a good deal of his servants!

Still, if he got there first, there was nothing to worry about. That, after all, was the important thing. For the moment, he forgot rivals and kings and diplomacy and thought only of the fact that soon he would know if the Spice Islands and Cipango lay where he had pictured them. If he were triumphantly proved right in *his* geographic concepts, what did he care for anything after that?

For then, all the questions would be answered.

XXII

Coasting Voyage

"Land!" came the cry from the maintop.

Gabriel Duchesne passed the word to the quarterdeck.
"Where away?"

"Two points on the larboard quarter, sir!"

Caboto and his captain exchanged wide smiles. For the second time in two years they had crossed the vast and unpredictable Ocean Sea and made a landfall on the continent of "Asia," this time somewhat north of the original discovery.

"Bring her up into the wind, please, Captain Duchesne!"

By the time the ship lay to, Caboto had got to work with his quadrant. Though it was light enough to see, a few stars were still visible in the dawn sky, and the sea was nearly still. Too good an opportunity to waste. He got a star fix quickly, made his calculations, and found the results agreed fairly well with his dead reckoning. Meanwhile the ship was stirring.

"Land?" Sleepy voices came from all over the ship. "I thought I heard the lookout—"

"Was somebody shouting?"

"It's land, Father!"

"God be praised!" said the priest.

Figures rose from rough beds on hatch covers and there was a scurry of spreading excitement.

"What's to do, eigh—what's to do?" The Yorkshire shareholder, John Cair, came hustling up from the maindeck, to stare off at the western horizon. "Is it land, Master Cabot?"

"It's land!"

Michiele gave an exuberant shout—

"*Viva* Caboto! *Viva* the Captain-General!"

A bellow came back from the lower deck and the bosun led the hands in the cheering. The goat tethered to the port cannon added her vociferous "baaahs" to the general rejoicing, and the fat Londoner, Master Thirkell, came hurrying on deck to shake hands with Caboto and his fellow-shareholders with a self-congratulatory air, as if he had done it all himself. In a way, he had. King Henry had, as usual, tightened his purse strings at the lost moment, and Thirkell's money had come to the rescue.

Caboto was not commanding the *Matthew* this voyage. His favorite ship had been away on charter to the Azores when the expedition was due to leave and he had been given as his flagship a small fast caravel called the *Catherine*. Early in the voyage, not surprisingly, she had outrun the trade ships. In one of them was Sebastiano, who had chosen to sign on with Robert Thorne, his father approving the decision. Sebastiano would show more responsibiilty, and perhaps more humility, under another master than his father. Moreover, the boy could make a chart record of the coast as he saw it, which later he could compare with his father's. This way they would have a double check and additional information.

"I don't see any land," grumbled Thirkell.

"You will soon. Look beneath that cloud cluster."

"Cathay!" marveled the Londoner, "after only twenty-eight days. That is—" he peered up at Caboto suspiciously. "You're sure it *is* Cathay and not some island?"

"I cannot be sure, of course, until I have thoroughly examined the coast, but I believe it to be a northeastern cape of Tartary. Cathay, strictly speaking, should lie farther south."

"We're still alone." Thirkell looked to the east.

"I doubt if we'll see the rest of the fleet until we reach our rendezvous—Kinsai."

"Kinsai," sighed Michiele with rapture. "Polo says the Chinese maidens there are the loveliest in the world—generous with their charms too. And we'll soon be there!"

"*Calma*, Michiele! Not all that soon."

"When, exactly?" demanded Thirkell.

"I hope not later than the end of August."

"August!" cried Thirkell indignantly. "But this is only the middle of June!"

"We may arrive sooner. I hope we do."

"*I* damn well hope so too," said the Londoner with a grim expression. "How can we be sure of meeting the trade ships at this Kinsai when we don't even know how long it will take to get there?"

Caboto controlled a rising irritation. He had by now discovered Thirkell to be a distrustful man and a faultfinder, certain that he himself was the only one capable of management and direction.

"We cannot be sure, naturally, of anything. We *know* only that we are some two thousand miles west of Europe, and approximately forty-seven degrees north of the Equator. If this is the mainland, as I believe, we should find a large city on a river basin in about 45° North, the latitude of St. Nazaire."

"Who says so?"

"I have seen a chart drawn by the Florentine, Dr. Paolo

Toscanelli, based on a study of Marco Polo's travels," said Caboto, exerting all his patience. "I have myself studied Marco Polo's book for mention of positions and distances. Also I have talked with the camelmen of Mecca who told me the spices came from far to the east and that there were large cities to the north from which the Chinese merchants set out."

"So you don't actually know what latitude or longitude the city of Kinsai lies in, but you *think* it's around 45° North. How long will it take us to sail there?"

"That is quite impossible to tell. It depends on the wind, on the lie of the land, on—"

"Just give me a rough idea!"

Whatever Caboto said, he would have it thrown up to him later if he was wrong. Nevertheless he gave the question his best consideration.

"If this land is continental, we may suppose Kinsai to be distant roughly three hundred leagues," he said slowly. "Last year I covered the same number of leagues in a month, at the rate of ten a day, sailing in fifteen hours of daylight. That is an average of two knots an hour, anchoring and standing off and on during—"

"But you were running in close then, having a look at things," cut in the Londoner impatiently. "This time we're going direct, no anchoring, no fooling about."

"I'm afraid not."

Thirkell stared. His several chins began to work threateningly.

"We must still run as close as we can," said Caboto firmly, before he could speak, "consistent with safety, that is."

"Ridiculous!"

"Eigh, man!" Cair growled in support. "It's daft." Even the priest began to look rebellious.

"Surely I am right in saying, Master Cabot, that this was

not to be a reconnaissance voyage like the one last year?"

"No, Padre, but—"

"Exploring may come first with you," cried Thirkell, "but not with us. Cair and I are businessmen! We've got money invested!"

"We must waste no time," urged the friar. "The heathen must be converted. The Great Khan must be persuaded as soon as possible to join us in driving the Moor from Jerusalem!" The priest's eyes, lit with fervor, reminded Caboto of Father Ferenco's that day in Alexandria. "I must see the defeat of Islam in my lifetime!"

"Happen we'd best take a vote," suggested Cair.

Caboto stiffened.

"There will be no vote," he said coldly. "It is I who am in command of the expedition. It is I who make the decisions!"

"But why, Cabot," groaned Thirkell, "why take the time to explore *now*? You're supposed to reach the Spice Islands ahead of the Spanish. This is a race we're in, man! A race for the richest trade monopoly on earth."

"I know that as well as you, sir," snapped Caboto. "It is my thankless task, however, to get us all there safely. To do so, I must see that matters are kept in perspective. It will do no good to dash blindly ahead or blunder aimlessly from island to island as Colombo has done for the past seven years—"

"Trying to persuade himself that he has reached the continent," chimed in Michiele, "when in reality he is only halfway."

"Is he? I'd feel easier in my mind if I could be sure of that."

"Aye, Master Cabot, there's nowt to tell, is there, where that lad's got to by now?"

"Do you think you are wiser than Columbus, my son?" reproached Fra Antonio.

"This was all explained to you in London, gentlemen," said Caboto wearily. "Colombo chose only the theories which suited him and so came to the conclusion that the Indies lay only five thousand miles from Europe. But I too have poured over the maps of Ptolemy and the book of Marco Polo and have asked myself the same questions— 'How wide is the earth, how wide the land mass of Europe and Asia, how wide the sea remaining?' and I have satisfied myself, regretfully, that the distance is much greater than Messer Colombo reckons, certainly in lower latitudes. I could not, like Colombo, delude myself that the way was shorter than it was. I could not whittle down my estimates to make the plan acceptable to a sponsor. Instead, I reasoned that by sailing in high latitudes, across by the north where the globe is narrower, I could reduce the sea voyage by nearly half. Meanwhile, as you know, Colombo set out from the Canaries and found land after only thirty-three days. It was too soon. He could only have got half the way in that time."

Then he told them what he had heard and seen in Barcelona when the Great Man came home from his voyage.

"I was there," he said, "in the courtyard of the castle among the crowd, and I heard Colombo describe the land he had found—houses made of grass, trading ships formed of hollowed-out logs, and a lack of everything which spells to us civilization. Therefore I knew from my reading of Marco Polo that he had not found what he sought."

"He brought back gold and spices," argued Thirkell.

"Did he? You would not have thought so if you had seen the shoddy gold ornaments worn by his sailors, the nameless seeds and powdered bark he offered in place of cinnamon and cloves and pepper."

"But what of those lads he brought back wi' him—Indians!"

"Indians? He brought back savages," cried Caboto scornfully, "without clothes, without religion, without knowledge of architecture or trade, creatures fit only as he said for slavery!"

"They might have been inhabitants of offshore islands?" ventured Padre Antonio.

"They would need to have been from islands very *far* offshore, Father. They had had, obviously, no contact with the officials of the Khan or merchants or trading vessels. If they had, they would have known that the Spanish were not gods descended from heaven. No, what Colombo has found are some islands in mid-Ocean. We, with our coastal approach, will reach India before him. Yes, in spite of a slow start! Meanwhile, by traveling slowly and cautiously, we will make sure that we do not repeat Colombo's mistake. I shall send the pinnace into bays and rivers to make sure they *are* bays and rivers, and not channels between islands. I must test for currents and for mixture of fresh water with salt. I must measure depths and drift. All this will take time. Once I am absolutely sure, however, that the land off there is Asia, I shall sail direct to Kinsai. Caping—that is, sailing from one salient of land to another—will not take so long. Then at Kinsai we can secure guides to take us quickly the rest of the way to the spice lands."

Thirkell's tone was now decidedly milder.

"Well, that's not as bad as I'd thought."

"You'll not muck about on shore?" asked Cair.

"Only if I find a town—or, briefly, to renew our stores of wood and water."

"Very well then," said Thirkell pompously, "if you can promise that—"

"I promise you nothing, Master Thirkell," said the Captain-General sharply. "I merely tell you what I intend to do."

"Well, so you have!" Thirkell looked at him sulkily. "And as long as you've got the crew behind you, you can do as you please, I suppose. But don't forget—if you let Columbus or the Portuguese get there first, you'll have some explaining to do, not only to the shareholders but to Henry VII!"

"I shan't forget." Caboto shrugged off his annoyance, added lightly, "Master Thirkell, you worry too much. Remember, the Spanish and Portuguese will be having their own troubles. Colombo, I am told, set sail far to the south this year, hoping to boost his badly fallen reputation by finding that rumored Southern Continent. He will have to sail as far north after his landfall as we must sail south, and in that low latitude he will have had a longer initial voyage. As for da Gama, if he sailed east around Africa as I suspect, we have a long head start of him."

As usual, with a combination of superior knowledge and persuasiveness, he won them to a more cheerful view.

"It's what, the fourteenth of June now—"

"And a month, you say, ought to find us in Kinsai?" asked Thirkell.

"I make no promises, but I would think so. Of course," added Caboto confidently, "we are sure to see Chinese coastal towns and fishing villages long before that." He raised his voice to Gabriel on the lower deck— "Captain Duchesne!"

"Aye, sir?"

"Set a course south-southwest, sounding at regular intervals."

"Aye, aye, sir! All hands to the sheets!"

"And now, my sons," said Fra Antonio, clasping his hands and falling on his knees, "we must give thanks to God for bringing us this far safely."

The whole company, except those needed to put the ship on her course, knelt obediently.

"Oh God, Father of all, and through the intercession of the blessed Mother, our advocate on high—"

"Raise up tacks and sheets!" The captain shouted.

Caboto, kneeling with the rest, was conscious all the time of Gabriel's voice raised above the prayer, of the ship's noises, of the wind's direction and the feel of the deck under his knees. At the same time his thoughts ranged far and wide.

"Hands aloft to loose tops'ls!"

"We thank Thee for bearing us safely across the turbulent seas—"

Caboto thought of the dreaming boy of Genoa, of the young seaman making his first voyage over the Aegean, and he felt a little humble to think that he had done more than he had hoped. He had traveled halfway around the earth, much farther than his old hero Pytheas, and here he was at last—Giovanni Caboto whom the English called John Cabot, within arm's reach almost of all the gold and spices of the East. He had much to be thankful for!

"And so we entrust ourselves to Thee once more, O God, imploring Thee to lead us to the Great Khan's city—

When he got there, he would have to exert himself, use the utmost tact and diplomacy. His role was a complex one —pathfinder today, administrator tomorrow, later perhaps commander of armies in the field!

"—where we may find allies for the crusade against the forces of the Infidel."

"Sheet home!" cried Gabriel. "Make all fast!"

Meeting the morning breeze sweetly on their beam, the flutter of the rigging ceased and the wind began to sing in the taut shrouds. The priest began to sing the *Salve Regina* and voices joined in from all over the ship—

> *Mater misericordiae*
> *Vita, dulcedo, et spes nostra, salve*
> *Ad te clamamus . . .*

By the time the singing ended, the morning haze had dissipated. The sun was going to be hot, and Caboto was suddenly ravenously hungry! He sent the ship's boy to bring bread and cheese to the deck, unable to bear the thought of his cabin on such a day.

"By the mark, fourteen!" sang out the leadsman.

"Wear ship!" ordered Gabriel. "Raise up tacks and sheets!"

"By the mark, thirteen and a half!"

"Let go and haul!"

The ship, tiny on the waste of water, wore around in a flurry of spray and canvas.

"Steady as she goes!"

So the *Catherine* settled down to work, bobbing along in light airs from the northwest, tacking continually, poking her nose into bays and inlets and harbors, while all on board looked hopefully day after day for signs of Oriental civilization and for the great trade ships sailing across the Sea of Chin to Cipango. Concerned with mapping the land and charting the waters, examining river bottoms, sea currents, tides, and depths along this unknown shore, Caboto was not at first aware of how the days were lengthening into weeks, with still no signs of civilization. Fortunately Michiele, long an ardent reader of *The Travels of Marco Polo*, kept shareholders and priest amused and out of Caboto's way by regaling them with descriptions of Cathay and Cipango.

"It's a pity we didn't see the capital, but of course Cambulac is hundreds of miles inland."

"That's where the high mucky-muck bides, eh?"

"Oh the Khan is always on the move about his great realm, Master Cair, but yes, Cambulac may be said to be his headquarters. It is a truly amazing city, completely surrounded by a wall twenty-four miles long, with a palace at each corner. In the center is the Khan's huge edifice, its inside walls covered with gold and silver, and painted with beautiful pictures. The great hall of this palace is so vast, it seats six thousand guests at a time! The roof is varnished over with brilliant colors, so it glistens like crystal for miles around. In the palace stables, the Khan keeps a thousand pure white horses and five thousand elephants."

Cair snorted disbelievingly.

"Five thousand elephants? Eigh now, you don't expect us to believe that!"

"You're just like those who doubted him in his lifetime, Master Cair! But listen to this—when they asked Messer Polo on his deathbed to admit before God that he had at least exaggerated, he whispered with his dying breath, 'I have not told you the half of it.' One must remember that Cathay was a rich and cultured nation when Rome was still undreamed of. I for one believe every word he said."

Jogging slowly south-southwest down the continent in the company of light airs, fogs, calms, and an occasional school of porpoises, it became the established thing for Michiele to describe Cathay and the Indies in detail.

"Cambulac contains, as well as the Forbidden City, ten principal market squares, each capable of holding fifty thousand people. In the shops, the people—"

"Hold on, Master Barber! What *about* the people? I always like to know something of my prospective customers."

"The people are very rich, very cultured. The merchants and their ladies do nothing with their own hands, but live as delicately as kings and queens, and even the poor people dress in silk. To give you some idea of their numbers, every day a thousand loads of raw silk come through the gates of Cambulac to be turned into clothing for the inhabitants."

"Must be fair jammed wi' folk. Worse than towns in Yorkshire on Fair day!"

"They live very comfortably, however, on streets so broad and straight you can see from one city-gate to another."

The days passed.

"Kinsai in the province of Manjii is even larger than the capital," said Michiele. "A hundred miles in circumference, with many canals and twelve thousand stone bridges, beneath which Marco saw large ships pass."

"It gets larger every time you tell it," complained Thirkell.

"*We've* seen nowt of bridges or ships," remarked Cair.

Fra Antonio fingered his wind-worn cassock sadly. "Nothing but trees, rocks, sand, and grass."

One day to make a change and to raise their spirits, Caboto took them ashore with him in the pinnace. As he had hoped, a fine harbor lay behind the island he had seen from the sea and two rivers debouched into it. Where the rivers met, he landed and sent the crew to fill the water casks while he tried a sun-sight with his quadrant. The others wandered about for a bit, but the silence of the forest depressed them and discouraged any wandering far from the beach.

"Looks like another dead end!" Thirkell looked around with grim distate. "Tell me this, Master Barber, what's the country *around* Kinsai supposed to be like?"

Michiele hesitated, trying to remember.

"The city lies in the basin of a great river—"

"You told us that!"

"And along this river are towns and cities."

"The country, man, the country!"

"I can't remember," said Michiele uneasily. "I know he said the roads enter the province from Cambulac and that roads lead out toward Zaitan, the spice depot of the south, and on these roads are inns every twenty-five miles to serve the men of the postal service—"

"Roads! Inns! Postal services!" snorted Thirkell, "There must have been mention of farms!"

"I suppose so—"

"A city a hundred miles about, pack-jammed with folk—they'd need farms for a thousand miles around!"

"There were gardens and orchards in the city—"

"Gardens!" shouted Thirkell. "God-a-mercy, Barber, gardens wouldn't feed that huge population. Where did they get their fresh meat and fish and vegetables?"

"Well," faltered Michiele, "he may have mentioned farms and villages—"

"Then where are they?" Thirkell waved his arm at the forest. "We're supposed to have reached Kinsai by now, according to Cabot—but look! Look at that virgin land, those forested hills that run back a hundred miles and more if I'm any judge. Where are those coastal towns and fishing villages we were supposed to see long before we got to Kinsai? It's near the end of August and we've not seen so much as a grass hut!"

"We've seen people," Michiele argued. "Figures running on shore—"

"Beasts, more likely."

"Those fires we saw at night."

"It's not good enough!" exploded Thirkell.

"The Captain-General made no promises," flared Michiele, getting angry in his turn. "We may be a few degrees off—"

"More than a few! We've wasted time—" Thirkell turned and saw Caboto packing up his instruments. "Cabot! I want to talk to you!"

Smiling, tucking his quadrant away in its case, Caboto came toward them across the sand. He opened his mouth to speak, but Thirkell was ahead of him.

"Where are those Oriental towns you talked about? Where are those blasted fishing villages?"

"Aye—and farmlands and country fairs!"

"Where, my son, is Kinsai?"

Caboto stared at them, his smile fading. He saw Michiele shrug helplessly.

"What's our present latitude?" demanded Thirkell.

"Roughly 41° North."

"There! You said you'd find Kinsai at 45 degrees," accused the Londoner.

"If I said that," snapped Caboto, "I was mad. But I did not. I said that, according to my best information, we would find it somewhere in that vicinity. Obviously my information was wrong."

"Eeeh! Loovely!" said Cair with bitterness.

"You mean the chart that fellow—what's-his-name, Toscanelli—made is no good?"

"Master Thirkell," cried Michiele, angry on his friend's behalf, "can't you be reasonable?"

"Peace, Michiele." Caboto stared at the silent trees, the empty sea. "How could Toscanelli know for certain, since he was never here? He was a doctor, a brilliant mathematician, an astronomer. He did his best, but it seems clear now that he put the Chinese cities too far north."

"Then we're traveling in the dark!" Thirkell cried.

"Of course!" blazed Michielle. "Are you just realizing that?"

"Why didn't you make that clear in London?" Thirkell glared at Caboto. "You only talked there of the riches of the Spice Islands, the wonders of Cipango."

"That is altogether untrue!" Caboto too was angry now. "Everything—all my geographic concepts and my sailing plans were discussed openly and exhaustively before King and Court. You had the chance then to challenge any statement. If you listened only to Polo's descriptions of Cipango's golden streets, I cannot be blamed for that!"

"Peace! Peace, my sons," begged Fra Antonio. "We must not quarrel. What does Marco Polo say of Kinsai? He at least was here and saw for himself."

"True. He saw places, found out the distances covered on a march, noted the position of Polaris at intervals, but he was not a geographer, Father. Not a cartographer. Simply a traveler, with an observant eye. His geography is actually vague in the extreme. He calculates the height of the Pole Star in cubits and is astonished to lose sight of it altogether in the Indies. His bearings and distances are rough-and-ready, and he generally ignores such things as compass points and variations."

"And this—" cried Thirkell, enraged, "is the man on whom both you and your Florentine doctor pinned your faith—and *our* money!"

"By San Giorgio!" roared the Captain-General. "What did you expect? Signposts? Road maps? We are here to *find* the way!"

"It's not why I'm here! I'm here for business—to open up trade with the Chinese, not to play at hide-and-seek!" Then even Thirkell seemed to realize that he was beating a dead horse, and his tone changed, grew almost plaintive. "Cabot, if we don't soon stop this dawdling in bays and rivers, we might as well give up and go home. Give us a date, just give us a date when you'll stop exploring and head for Kinsai!"

There was a long pause while Caboto looked at Thirkell inscrutably. Then—

"As a matter of fact," he said in a weary tone, "that is what I was coming to tell you just now. My latest calculations show that we have now covered some six hundred leagues of coastline without finding a gap in the land. The exploratory part of our expedition is finished."

Thirkell's jaw dropped ludicrously.

"I am convinced now," went on Caboto, "that we are coasting a mainland. No islands could be so great nor have such large rivers."

"Heaven be praised," murmured Fra Antonio.

The other two were silent.

Seeing the return of the men with the water, Caboto

called to the bosun to launch the boat. "Come, gentlemen, we must not waste time admiring the scenery!" They followed him meekly. "We go now as directly as possible to Kinsai."

As they scrambled to their places in the boat, the Yorkshireman looked back at the shore.

"Fair puzzles me the way they leave such places to the beasts and birds. *This* place'd make a rare port."

"Yes," agreed Caboto thoughtfully, "it would. I've wondered myself why they haven't developed this coast, with all its rich timber and deep harbors. I suppose the answer is that the country is so huge they haven't needed to. Civilization has grown toward the south, toward the spice centers of Kattigara and Malaieu. However," he added with revived buoyancy, his good humor restored at the prospect of the coming voyage, "we'll know all about it some day."

Privately, he made up his mind to question both Toscanelli and Marco Polo from now on. He must keep to the few facts he was sure of—the fact that the world was round and therefore Asia lay west of Europe; the fact that he had certainly found a continent, therefore it was Asia; the fact that spices did not grow in temperate regions, therefore the Indies lay farther south and west. He would discover everything else by actual experience! If he did not find the Chinese and Indian cities before he reached the Equator, he would be bound to find them there. No more rash promises! Forty degrees of sailing might take months.

So the *Catherine* headed to sea again, this time with decision. Kinsai was the goal, but the coast line had to be kept in sight at all times. Occasionally they had to spend time searching for a new cape where the line of shore was temporarily broken.

"Zaitan," lectured Michiele, "is the port where all the spices from India are landed, as well as the pearls and precious stones. Zaitan is a huge center with ships converging on it from all points of the compass—"

Three pairs of eyes turned lugubriously to look at the sea. Not a city. Not a sail. Michiele continued stubbornly.

"—and for every shipload of pepper that goes through Alexandria for the European market, a hundred are brought to Zaitan. The ships are much larger than ours, many of them with four masts, carrying crews of a hundred men, all well armed. There are first-class cabins, as many as sixty to a ship, one for each merchant, and fruit and vegetables are grown on board for food to keep the passengers in good health."

Thirkell reflected sourly on his late meal of cold salt pork and dry biscuit, washed down with stale water. The goat had stopped giving milk and had been sacrificed to the stewpot weeks ago. The rum had given out too.

"The artisans of Cathay are masters of every rare and wonderful craft and each has his own guild. They are an industrious people, quiet and good-mannered, always happy to see foreign merchants."

"Glad to hear it." Thirkell looked at the *Catherine*'s two tiny cannon. "We wouldn't stand much chance against those ships you mentioned."

"Of course we won't have to fight. They'll be our allies," said Michiele confidently.

The weather was too good to last. In late September, a storm swept in from the east, driving the *Catherine* toward a lee shore. For twenty-four hours, she fought in wind and spray, Caboto and Gabriel struggling to save her. The way the wind was blowing, they could only hold her off the rocks and pray for the wind's direction to change. Instead, ironically, it died suddenly altogether, whereupon the current and the set of the sea sent the *Catherine* drifting helplessly toward the reef she had so far managed to avoid. There was no bottom at anchoring depth outside the reef. Not the sweeps nor even the pulling power of the men in the pinnace and long boat could hold her. Suddenly in sun and calm, with not so much as a cat's-paw of wind to hold her back, the *Catherine* was washed on to the reef among the breakers. She struck with a horrid rasping sound of keel on rock, and stopped dead.

"Clew up! Aloft and stow!" shouted Gabriel. The sails were got off as quickly as possible, so as not to cause further damage by driving the keel along the rock and possibly ripping out the ship's whole bottom.

"Tide's falling," said Caboto, still hoping against hope. "She's not working much."

"Not making any water yet, sir," reported the bosun.

If they acted quickly, they might be able to haul the vessel off before the tide fell too low. The crew swarmed aloft to send down the masts and yards, stripping the ship down to a hulk. Then out went both boats to run out anchors on long cables and with the aid of capstan and windlass to try to heave the ship off the rocks. But it was no use—the *Catherine* would not budge.

There was nothing to do but wait through the fall of the tide and its rise again, pumps working all the time. At top of high water, the vessel floated off the reef and, though she did not sink, the water was up to her chain plates. Any breeze that came now would send her back on the rocks and doubtless smash her to pieces. There was only one thing to do.

"Take up the masts and spars, rig them and we'll run her ashore."

Masts and spars were hauled up from where they had been floated overside, and rigged again. With the sails spread to catch the faint rising wind, the *Catherine* headed sluggishly for an opening in the reef. Luck was now on their side. They made the passage in safety and found a sheltered bay with a sloping gravel shore. Almost indifferently, the *Catherine* drifted on to the beach and toppled over on her side. In the part of her hull above water they saw a huge rock jammed into the largest hole.

There was no hope of fothering a hole like that! Caboto saw at once that the hull must be completely repaired, and both Gabriel and the bosun were in agreement.

"We'll never make it now," said Thirkell in despair.

"We'll make it," growled the Captain-General, "if we have to rebuild this ship from stem to stern!"

"Too late," moaned the Londoner. "The Spanish will be there ahead of us." But even Thirkell realized that complaining now was pointless. The storm was an Act of God and nothing could undo the damage. They were lucky to have saved their lives.

They would be here for months now, Caboto knew, though he made light of the delay in public conversation. First, everything had to be heaved out of the ship, piece by piece, and carried ashore. Tents were raised to give shelter for the precious stores and ammunition. Other shelters were built with tree branches for living quarters. Later, all would have to be carried back to the ship and restowed.

Cables were now fastened to the nearest trees and by them the ship was hauled above high tide and there careened—laid over on her side, with the weight of her two cannon slung from a yard to hold her in position.

It had been weeks since they'd touched shore. Now, with time to look about a little, the men of the *Catherine* saw that the character of the land had changed. Pine and spruce had given way to groves of opulent oaks and swampland. Instead of meadows filled with daisies and buttercups, they found woody patches of honeysuckle and wild jasmine. That night as they rested in unaccustomed luxury on beds of moss and branches, they smelled night-blooming nicotania.

"We are 36 degrees north of the Equator." Drowsily, Gabriel considered as well as he could the assumed length and direction of Asia's shore line. "We have still a long way to go."

"Yes." Caboto stared into the darkness. "Unless, when the ship is repaired, we turn east and try to find Cipango?"

"Why not?" cried Michiele from his place on the other side of the shelter. He raised himself on one elbow. "If we miss Cipango, there are those hundreds of islands out there—"

"Fifteen hundred miles offshore," Gabriel reminded him.

"If we could be sure of finding spices, it might be worth a try," observed the Captain-General, "but we must remember that spices do not as a rule grow so far north."

"But if Cipango is full of gold and pearls—" began Michiele.

"Golden roofs, golden pavements, Michiele, are not negotiable in Europe. Those rose-colored pearls Marco Polo speaks of—if they exist—may not be of sufficient value to make the journey worthwhile. We know for a fact that in the south lies the region where spices do grow in great quantities, and there is gold too." Talking about it, Caboto found he had already come to a decision.

"I suppose you're right," admitted Michiele. "All the best things are found in warm climates, as everyone knows—"

"Including Paradise," said Gabriel seriously.

"It is there too," said Caboto, "that we will find the strait though which Marco Polo sailed to India on his way home."

"Yes, *mon ami*. Cipango is too speculative." This was Gabriel's opinion too.

"Marco never saw Cipango himself, after all," Michiele reflected. "He got a description of it from others."

"Yes," decided Caboto, "we must continue south and southwest, and simply pray that the others do not reach the Strait before us."

"But first—the ship."

Caboto decided it would be wise to find things for their passenger-shareholders to do while they were ashore—in other words, to keep them busy and out of mischief. He therefore appointed Michiele, the priest, and Messers Cair and Thirkell as his commissariat, issuing crossbows and matchlocks, as well as materials for constructing traps, warning them however not to range so far in search of game that they would lose themselves or reach beyond the sound of a cannon shot from the ship. It was not an impossibility—they had already seen quantities of rabbit, deer, squirrel, partridge and duck very close to camp.

Their skill at first was negligible but improved with practice, and the meat provided a welcome change to the appetites of men used to salted meat, fish, and dry biscuit. Grapes too were found, and smaller berries. The digestion and complexions of the Europeans almost at once showed a change for the better, and many minor ills of shipboard cleared up. Rheumatic pains were soothed by the day's hot sun and sleeping at night in warm dry beds. The men worked with vigor and good will under such conditions.

Having set all in operation, Caboto went for a short walk alone to investigate his new temporary domain and, looking around, he wondered rather wistfully if there might once have been a Chinese city on this spot, one wiped out by war or pestilence since Polo's time. But in that case, surely, there would be ruins—remains of some sort. No, this land had never known anything but trees, rocks, and sand.

In spite of everything, he was not unhappy. He had been plagued since Bristol by a cranky rudder, and he meant to have a new one made here, with new straps and pintles forged for the purpose. He would seize the opportunity too for a complete overhaul in a place where wood was plentiful and living easy. He would have a new foresail cut and roped to replace the one blown out in the storm and he would have to have the *Catherine's* bottom thoroughly coated with tallow to keep out shipworm. It would also be a golden opportunity to rummage—that is, to change ballast. This had been his ambition ever since England where, despite his pleadings, the ship chandlers had put sand in the hull instead of stone. Sand grew foul quickly, tended to get into the pumps and clog them, and it smelled to high heaven. He would have the bilges scrubbed and sprinkled with vinegar to keep them sweet. It would save time in the end, perhaps lives too, in the long run. The time would not be wasted.

On the twelfth morning of their stay on land, at midday, they heard a shout from the seaman on guard at the point. Caboto, as startled as the rest, turned and saw the man's arm pointing toward the sea and a moment later three canoes appeared. The natives saw the Europeans at the same moment and stopped short, backing water confusedly. The two groups looked at each across the short expanse of water for a long frozen moment, then Caboto detached himself from his company and walked slowly down to the water's edge, smiling and holding out his hand in a gesture of greeting.

"Bring something from the cask," he said quietly, "some beads, a few bells." He wanted desperately to communicate with the strangers, though his heart sank at sight of them. With their dark, naked skins and feather headdresses, they were too reminiscent of Colombo's "Indians." They could not, however, be the same sort of men! After all he, Caboto, knew for a fact that he had reached the Asian mainland.

He wondered if he looked as strange to the natives as they did to him. He saw himself with their eyes—fair head bare in the sun, dressed in dark breeches and light shirt, sword hung at his waist. Now they paddled, gingerly, a little closer, but stopped well out of spear's range. The group behind Caboto remained silent. Martin Brewer, the bosun, passed the beads to the Captain-General and a bell in his hand tinkled. The natives turned, startled, toward the sound. Caboto beckoned enticingly with the beads and saw them confer together for a moment, then pick up their scoop-shaped paddles.

They came in swiftly, stepped out of the canoes in shallow water and stretched out their hands for the baubles. Then, before Caboto could say a word, they leaped back into their boat again and pushed off.

"Shall I shoot?" asked Martin.

"No! They'll be back."

Michiele came out of the forest, a brace of wildfowl on his shoulder, just in time to see the departure. He hurried to stand beside Caboto, gazing after the men wonderingly.

"They aren't Chinese—not the Chinese I've read about."

"No," said Caboto heavily, "they're not Chinese."

"I don't like it," said Thirkell, coming up too. "They may make trouble."

"I don't think so."

"We ought to be away from here as soon as possible," insisted the Londoner.

"My dear Thirkell, we can't leave until the ship is ready."

"How long are the repairs going to take? What more is there to do?"

"What more?" repeated Caboto, incredulously. "There are trees to be cut down, wood to be made into boards and carved to fix the *Catherine*'s hull. There's a new rudder to be made and fitted. After that, there's the bottom to be caulked, the ballast to be changed, fresh meat brought in and salted. And at the end, there's the putting back of the cannon and stores, re-rigging, reloading, swaying up the ship, and—"

"Stop! That's enough! How long?"

But Caboto was not to be caught that way again.

"From three to six months, possibly longer—depending on the weather," he said firmly.

"God-a-mercy!"

"It might be worse," pointed out Michiele. "We might have been at the bottom of the sea. Make the best of things for once, Thirkell, and try to look cheerful."

"It's not your money that's invested! Or Master Cabot's!" growled the Londoner.

"No," said Caboto quietly, "only our futures. Only our lives."

"I was told in London this would be a sure thing."

"Were you so?" asked Caboto with sudden contempt. "And you believed it? By San Marco, you're a fool then. If this were a safe and easy business, Master Shareholder, what profit would there be in it for men like you? A hundred —a thousand—would have been here before you!"

"We're lucky to be alive," said Michiele again.

"We mayn't be for long," said Thirkell sulkily, "if those natives come back tomorrow in force."

"They'll come back," said Caboto dryly, "to trade. Trade is something *every* man understands."

He was right. The following day, the natives came back with twenty or thirty others in half a dozen canoes, bringing fresh-caught fish which they offered in exchange for trinkets. This time they dared to remain for a while. They smiled, touched head and breast in ceremonial fashion, and seated themselves cross-legged to watch with curiosity the work going forward on the ship.

They were handsome fellows, light brown in color, very mannerly, showing no fear of swords or hand guns, which suggested to Caboto that they had seen no Europeans before. There was no communicating with them in words. Questions from Caboto drew forth only a long polite-sounding speech, after which they solemnly departed.

About once a week after that, the natives would appear with furs and pieces of worked leather to trade for bells and red cloth. All Caboto could make out with his hopefully pantomimed questions was that there were cities near, with many people and much gold—but he suspected they were giving him the answer he hoped for in order to be agreeable.

No gold was seen on them, only a few copper ornaments worn about the neck. They had no spices, except a root called *sassafras* which they used for medicine as well as flavoring.

One evening they came bringing a whole venison with them and other good things, and made signs that they desired to feast. They had also brought their womenfolk for the first time, which caused Caboto uneasiness. He sent Gabriel around the men to make it known in no uncertain terms what would happen to them if they interferred with the native women in any way.

So the feast was an amiable one on both sides. The Indians —Caboto, despite himself, fell into the habit of calling them by that name—had brought melons, walnuts, cucumbers, some conies, and fresh salmon, as well as the fat buck. In return the white men offered wine and salt bacon with ship's biscuit from the stores, also fresh clams dug that morning.

Under the wine's influence there was much giggling and horseplay and the Indians' manners deteriorated considerably. Watching them gorge themselves with food—one of them stuffed a whole roast pigeon into his mouth at once— Caboto thought wryly of Michiele's description of the men of Cathay—

"They live in large mansions inside gardens. Their wives and children are very delicate and wear embroidered silks, and are very modest and retiring. The ladies walk with their

eyes on the ground and do not speak. The men behave like
gentlemen and eat with great propriety, and their speech is
very polite, almost ornate."

Caboto listened to the high-pitched stutter of vowels and
saw the women in the shadows eating food flung back to
them by their menfolk, wiping their mouths and their hands
on the hair of their dogs! He heard himself say, in a sour
echo of his own words that day in Barcelona— "Are these
the men of Cathay?"

"We're not in the tropics yet." But in Michiele's tone
Caboto thought he detected the first note of uncertainty,
though the little barber hastened to dissemble it. "These
people are obviously barbarians living on the outskirts of
Cathay or Manjii—men Marco Polo never saw!"

"Michiele, who would have thought the North of Asia to
be like this?" Caboto kept his voice low. "Wilder and more
undeveloped than we ever imagined."

"Yes it is, but do you know," said Michiele, meeting his
friend's eyes with something like defiance, "I like it! It's
good to wander free, under the open sky, getting one's food
with one's own hands! It—it satisfies something in me. I *like*
this country!"

Caboto smiled.

"It's the gourmand who speaks there! You'll miss those
fine dinners when we go back to the ship."

"I'll miss more than the food," said Michiele seriously,
"I'll miss the smell of the earth. I'll miss the flying glow-
worms and even those strange insects that stung Thirkell in
a momentarily exposed part of his anatomy!" Michiele chor-
tled happily at the memory, then sobered. "It's an exciting
land, all the same. The trees, the birds, the abundance and
vastness of everything!"

"I can see you'll have to be dragged aboard the *Catherine*
next spring," said Caboto, but he felt what his friend felt.

Again he was puzzled by the fact that the Chinese had neglected this rich territory. If this was considered by them to be poor land, what must the interior be like!

It was almost summer when the ship was fit again for sea, and none too soon. The natives had gradually turned angry and distrustful—resenting, perhaps, the Europeans making free for so long with their hunting grounds. There had been incidents too, connected with the women. There was no outright aggression, but pieces of ironware and other articles began to disappear from camp and once a grass fire was set too close to the shelters and burned one of them down. They parted therefore with mutual satisfaction, the Indians even waving with a sudden resumption of friendliness when the *Catherine*, now a taut trim ship again, slipped through the gap in the reef and headed for the open sea.

"*The watch is called,*" sang the grommet gaily, turning the glass so the sand ran down again, "*the glass floweth. We shall make a good voyage if God willeth!*"

"Was that sand all out?" shouted Gabriel suspiciously.

"Aye, aye, Captain!"

All was normal again.

The ship sailed south and west until the land took a quarter-turn east and brought them into a region of coastal islands and lagoons dotted with thousands of fishing birds. Here Caboto noted a strong current thrusting up from the south. The sea was a deeper blue now and more saline, with a higher temperature.

The days passed.

The weeks passed.

Midsummer— and still no sign of cities.

The salute to the day had grown dull, repetitious. Devotions began to lose their meaning and it seemed to the men of the *Catherine* that they had been sailing down this uninhabited shore for a lifetime.

"I haven't thought of the other ships in the expedition for weeks," gloomed Thirkell. "Wonder what's happened to *them.*"

"Same as us, I reckon," sighed Cair, "still looking for Kinsai."

"Well, there is no turning back now," said the priest. "What we seek lies ahead."

"If it lies anywhere. It's all so damn useless! Every day the same. Nothing to show for it."

Even Michiele began to show marks of strain.

"How can you remain so calm and cheerful?" he asked Caboto plaintively.

"Michiele, if I ever gave in to my own fears and anxieties, it would be the end for all of us!"

"I suppose so. I don't have your faith—or your self-control." Then, in sudden anger— "Was Marco Polo a liar then? *Marco Milione,* they called him, after all—liar and braggart!"

"*Calma, amico mio.* Why should he have lied? And indeed, we know that much of what he said was true. He was simply unfamiliar with astronomy and navigation. It's all right, Michiele. We just haven't gone far enough."

But both were remembering what they had seen on their latest tour ashore. (It had become a policy of Caboto's to land every now and then. Having seen what change and fresh food could do for the crew, he wanted them to have fresh meat occasionally and a chance to stretch their legs and wash their clothes on shore.) The shore line they had last seen was one of muddy reeds and twisted mangroves, of tangled vines and dead cypress trees in shallows full of alligators. Then, returning to the ship, they had seen to the south a sea of rippling grass! Miles and miles of wet greenery, broken occasionally by a jungle of mangrove. So even the land was failing them. It had gone awash! Caboto called this area the Land of Drowning Grass, and he carried the memory of it to sea with him—a silver desert of water with vultures hovering in a burning sky.

That night the sun went down in gorgeous crimson fire and the sea's surface was broken by schools of seal and dolphin, heralds of a storm the like of which Caboto had never known. When things had seemed as bad as they could be, they grew worse—

At first it was almost a relief to the men of the *Catherine*, the wind blowing away the pall of inertia and boredom, keeping them too busy for doubts and wonderings. But soon, their spirits began to be beaten down under the continuous flailing wind and rain. The storm came from the southwest at first, fortunately driving them offshore, but after days of thrashing about in what they had thought was open sea, they were frightened out of their wits by the sight of land to larboard! An island? At any rate, they knew they now had land on two sides to worry about.

Fearing they were in some large bay or gulf, they sailed blind, pressed by the wind and threatened by lee shores, standing off and on as best they could, praying to see breakers or reefs in time.

Then one morning the wind turned 'round and blew from the northeast. There was some comfort in this, though not much, for they were at least being blown in the right direction. This wind was easier, but just as steady. There was no beating against it even if they had wished. It drove them west and south for a week and a day, and somehow they stayed afloat, though the sails were badly mauled and a hole had had to be fothered in the hull below the water line. The pumps were going continually, not only because of the holing, but because the shipworm was particularly bad down here in the tropics, making damaging headway against the ship's fabric. Then on the ninth day, the sun blazed forth, the sky turned as blue as cornflowers, and a small but lovely island appeared off the bow—a true, tropical isle with coral reefs and gleaming white sand. They anchored and took the pinnace through a gap in the reef.

Some of the men wept as they stumbled ashore in the sun, warm and dry for the first time in weeks.

That night, Caboto took his first star fix in a fortnight and found he was somewhere about 18° North—south of Colombo's original discovery, though naturally, he felt sure, far west of it. Caboto rubbed his tired eyes and studied the line of his chart, which showed the long, long voyage down the coast, breaking off short where the storm had hit. Where was the land? But they were at least nearing the Equator. Only a little way now and they'd find the islands and the strait leading to India . . .

They remained in their tropical heaven for a week, resting, getting clean, drinking fresh water and the milk from coconuts, and making themselves ill on unfamiliar fruits. There was no game on the island, however, and they saw no other human beings. The place was deserted, though there were signs of past habitation—a palm-thatched hut, the remains of old fires. There were trees of many varieties, but none they could identify as spice-bearing. Perhaps it was the wrong time of the year for the fruits. They wanted to stay there forever, drowsing away their days in sun and rest. Even Thirkell and the priest succumbed to this western Land of Lotus and when the time came for Caboto to announce their departure, there was rebellion.

"What! So soon?"

"So soon, Master Thirkell?" Caboto raised an eyebrow. "There was a time when you thought we had no time to waste."

"That was months ago—years ago! Too late now—time's gone by." Thirkell was a changed man. The hardships, the limited diet, and then the terrors of the storm had thinned him down almost to the point of haggardness. His formerly plump jowls hung in drooping folds. All he wanted to do was eat and sleep. If Caboto would let him, he would remain in this paradise for the rest of his life, or so he believed then.

"We've got to go. This island promises no unlimited supply of food," Caboto pointed out, "and our own supplies are very low. What we have eaten here, moreover, has often made us ill. Every day we stay, the worm makes further inroads into the ship's structure. We have no choice."

"Very well," said Thirkell, "but where?"

"First to a place where we can make repairs, then south again to the strait—"

"No!" cried Thirkell. Cair came and ranged alongside him. Martin Brewer and some of the men began to drift nearer.

"No more looking for the Spice Islands," said Thirkell definitely. "If I can't stay here, I want to go home."

"Hear, hear!" said Cair loudly.

There was a mutter from the men. Gabriel and Caboto looked at each other. It was what they had been fearing.

"Hush," Michiele said to Thirkell anxiously, "you don't want the crew to hear talk like that!"

"I don't care if they hear!" shouted Thirkell. "It's their business too. Maybe they feel the same way. How about it, men? Do you want to go home?"

"Aye! That we do, sir!"

"Brewer," snapped Gabriel, "be quiet!"

"The Captain-General himself, sir, said the ship's in bad shape," Brewer said doggedly, "what with the worm and the damage we took in the storm. We'll be lucky if we get home at all, seems to me." The men nodded and muttered approval.

Caboto stood back for the moment, let Gabriel speak for him, knowing they were of one mind.

"Now, look, men," the Burgundian tried persuasion. "We came through the storm—"

"Aye, by a miracle!" said Cair.

"We're not apt to last through another," the bosun said.

"The holes can be mended—"

"Not the worm holes, Cap'n!"

"We can stop those with caulking."

"Using what for pitch? It's near all gone."

"We'll take resin from trees."

"Nowt but palms hereabouts," Cair mentioned, and Gabriel threw an angry glance at him.

"We can live off the land until—"

"We can't live on fish forever! And fruit makes us sick!"

Now they all began to speak at once—

"It's not good enough!"

"We're for home!"

"Aye! Home! England!"

"I've wife and family to think on."

"Let's vote on it!"

Caboto stepped forward and at once the men grew silent. Up to now they had trusted him. They would listen at least to what he had to say.

"You may vote if you wish, but first let me speak." They waited. "We are in the tropics now, as you know—only ten or fifteen degrees north of the Equator. We may be only a few score leagues now from Kattigara, the great Eastern spice market. Think of that, men—Kattigara! I believe that the Strait to the Indies lies due west of here, for I have been noticing a strong western current which sweeps in that direction and which ought to carry us along Marco Polo's route to the Indies. Hold on just a few weeks longer and we will find safe harbor in the realm of the Great Khan!"

There was silence. Then men looked at each other. For a moment, Michiele hoped. Then Brewer shook his head.

"It's no use, sir. We're tired of lookin' for the Khan's cities. We're tired and sick of everything. We don't care no more about spices. We want to go home—home to our families—before it's too late."

"Aye!" cried other voices. "We want to go home!"

"If we don't go now," added the bosun, "the worms will sink the ship under our feet."

The voices rose, topping each other, growing to hysteria.

"We'll take the ship over and sail her home ourselves!" someone shouted.

"You can't navigate her!" Gabriel reminded them savagely.

"No more'n you can sail 'er without us!" Brewer came back.

"Sir!" Gabriel turned to Caboto. "I would advise putting this man in irons! He's obviously the ringleader—"

But Caboto stopped him.

"No," he said wearily, "I can see their point." That was the trouble. He could understand and sympathize with them. For the crew there would be no gold, no glory, no spice monopoly, only slightly higher wages for doing their ordinary work. They had nothing to gain by risking their lives further. All the rewards of success would go to the King and the shareholders. He had nothing to offer them personally. He was still a poor man.

And in any case, he could not sail anywhere without the willing co-operation of his men. If pressed too far, they could overpower their officers, sail to the nearest tropic isle, and perhaps never return to England. He had done all he could. If the race was lost, it had not been for lack of trying. If, by some miracle, his rivals had not beaten him, he would come back another day. He—or another.

"They're tired of being tired," he said, "sick of being always sick and wet and hungry. We'll go back. Try again another year."

They raised a cheer, but he silenced them, his face bleak. "Don't cheer too soon. Before we put the ship about, we must find a place to heave her down and do what we can with our remaining pitch to make her seaworthy. You know as well as I that there is no suitable beaching place on this island, even if we were able to bring the ship through the coral. Without extensive repairs, we will never reach England."

With this they were content, priest and shareholders also expressing their willingness to give up the search for this year. Only Michiele and Gabriel, knowing there might be no second chance for Caboto, were silent.

Caboto had one faint hope which he admitted to no one. As they sailed in search of a beaching place, they might find the strait first! He had every excuse to sail south at the moment, for the wind was still dead against them. The *Catherine* was therefore steered as before, south-southwest, which was as close as she could come to the wind.

On the sixth of September, a year and five months after their departure from England, they sighted a shore running east and west. Caboto sailed along this coast for days, looking for a likely landing place, but the wind was offshore now and they could not beat in against it. They tacked, keeping the land just in sight, Caboto fretting at the need to sail east when west beckoned. Thirkell was the first to grow restive.

"I thought we were going to land and make repairs."

"We will," said Caboto wearily, "as soon as we can." After all these months, Thirkell should know the impossibility of driving a ship like a team of horses. The only means of movement was the wind striking the sails from certain angles. At the moment, Caboto observed, it seemed to be striking now from one direction, now from another, backing and filling the sails irritably, but never blowing in the *right* direction.

The bosun went up to the captain with a worried frown

and touched his hand to his forelock. What he said to Gabriel, Caboto could not hear, but he recognized the note of urgency. In a moment, Gabriel turned and looked up at Caboto, the same worry imprinted on his own face. Caboto leaned over the rail—

"What is it?"

"Leaking's heavier on the port side. Brewer thinks the pumps won't be able to keep up with it much longer."

"I'll come down," said Caboto, refusing to let consternation show on his face.

At that same moment, a hail came from maintop, loud and excited—

"Sail!"

Every man on the ship froze in his steps, incredulous. Again the cry came, wavering, joyous—

"Sail ho! Sail dead ahead, sir!"

XXIII

The New World

There was a surge to the rail, eyes squinting against the afternoon sun. A dot far out. A sail!

"Hull down yet." Gabriel's voice quivered and Caboto did not trust his own voice at all. "She must be one of ours, followed us down the coast!"

Caboto knew it was too soon to say. Yet who else would have a ship in this part of the world? The Chinese, of course. Spanish or Portuguese, *per favore, Dio, no!* And yet, he knew, it could be.

A gust of hot wind took the *Catherine* all aback and Gabriel shouted angrily, but it was no fault of the seamen who from recent dull misery had suddenly turned to hope and excitement. A freak wind had caught the topsails and fluttered them in wild independence. An eerie moan came from the rigging. Caboto looked at the water—oily with long swells—and glanced up at a sky full of veiled cirrus clouds. More trouble. Not now, he protested silently, not now when at last they had met another ship! The wind turned around again and settled, happily, on the direction he needed.

"We'll meet her," he told Gabriel quietly and the captain

nodded, hurried down to the main deck to set the crew to the lines. The *Catherine* was soon moving at fair speed on a course which would eventually, if the wind held, bring her across the stranger's bows. Let the storm hold off a few more hours!

It would be another hour at least before the ships met. Caboto seized the opportunity to go to his cabin, calling to his boy to unpack his one good suit of clothes, which he had saved for just such an eventuality as this. While the boy shook out the feather on the hat and passed a rag over his shoes, Caboto hurried into a wine-colored tunic and doublet, wrinkled from packing, and pulled on his best pair of hose. It was really too hot for clothing, but it was important to uphold the dignity of his office. What if he were about to meet the Khan's men at last! And what about language—communication? A dozen possibilities occurred, a score of anxieties beset him. What to do if the ship were an enemy? He thought of the King's express command to avoid trouble, which in essence meant to avoid the ships of Spain and Portugal. He could hardly turn his back on the ship, not even knowing her nationality. In any case, he knew quite well he had no intention of missing this meeting! After a year and a half of silence, here was a chance at last to make contact with men who had perhaps left Europe this year. A chance to get information, if only as to what the strange ship was doing on the east coast of Asia. He could decide nothing in advance of this knowledge, he realized suddenly, and was calm again, looking no farther ahead than the meeting, feeling oddly as if it were the only thing in the world now that really mattered. He emerged from his cabin, alert, straight-backed, ready for whatever came.

On deck he saw that the other ship was hull up now on the queerly shining water. He felt the sun hot on the back of his neck and heard his companions trying to guess the stranger's nationality.

"She must be English!" said Fra Antonio with more animation than he had shown in months.

"Dutch!" said Cair positively.

"Nonsense!" Thirkell said. "Spanish!"

"She's standing straight for us, anyway," remarked Michiele and, catching sight of Caboto, eyed his friend's wrinkled splendor with a dubious eye.

"Aye, she means business," the Yorkshireman agreed.

"Anyway, something's happening at last! Can you make her out?" Michiele asked Caboto.

"A *nef* I think."

"Converted, yes." Gabriel had come up to stand beside them. "Not English. Too big."

"Not an eastern rig either," said Caboto, relinquishing that hope for good. "And if she is Portuguese I shall be most surprised."

"Colombo?" suggested Gabriel.

"*Basta!* I hope not. Just once I should like to be ahead of him! I'm told he generally sails in company and this ship is certainly alone. She does look Spanish though." He hated to think that any Spaniard had reached this far west.

"Shouldn't she be showing a flag by now?" asked Michiele.

"We're not," pointed out Master Cair.

Fra Antonio moved uneasily.

"That would be giving ourselves away, surely. If she is Spanish—"

"What if she is?" growled Thirkell. "We've as much right here as anyone!"

Caboto in any case had made his decision.

"Hoist our colors." Though she were a vessel straight from Hell, he meant to speak to her!

In silence they watched the Cross of St. George flutter to the top of the mast.

"Look!" Almost simultaneously, a flag broke out at the stranger's peak—the red and gold standard of Spain!

"Spanish, by Heaven!" cried Thirkell with a kind of relish.

The little priest, however, looked alarmed. He was no coward—otherwise he would not have been on this voyage. It was only that, apart from his religion, he was a man of peace.

"We could still run away, I presume?" he asked Caboto.

"We could, Father, but we won't." Caboto did not elaborate. History had taught him, among other things, that those who ran away generally had to keep on running. The weak did not, as a rule, prevail—even in keeping the peace!

"There's no doubt she too wants a meeting," said Thirkell.

"What if they've come to say they've found the Indies?" asked Cair.

"If we've failed," answered Caboto shortly, "we might as well know it."

Gabriel was shouting up now to ask if Caboto wanted the pinnace.

"I'm not sure. Clear away for launching, just in case. And strip the guns."

"Aye, aye, sir."

"I think I can make out more than two guns on her."

"No doubt. No more than four though. Those old *nefs* are inconvenient for mounting cannon." Caboto added in a lower tone— "Stay with me, Michiele. I want you at the meeting."

"Of course." Michiele paced excitedly. "By San Pietro and San Paolo, it will be good to see a set of new faces!"

Caboto gave the order to wear 'round.

"All hands to the braces!" shouted Gabriel. "Smartly there!" He was anxious his ship should not disgrace herself before the Spaniards.

"Back mizzen tops'l!"

Feeling grew tense as the *Catherine* successfully executed her maneuvers and the Spaniard came running down from windward under full sail. The other was close enough now so they could see the crew at their stations, ready to haul on the lines at command. She luffed up expertly and stood proudly, sails aflutter, in the wind. A newish ship, Caboto thought, not too long out from Spain. Rapidly the stranger's canvas was taken in and secured.

And there the two ships lay hove to a hundred yards apart, in a sea that moved like heavy satin.

A boat was put over the side of the Spaniard and that was one question settled—who was to visit whom. The air was hotter than ever now and the sky had turned a greeny-gold color.

"Two in the boat, besides the seamen," pronounced Thirkell. "One in black, with a feathered hat. The other looks like an officer."

Caboto descended to the maindeck to wait with Gabriel and Michiele. They watched the small boat approach with speed across the oily waves, and their hearts beat faster than usual.

"That gentleman in black," said Caboto suddenly. "I know him!" He racked his brain, but the name would not come.

"His clothes are as wrinkled as yours," said Michiele with some satisfaction. "He must have been keeping his in a seabag too."

"Constantinople! That's *where*! But who—" What was the name?

There was a hail from the boat in Spanish—

"Señores! May we come aboard?"

Captain Duchesne replied in the same language—

"By all means!"

He was at the ladder's side when the gentleman in black

came up. Caboto, advancing to meet the visitor, saw a tall fair man of fifty with arrogant eyes and a mouth tightly tucked in at the corners, and recognized him. He had been trying to think of a Spanish name, but this man was from Florence! Vespucci! The young man in the *souk* that day! Vespucci. Amerigo Vespucci!

It was a moment of high drama.

Caboto bowed. The bow was punctiliously returned. Then Vespucci was joined by the Spanish officer, a stocky man in sensible seaman's clothes, a man with a blunt intelligent face. He divided his bow between Captain and Captain-General. Emotion ran like a fine thread from the little group in the ship's waist, past the gaping seamen and up to the tight little group on the quarterdeck.

"A happy meeting, Señores!" said Caboto in Spanish, adding in his native tongue— "Signore Vespucci, is it not?"

Vespucci bowed briefly.

"*Buon giorno,* Signore." His voice was coldly formal as he turned to introduce the man beside him. "Señor Juan la Cosa."

La Cosa, thought Caboto. There were two La Cosas associated with Colombo—this must be the map maker of the second voyage. Some of the zest had gone suddenly from this meeting. He welcomed Señor La Cosa, introduced Gabriel and Michiele, and took the visitors to the quarterdeck.

"You didn't seem surprised to meet Caboto here on the coast of Asia," said Thirkell bluntly in English when they had been introduced. "You knew about our expedition evidently."

Caboto translated his remark and the Florentine's reply—

"Naturally, Señor. The departure of your ships last spring was noted in Spain with interest."

"I've been looking forward to this meeting, Señor Caboto,"

said La Cosa pleasantly. "We are, after all, professional brothers. In Seville, I saw and admired some of your fine mapwork."

"Thank you," said Caboto dryly. The chart of last year's voyage had got to Seville evidently, no doubt through the agency of the indefatigable John Day. "So a copy of my map has found its way to your Admiral. It is as well perhaps that other nations should know at once what the English have discovered and are prepared to hold," he added with meaning and found himself wondering about the sheepskin roll under La Cosa's arm. At the thought of what might be drawn there, his mouth watered.

"I do not wish to sound rude," interjected Vespucci, "but I understand a storm is brewing. Our business ought to be conducted with dispatch."

"True," said La Cosa, "I was forgetting."

"By all means. If you gentlemen will come to my cabin—" Caboto caught Michiele's eye and the barber followed, leaving the other three to nurse their curiosity as patiently as they could.

The four of them could just get around the chart table, wedged in on benches and stools. Caboto's grommet brought wine and mugs. Vespucci began at once.

"You may wonder what *I*, a banker of the Medici, am doing here. To make a long story short, our branch in Seville supplied the ships of Colombo on the last two voyages and through my association with the Great Admiral I became interested in exploration. I studied the sciences of astronomy and navigation and in March of this year sailed with an expedition from Spain under the command of Don Alonso de Ojeda." Ojeda! One of Colombo's old lieutenants. So Ojeda had a command of his own now. Poor Colombo. Everyone was anxious to make use of the path he had found and with profit to themselves.

"Where is the Admiral now?" he asked, not really expecting an answer.

"He is in Española at the moment," said Vespucci, "detained there by administrative affairs." Española? Yes, of course, one of the islands Colombo had discovered, now apparently his headquarters.

"And suffering sadly from rheumatism and sore eyes," added La Cosa, "from dissension and rebellion too, among—" He stopped at a warning look from Vespucci. "But that's by the by. To get on with the story—?" He looked at his companion.

"Yes," said Vespucci in a chill tone. "To continue. We sailed with Don Ojeda's fleet, but separated from his other ships when we reached the landfall at Trinidad."

"Trinidad?" A new name to Caboto.

"Colombo's landfall last summer. You would not know of course what has been happening."

"I know he set out to look for a Southern Continent."

"He found it."

Caboto drew in his breath. So Colombo had succeeded to that extent at least.

"He sailed with six ships last summer to find the land written of by Ptolemy and talked about by the Carib Indians. He found in fact that there was mainland south of the islands he had discovered and now I can confirm—"

"South! Surely you mean south*west*?"

"No, Signore Caboto," said Vespucci firmly, "a trifle south*east* if anything." He waved an arm. "Off there, its northern coast runs east and west—"

"How do you know?" cried Caboto.

"Because I followed it up from below Colombo's landfall," Vespucci added with pride. "I discovered a great river some distance below the Equator and followed the coast north again to Trinidad and along this coast. It is certainly a continent. I call it *Terra Crucis*! I—"

"Wait!" begged Caboto, still confused. "You said this land —this continent—lies south or south*east* of the islands discovered by Colombo! But that is impossible!"

"Not at all. Española—as well as Juana, San Salvador, and a part of Cathay called the province of Manjii—lie to the north of us now."

Caboto felt like a man in a bad dream.

"Here," said La Cosa, unrolling his map, "let me show you." Caboto grasped for it eagerly, looked, and saw the Spanish flags planted along a string of islands running down to a separate coast line marked *Terra Crucis*. "Vespucci is right, you know. The islands are here. And here is the continent. The size of its rivers, the tremendous amount of fresh water running into the sea at various places leaves no doubt of the matter—"

Caboto heard no more. Here was a perfect avalanche of all his cherished long-held beliefs! As he tried to absorb the shocking fact of Spanish achievement, he felt Michiele jerk against him..

"But the Spanish islands are in mid-Ocean!"

"I'm afraid not," said Vespucci smugly. "Actually the nearest of them lies just over the horizon."

"You lie!"

La Cosa flushed, half-rose to his feet, bumping his head on the bulkhead. Caboto laid a hand on Michiele's arm.

"*Calma*, Michiele. Patience—"

"Signore Ferari insults me," cried Vespucci, while La Cosa swore and rubbed at the side of his head. Caboto gathered his wits.

"*Per Dio, amico mio.* They do not lie. What would be the use? It will be easy to verify. The chart shows the situation and we must accept it. Colombo is here, like us, on the very edge of the Asian continent. We were mistaken." Bitter admission, but it had to be made. "Signores, I apologize for my friend. It is not his fault. It is mine. I had not thought—" he said it with difficulty, "the Spanish were so far west."

Michiele too stammered an apology. Deafened by his jumbled thoughts, Caboto only half-heard Vespucci continue—

"Therefore, since my calculations show we are now directly south of Española, with our last flag planted on Cabo de la Vela yesterday, we are in Spanish waters and you, Signore Caboto, are a trespasser!"

The last words came through clearly enough. Caboto woke up with a vengeance.

"Trespassing? Impossible!" He summoned up all his resources for battle. "I sailed from the north and west into a sea open to all. Obviously, from your map, you have not sailed west of this cape." He pointed to the spot. "Where your Spanish flags end, therefore, our English ones begin!"

There was a pause. Vespucci's lips thinned. He began to remind Caboto of the Treaty of Tordesillas and the Papal Bull, but Caboto made an impatient gesture.

"The bull is illegal," he said flatly, "and the treaty binds only Spain and Portugal. We will respect Spanish rights to what they have already discovered, but we do not—and never will—recognize in advance any Spanish rights to discoveries not yet made."

"You refuse to leave?" asked La Cosa, after a pause.

"I do." Caboto had not, naturally, forgotten the promise to his men, but he did not allow himself to think of it for the moment. These men must not have the satisfaction of knowing that the *Catherine* had no choice about leaving or staying. "Land belongs to the nation whose emissaries find it, and the country able to hold it!" He must deceive them, if he could, into thinking the *Catherine* was still seaworthy and would fight to prevent the Spanish from venturing farther west into Marco Polo's strait. La Cosa gazed at his fingernails thoughtfully.

"You've been away some seventeen months now," he said casually. "Is that not so, Señor Caboto?"

"That is so."

"Your stores must be low."

"We will manage."

"I noticed as we came aboard that your hull had suffered some damage."

"It is not serious."

"Tell me," said La Cosa innocently, "have you had much trouble with the *teredo* worm?"

"A little." Caboto made a valiant effort to appear indifferent, but his heart had begun to sink. Their condition, after all, was too apparent to an experienced eye.

"Come, come, Caboto," said La Cosa briskly, "you know you have not a proper ship under you, but only a sieve that could sink in the first bad storm. Our ship is fresh still, provisioned for another eight months, and we have a base at Española. Just over the horizon lie a dozen Spanish ships, hundreds of Spanish marines and settlers. You are outnumbered, surrounded! Anywhere you sail, except west of course, you will run into our islands or our ships. And let me tell you, my friend, they are not all officered by men as nice as Vespucci and myself. Ojeda for instance, if I am any judge of that hot-blooded *hidalgo*, would have blasted you out of these waters by now, without asking first for an explanation."

"But as you pointed out," Caboto fought on, "I could still sail west."

"We would prevent you," cried Vespucci. "We could blow you out of the water."

"Try!" said Caboto fiercely. "Has it occurred to you that here on my ship at this moment *you* are at *my* mercy?"

"We have taken precautions, naturally," Vespucci rejoined coldly. "If we do not return at a certain hour, our first officer has orders to run back to Española for help. You would have a dozen ships at your heels before you were a league on your way!"

"If they knew where we were going perhaps," said Caboto, fighting to the finish.

"Come, come, my friend, that's easy!" La Cosa laughed. "Like ourselves you are looking for the Spice Islands—and the Spice Islands lie to the west."

"How do you know we haven't already found them," cried Michiele.

"Because you would not be wasting time here if you had. It must be equally obvious that *we* have found nothing in the south. What remains?" La Cosa left it to Caboto. There was no need for an answer. Caboto saw that his cause was hopeless. These men understood as well as he that the only remaining area to search was this strait they were in. The Indies *must* lie due west. There was nowhere else for them to be. La Cosa now made this quite clear.

"We are in the Strait of Malaieu at this moment," said La Cosa. "The Spice Islands and probably the Chinese cities lie in this strait due west of here. Incidentally, you are quite certain the shore you coasted along was mainland?"

"Quite certain," said Caboto despondently. With half his mind he was considering, and discarding, the idea of challenging the Spanish to a fight. He remembered the words of Henry VII. The English and Spanish governments still enjoyed friendly relations on the surface. Until that marriage was arranged, neither country wanted—an incident. It was bitter though to face the fact that he must sail off and leave the field to the Spanish. Return to England and admit failure! In deep agony of spirit, he ran over in his mind again all the possibilities—always he came back in the end to a crippled ship, weary mutinous men, the scarcity of food and other provisions.

"Incidentally," said La Cosa, not too hopefully, "I don't suppose you'd care to show me *your* map."

Why not?

"It's not a matter of politics," explained La Cosa, "as far as I'm concerned anyway. I'm just a poor devil who collects facts for kings and councilors and time-servers. What matters to me is the maps themselves."

This stirred Caboto out of his lethargy.

To him too, it was the maps—the knowledge—that mattered. He remembered the thrill of seeing that first map in the scriptorium with Fra Andrea.

"Yes, why not?" he said aloud. "Let our countries lay claim to the whole world if they like! It is one thing to make a claim, another to enforce it. These matters, anyway, are usually settled in the end by force or diplomacy, not by flags drawn on maps. But the maps will remain long after we, and our kings and diplomats, are dead."

"Well said!" cried La Cosa, regarding Caboto intently, almost with affection. "You are a man after my own heart."

He leaned eagerly over the map and chart Caboto spread out on the table.

"This was my route," said Caboto. His finger slid down the long coast. "I have estimated that we sailed some two thousand leagues altogether."

"Two thousand!" La Cosa glanced up with frank awe. "I must congratulate you on your seamanship as well as your draftsmanship, it seems." He stared at the map again. "So that is the eastern coast of Asia. No cities at all?"

"None."

"Strange. However—" La Cosa hesitated a moment, asked

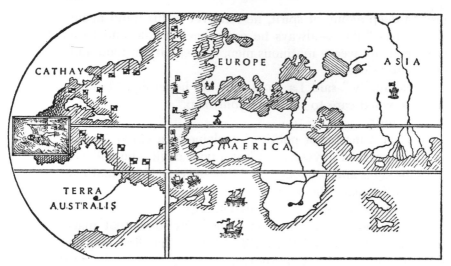

La Cosa's map, 1500

bluntly, "Have you any objection to my showing your coast on my map—provided of course that I mark it as an English discovery?"

"None in the least—if I may add your map to mine."

"Fair enough!"

Quills and ink and fresh sheepskins were produced from Caboto's sea chest and two maps were redrawn so as to include the additional information. They were in the end nearly identical. They showed the whole coast of "Asia," the islands of Colombo, and the coast line discovered by Vespucci in the south. The sea to the north was marked "Sea Discovered by the English." In the south, the Spanish flags marched along the Southern Continent's coast line and through the line of islands. In between lay that mysterious opening—the strait leading west to the Indies. Marco Polo's strait! Or so they hoped.

Caboto looked at the coast on La Cosa's map marked "Province of Manjii."

"That cannot be right, Señor. The mainland lies beyond, according to my calculations. I believe it was that island, Michiele, we passed on our left just after leaving the Land of the Drowned Grass."

"I knew it!" cried La Cosa unexpectedly. "The natives called it Colba, an island, but the Admiral would not hear of it. He made us all swear that it was part of the mainland!"

Triumphantly, La Cosa closed in the line of the coast to shape the island and at that moment there came a rap on the cabin door, which opened immediately. Gabriel looked in, apologetic but worried.

"Wind's increasing, sir. I think we're in for a gale."

Vespucci rose hurriedly.

"We must get back to our ship."

"Right!" La Cosa rolled up his maps, his face agleam with pleasure and perspiration. "*Dio mio!* No, it would not do to be stranded on an English ship at this stage of the game."

Caboto escorted them to the ladder, and there Vespucci turned for a last word.

"I have your promise, Signore, that you will not follow us?"

"You have my word," Caboto answered heavily. "As La Cosa points out, I have no other choice—at the moment."

"Don't take it too hard, Señor!" La Cosa gripped his arm briefly. "I could find it in my heart to wish you had been more successful—" he chuckled, "only it would mean that Vespucci and I must have failed in that case. Seriously—I wish you luck—God's truth, I do! A safe voyage home."

"*Gracias*, Señor. May we meet again some day on more even terms."

At the last moment, Caboto thought of a dozen things he would have liked to discuss with La Cosa, a score of problems which had worried him on the voyage—but it was too late now. La Cosa waved from the boat as it toiled back through a rising swell.

The fascinating problems of navigation and cartography faded from Caboto's mind with their departure and a black pall of failure and despair settled down on him.

"I'll keep them away," said Michiele quickly, divining out of his long affection for this man that Caboto's most pressing need at the moment was privacy. He pressed his friend's arm briefly and hurried off to field the shareholders before they could reach Caboto, turning them away to the rail to give them a guarded summary of what had been said. Caboto retired to his cabin.

It was too small for him in his present mood, but it was his only refuge.

Man is always, essentially, alone. He is especially alone with his mistakes.

Caboto chewed on his mistakes the way a man will bite on a painful tooth. He had made so many! He had trusted Marco Polo too implicitly—and Toscanelli. He had been mistaken in believing that Colombo had come only halfway across the Ocean Sea. He had been wrong to believe the Chinese cities lay on the coast. He had even made Colombo's mistake about the "Indians"!

Giovanni Caboto sat slumped over his chart table, head braced in his hands, staring at nothing. For a while he tried to picture the strait in its entirety, imagining how it led through the islands of spicery to the Indies. So near, yet so far. Then his eyes focused on the map and the strait was simply an empty space, a question mark . . .

The heat was terrible now. He stripped off his velvet and flung the gaudy stuff on his bunk, pulled on his seaman's light breeches. Bare from the waist, he stood staring down at the map, seeing where the sweat of his hands had marked the sea off the coast where Cipango ought to be. He went to rub it off, thinking it was dirt, but the spot remained. He stared at it, stupidly, his thoughts idly wandering—

Cipango.

He'd forgotten Cipango. They'd all forgotten it in the recent discussion.

Thoughtfully, he tugged at his gold earring.

An idea stirred briefly, and died.

Strange, he thought next, that the Spanish hadn't put Cipango on their map. They must have found it! It stood directly in their way. Not just one expedition, but several— thirty or forty ships—had crossed the Ocean Sea in varying latitudes since 1492. Had not even one of them stumbled on Cipango—or the many islands that stretched north and south across Asia's coast? According to Marco Polo.

The idea stirred again. His brain began to wake, to move faster.

Why had they seen no Chinese ships? That had bothered him ever since the shipwreck and the rebuilding of the *Catherine*. They ought to have seen at least one Chinese junk crossing the Sea of Chin between Manjii and Cipango—but they hadn't! It was almost as if—as if Cipango did not exist— never had existed!

Marco Polo was definite about it though. "*Cipango is an island toward the east, in the high seas, fifteen hundred miles from the continent. It is a very large island.*"

Then—the way a man will leap a ditch hardly knowing it's there—so Caboto's mind leaped a gap.

There was no Cipango because Cipango wasn't there. If there was a Cipango, it must be somewhere else. And if it was somewhere else, so was Asia.

What he had found was not Asia!

The shock of it rocked him off balance.

Then—if what he had found was not Asia, what he had found was a new continent!

Caboto stared wildly into space. He did not even question the new theory, so sure was he. Why? Words spoken a long time ago echoed along the corridors of his brain, Fra Andrea's voice saying, *"Strabo, however, does not agree with Hipparchus who thought there might be two seas with land between."*

Two seas. Land between.

Giovanni Caboto stared at the wall of his cabin, shaken to the core.

Not one island in a vast Ocean Sea, but two—one, the traditional combination Europe-Asia-Africa, the other Vespucci's southern continent and his own northern one. Two hemispheres. Five continents, not three—and the fourth and fifth unknown, undiscovered, until now!

He wanted to shout! He had been beaten not by the Spanish, but by geography. They had been beaten too. He pictured Vespucci and La Cosa patiently trying to find a way through a strait that might not even exist. Even if it did, even if there was a way through, they would still have another sea to cross! A wide one if Eratosthenes had estimated the world's circumference correctly. He pictured the Spanish ship sailing, sailing, still thousands of miles from Cipango and the Spice Islands. Poor Vespucci, poor La Cosa. He began to laugh. He laughed so hard Michiele heard and, shocked, came running in.

"Giovanni, my poor friend, don't take it so hard!"

But Caboto couldn't stop.

"Think of it, Michiele! No Cipango! No Asia!"

"Calma, calma," soothed his friend, thinking his captain bereft of his senses.

"I'm not mad," spluttered Caboto, "nor unhappy! I have found a new world, Michiele—two new worlds!" Yes, two. For, in the sense of understanding *what* had been discovered, he—Giovanni Caboto—had discovered both. He was

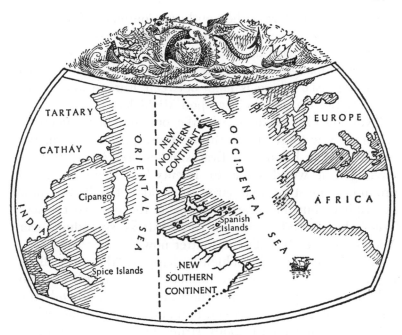

Cabot's concept of the world

the only discoverer! "Vespucci still thinks his southern continent is just south of Asia—whereas I know there are two continents, joined perhaps in the middle, perhaps not, and neither of them are Asia!" He sobered suddenly. "Ah, Michiele, think of it! Fra Andrea was a good prophet—for now, after all, I can say I have walked where no man (no Christian man at least) has ever walked!"

Michiele stared helplessly.

"You don't understand what I'm talking about, of course. How could you? Look, my faithful friend—" Caboto drew a fresh sheepskin from his chest and spread it on the table. With a quill dipped in ink, he rapidly drew a picture of the world as he saw it now, nearly complete. "Here, Michiele, is

the Old World. Here is the Southern Continent of Vespucci
—here is our Northern one. And here between—who knows?
Over there, perhaps another two thousand miles away, lie
Asia and Cipango. Do you see now? We are not in the sea
adjoining Asia. There is *land* between Europe and Asia!"

"How can you be sure?" gasped Michiele.

"Nothing else makes sense. We ought to have guessed,
when we saw those empty shores, those primitive men. We
ought to have listened to Eratosthenes and Alfragan, who
envisaged a world close to twenty-five thousand miles
around. It must be that large, to hold not only this new
hemisphere but an ocean as large as the one we crossed!
We—" he paused, aware of the distress spreading over
Michiele's face. "What's the matter now?"

"If it is true," cried Michiele unhappily, "there is still no
cause for celebration. You're no better off. You still have no
gold or spices to take back to the King of England. Only the
bad news of a barrier between him and the riches he seeks."

"Barrier?" repeated Caboto, struck by the word into mo-
mentary silence. "Yes," he said slowly at last, "they'll call it
a barrier. Naturally. But to us, Michiele, it will be much
more! That realm of tall trees and vast meadows! Enough for
all the masts and all the cattle in Christendom. The teeming seas, the fertile soil—food to feed a million people! The
birds, the furs, the minerals—you said it yourself, Michiele,
it's an exciting country! A barrier? Well, they may call it
that, but some day England may thank me for it!"

He heard the cabin door open and was aware of Michiele
going to speak with Gabriel, but mostly he was thinking
of the future—

New horizons beckoned! The last burden on his heart
lifted. The earth was round! That much was still true. That
was the thing to remember. It was larger than most people
had thought, that was all, but it was as round as ever. One
needed only to keep on, to cross the barrier, cross another

sea, and come at last to—to Asia? Almost certainly. But to be sure, one must go and see!

Very well! He would go back to England, tell what he had found—tell them about the new world he had discovered—and persuade the King to send him out again with a new expedition.

He thought of Colombo, his rival, and, for the first time, felt close to him in spirit. They had both made mistakes, but both had persevered in the face of obstacles. Caboto thought he knew now what drove that tired, angry, arthritic man from island to island, in spite of illness and disappointment, searching endlessly. It was the thing he recognized now in himself—not just the need to achieve, to excel, to win glory and reward but—to *know*!

All this flashed through his mind during the few moments when Michiele was speaking with Gabriel at the door. Now Michiele returned to say anxiously, "Gabriel says to tell you he thinks it's going to be bad."

"I'll be there in a moment."

As he put the maps away, tidily, in his chest, he noted the sound of the wind and the violent motion of the deck. He heard the worried voices on deck and knew he should be out there soothing their fears, encouraging them as he had from the start. He lingered a moment longer, putting a shirt on over his breeches, feeling the deck planks move under his feet as if twisted by some unknown force. The priest's voice outside the cabin rose, even as he prayed, in a moan of anxiety.

Caboto hurried out. The sky was frightening now, the waters wild and empty. The wind tugged at his hair, but it felt good!

Storm ahead. One expected that. This, after all, was what he loved!

He took a last look at the sky—laughed, and turned to meet the storm . . .

HISTORICAL NOTES

Historical Notes

The following excerpts from letters and documents are used with permission of Cambridge University Press from *The Cabot Voyages and Bristol Discoveries under Henry VII* by James A. Williamson, from The Hakluyt Society series, No. CXX, Second Series, published by Cambridge University Press, 1962.

Part One
THE BOY CABOT

The facts, verified by source material cited below, are that John Cabot was a Venetian citizen—

"That a privilege of citizenship, both internal and external, be made out for John Cabot on account of fifteen years' residence, as usual. Ayes 149, Noes 0." Translated, Grant of Naturalization from Venice Archives of State, March, 1476.

that he was born in Genoa—

"I have seen the map made by the discoverer who is another Genoese like Columbus." Piero de Ayala, Spanish Ambassador to his Sovereigns, July, 1498.

that he had a father named Julio and a brother called Piero—

> "Messer Zuan Chabotto, son of the late Messer Julio, by right of possession has executed . . . etc. Messer Zuan Chabotto in his own name and in the name of Messer Piero, his brother, gives as surety, etc." Property transactions, Venice Archives, 1482-84.

and that he was an expert mariner and cartographer—

> "Messer Zoane Caboto by name, of kindly wit and a most expert Mariner . . . has the description of the world in a map and also in a solid sphere which he has made . . ." Letter of Raimondo de Soncino to the Duke of Milan, London, December 18, 1497.

Part Two

CABOT THE MAN

that John Cabot's wife's name was Mattea—

> "Messer Zuan Chabotto gives and makes over to Donna Mattea his wife, as security for her dowry . . ." Property Transactions, Venice Archives, 1482-84.

that he had three sons—

> "We have given and granted . . . to our well-beloved John Cabot, citizen of Venice, and to Lewis, Sebastian, and Soncio, sons of the said John . . ." First Letters Patent, 5 March 1496.

that he had been to Mecca—

> "He [Cabot] says that on previous occasions he has been to Mecca, whither spices are borne by caravans . . ." Letter of Raimondo de Soncino to the Duke of Milan, December 18, 1497.

that he may have been the Johan Caboto Montecalunya concerned in a port construction in Valencia—

"We have been informed by Johan Caboto Montecalunya the Venetian . . . that he has considered whether on the beach of this city a port could be constructed and, on finding that it could . . . he has designed and painted plans of them." Letter of the King of Spain to Diego de Torres, Governor General of Valencia, 27 September 1492.

We have Cabot's Letters Patent to show that he meant to sail over the northwest Atlantic to discover new lands—

"Be it known and made manifest that we have given and granted as by these presents we give and grant, for us and our heirs, to our well-beloved John Cabot, citizen of Venice . . . full and free authority, faculty and power to sail to all parts, regions and coasts of the eastern, western and northern sea, under our banners . . . to find, discover and investigate whatsoever islands, countries, regions or provinces of heathens and infidels in whatsoever part of the world placed, which before this time were unknown to all Christians, etc . . ." First Letters Patent, 5 March 1496.

As to the Voyages themselves—the abortive one of 1496, the successful landfall of 1497, and his plans for the third— these are mentioned in several letters and documents. Since most of the main facts are contained in the letter of John Day to the Lord Grand Admiral of Spain (almost certainly Columbus) this letter is quoted practically in full—

"And from the said copy [of the map] your Lordship will learn what you wish to know, for in it are named the capes of the mainland and the islands, and thus you will see where land was first sighted, since most of the land was discovered after turning back . . . He landed at only one spot of the mainland, near the place where land was first sighted, and they disembarked there with a crucifix and raised banners with the arms of the Holy Father and those of the King of England, my master, and they found tall trees of the kind masts are made of, and other smaller trees, and the country is very rich in grass. In that particular spot, they found a trail that went inland, they saw a site where a fire had been made, they saw manure of animals which they thought to be farm animals, and they saw a stick half a yard long pierced at both ends, carved and painted with brazil, and by such signs they believe the land to be inhabited. Since he was with just a few people, he did not dare advance inland beyond the shooting distance of a crossbow, and after taking in fresh water he returned to his ship.

"All along the coast they found many fish like those which in Iceland are dried in the open and sold in England and other countries, and these fish are called in English 'stockfish'; and thus following the shore they saw two forms running on land one after the other, but they could not tell if they were human beings or animals; and it seemed to them that there were fields where they thought might also be villages, and they saw a forest whose foliage looked beautiful.

"They left England toward the end of May, and must have been on the way thirty-five days before sighting land; the wind was east-north-east and the sea calm going and coming back, except for one day when he ran into a storm two or three days before finding land; and going so far out, his compass needle failed to point north and marked two rhumbs below. They spent about one month discovering the coast and from the above mentioned cape of the mainland which is nearest to Ireland, they returned to the coast of Europe in fifteen days. They had the wind behind them, and he reached Brittany because the sailors confused him, saying that he was heading too far north.

"From there he came to Bristol and he went to see the King to report to him all the above mentioned; and the King granted him an annual pension of twenty pounds sterling to sustain himself until the time comes when more will be known of this business, since with God's help it is hoped to push through plans for exploring the said land more thor-

oughly next year with ten or twelve vessels—because in his
voyage he had only one ship of fifty 'toneles' and twenty
men and food for seven or eight months—and they want to
carry out this new project. It is considered certain that the
cape of the said land was found and discovered in the past
by the men from Bristol who found 'Brasil' as your Lordship
well knows. It was called the Isle of Brasil, and it is assumed and believed to be the mainland that the men from
Bristol found.

"Since your Lordship wants information relating to the
first voyage, here is what happened; he went with one ship,
his crew confused him, he was short of supplies and ran into
bad weather, and he decided to turn back . . ." Letter of
John Day to the Lord Grand Admiral of Spain.

Additional details are supplied in the letter of Raimondo
de Soncino—

"Perhaps amid the numerous occupations of your Excellency, it may not weary you to hear how his Majesty here
has gained a part of Asia, without a stroke of the sword.
There is in this Kingdom a man of the people, Messer Zoane
Caboto by name, of kindly wit and a most expert mariner.
Having observed that the sovereigns first of Portugal and
then of Spain had occupied unknown islands, he decided to
make a similar acquisition for his Majesty.

"After obtaining patents that the effective ownership of
what he might find should be his, though reserving the
rights of the Crown, he committed himself to fortune in a
little ship, with eighteen persons. He started from Bristol, a
port on the west of this kingdom, passed Ireland, which
is still further west, and then bore towards the north, in
order to sail to the East, leaving the north on his right hand
after some days. After having wandered for some time he at
length arrived at the mainland, where he hoisted the royal
standard, and took possession for the king here; and after
taking certain tokens he returned.

"This Messer Zoane, as a foreigner and a poor man, would

not have obtained credence, had it not been that his companions, who are practically all English and from Bristol, testified that he spoke the truth. This Messer Zoane has the description of the world in a map and also in a solid sphere which he has made and shows where he has been. In going towards the east he passed far beyond the country of the Tanais. They say that the land is excellent and temperate, and they believe that Brazil wood and silk are native there. They assert that the sea there is swarming with fish, which can be taken not only with the net, but in baskets let down with a stone, so that it sinks in the water. I have heard this Messer Zoane state so much.

"These same English, his companions, say that they could bring so many fish that this kingdom would have no further need of Iceland, from which place there comes a very great quantity of the fish called stockfish. But Messer Zoane has his mind set upon even greater things, because he proposes to keep along the coast from the place at which he touched, more and more towards the East, until he reaches an island which he calls Cipango, situated in the equinoctial region, where he believes that all the spices of the world have their origin, as well as the jewels . . .

"He tells all this in such a way, and makes everything so plain, that I also feel compelled to believe him. What is much more, his Majesty, who is wise and not prodigal, also gives him some credence, because he is giving him a fairly good provision since his return, so Messer Zoane himself tells me. Before very long they say that his Majesty will equip some ships, and in addition he will give them all the malefactors, and they will go to that country and form a colony. By means of this they hope to make London a more important mart for spices than Alexandria. The leading men in this enterprise are from Bristol, and great seamen, and now they know where to go, say that the voyage will not take more than a fortnight, if they have good fortune after leaving Ireland.

"I have also spoken with a Burgundian, one of Messer

Zoane's companions, who corroborates everything. He wants to go back, because the Admiral, which is the name they give to Messer Zoane, has given him an island. He has given another to his barber, a Genoese by birth, and both consider themselves counts, while my lord the Admiral esteems himself at least a prince . . ." Letter of Raimondo de Soncino to the Duke of Milan, London, December 18, 1497.

We learn the date of the landfall, the name of the ship, and the dates of departure and return—

"This year on St. John the Baptist's day the land of America * was found by the merchants of Bristowe in a ship of Bristowe called the Mathew; the which said ship departed from the port of Bristowe the second day of May and came home again the 6th of August next following." Fust MS of a Bristol Chronicle, circa 1565.

that the King gave him a reward for his discovery—

". . . have given and granted unto our well-beloved John Cabot of the parts of Venice an annuity of annual rent of twenty pounds sterling . . ." Privy Seals, Public Record Office, 13 Henry VII, December, 1497 (Biggar translation).

and that the news of the discovery soon reached Venice—

"London, 23 Aug. 1497—That Venetian of ours who went with a small ship from Bristol to find new islands has come back and says he has discovered mainland 700 leagues away, which is the country of the Grand Khan, and that he coasted it for 300 leagues and landed and did not see any person; but he has brought here to the king certain snares which were spread to take game and a needle for making nets, and they found certain notched (or felled) trees so that by this he judges that there are inhabitants. Being in doubt he returned to his ship; and he has been three months on the voyage; and this is certain.

* The name "America" was of course not used in 1497, but was in 1565 when the Chronicle was written.

"And on the way back he saw two islands, but was unwilling to land, in order not to lose time, as he was in want of provisions. The king here is much pleased at this; and he (Cabot) says that the tides are slack and do not run as they do here. The king has promised him for the spring ten armed ships as he (Cabot) desires and has given him all the prisoners to be sent away, that they may go with him, as he has requested; and has given him money that he may have a good time until then, and he is with his Venetian wife and his sons at Bristol.

"His name is Zuam Talbot and he is called the Great Admiral and vast honour is paid to him and he goes dressed in silk, and these English run after him like mad, and indeed he can enlist as many of them as he pleases, and a number of our rogues as well. The discoverer of these things planted on the land which he has found a large cross with a banner of England and one of St. Mark, as he is a Venetian, so that our flag has been hoisted very far afield." Letter of Lorenzo Pasqualigo to his brothers at Venice, 23 August 1497, M.S. Diarii of Marin Sanuto, Venice, Biblioteca Marciana.

We learn what Cabot had in mind for his 1498 voyage and how the Spanish felt about it—

"London, 25 July 1498 . . . I think your Highnesses have already heard how the king of England has equipped a fleet to explore certain islands or mainland which he has been assured certain persons who set out last year from Bristol in search of the same have discovered. I have seen the map made by the discoverer, who is another Genoese like Columbus, who has been in Seville and at Lisbon seeking to obtain persons to aid him in this discovery. For the last seven years the people of Bristol have equipped two, three (and) four caravels to go in search of the island of Brasil and the Seven Cities . . . The king made up his mind to send thither, because last year sure proof was brought him that they had found land.

"The fleet he prepared, which consisted of five vessels, was provisioned for a year. News has come that one of these . . . has made land in Ireland in a great storm with the ship badly damaged. The Genoese kept on his way. Having seen the course they are steering and the length of the voyage, I find that what they have discovered or are in search of is possessed by Your Highnesses because it is at the cape which fell to Your Highnesses by the convention with Portugal. It is hoped they will be back by September. I will let Your Highnesses know about it. The King has spoken to me several times on the subject . . . I told him that I believed the islands were those found by Your Highnesses, and although I gave him the main reason, he would not have it. Since I believe Your Highnesses will already have notice of all this and also of the chart or mappemonde which this man has made, I do not send it now, although it is here, and so far as I can see exceedingly false, in order to make believe that these are not part of the said islands . . ." Letter of Pedro de Ayala to the Spanish Sovereigns, 25 July 1498 (Biggar translation).

and hints of what happened on the voyage—

"This year (1498) the king (by means of a Venetian) caused to man and victual a ship at Bristowe, to search for an Island, which he said he knew well was rich and replenished with rich commodities. Which ship, thus manned and victualed at the King's cost, divers merchants of London ventured in her small stocks, being in her as Chief Patron the said Venetian. And in the company of the said ship sailed also out of Bristowe three or four small ships fraught with slight and gross merchandises, as coarse cloth, caps, laces, points, and other trifles, and so departed from Bristowe in the beginning of May; of whom in this Mayor's time returned no tidings . . ." Chronicle of Robert Fabyan as rendered by Richard Hakluyt in the 13th year of King Henry the Seventh, 1498.

and hints that he may have reached the Caribbean by the end of 1498 or early in 1499, where he could have met a ship of Ojeda's expedition—

> "It is certain that Hojeda in his first voyage (1499) encountered certain Englishmen in the vicinity of Coquibacoa." Fernandez de Navarrete, Spanish historian, *Coleccion de los viages y descubrimientos.*

> "License to Alonso de Hojeda (1501) . . . to go and follow that coast which you have discovered, which runs east and west, as it appears, because it goes towards the region where it has been learned that the English were making discoveries; and that you go setting up marks with the arms of their Majesties, or with other signs that may be known, such as shall seem good to you, in order that it be known that you have discovered that land, so that you may stop the exploration of the English in that direction." Extract from the Patent granted by the Spanish Sovereigns to Alonso de Hojeda, 1501.

and how it was that Cabot might have met Vespucci and La Cosa—

> "When the flagship (of Columbus) returned to Spain in the fall of 1498 with news of the voyage to Paria (mainland of South America) Hojeda managed to get possession of the Admiral's chart and to obtain a license . . . for a voyage to that region. With Bartolome Roldan, Juan de la Cosa (the map maker of the Second Voyage) and a Florentine resident in Seville named Amerigo Vespucci (whose account of this voyage, pre-dated two years and not mentioning his commander, led to the continent's being given his name) Hojeda reached the Gulf of Paria, continued his voyage along the mainland behind Margarita where Columbus had left off . . ." *Admiral of the Ocean Sea* by Samuel E. Morison, Atlantic-Little, Brown and Company, 1942.

"Vespucci would seem to have left Hojeda after reaching the coast of what is now Guiana. Turning south, he is believed to have discovered the mouth of the Amazon and to have gone as far as the Cape of La Consolacion. On the way back, he reached Trinidad and sighted the mouth of the Orinoco . . ." *Encyclopaedia Britannica,* Vol. 23, 1963.

La Cosa's famous world map shows the "Sea Discovered by the English," a continuous coast line from around Newfoundland down to the Caribbean, as well as the Spanish Main and part of South America, with a vignette of St. Christopher filling in the isthmus between North and South America. His map was made in 1500, not long after his return to Spain. The fact that after Cabot's voyage of 1498-99 nothing more was said in England about sailing west to Asia, while expeditions going out in the following years went looking merely for "the new found land" or for a passage through or around the continent, suggest that at least one of the English ships got back to report what they had found— a barrier, a new continent, Cabot's New World.

SELECTED
BIBLIOGRAPHY

Selected Bibliography

Bakeless, John Edwin. *The Eyes of Discovery; The Pageant of North America as Seen by the First Explorers.* Philadelphia: Lippincott, 1950.

Beazley, Sir Charles Raymond. *John and Sebastian Cabot, The Discovery of North America.* London: T. F. Unwin, 1898.

Berger, Josef and Wroth, Lawrence C. *Discoverers of the New World.* New York: American Heritage Publishing Company, 1960.

Biddle, Richard. *A Memoir of Sebastian Cabot; with a Review of the History of Maritime Discovery.* London: Hurst, Chance, and Company, 1831.

Biggar, Henry Perceval. (ed.). *The Precursors of Jacques Cartier 1497-1534.* Ottawa: Government Printing Bureau, 1911.

Buehr, Walter. *Ships and Life Afloat: From Galley to Turbine.* New York: Scribner, 1953.

Burckhardt, Jacob. *The Civilisation of the Renaissance in Italy.* Translated by S. G. C. Middlemore. London: G. Allen & Unwin, Ltd., 1928.

Canby, Courtlandt. *A History of Ships and Seafaring.* New York: Hawthorn Books, 1963.

Chamberlin, Eric Russell. *Everyday Life in Renaissance Times.* ("Everyday Life Series"). London: B. T. Batsford, 1967.

Fisher, Herbert A. L. *A History of Europe.* Vol. 1. "From the

Earliest Times to 1713." London: Collins, 1935. (Fontana edition, 1960).

Hakluyt, Richard. *The Principal Navigations, Voyages, Traffiques and Discoveries of the English Nation.* London: J. M. Dent & Company, 1907-10.

Hale, John R. *The Age of Exploration.* New York: Time-Life Books, 1966.

Hazlitt, William Carew. *The History of the Origin and Rise of the Republic of Venice.* London: J. R. Smith, 1858.

Hobley, L. F. *Early Explorers to A.D. 1500.* Methuen's Outlines. London: Methuen, 1954.

Magnusson, Magnus and Palsson, Hermann. *The Vinland Sagas, The Norse Discovery of America.* New York: New York University Press, 1966.

Mahn-Lot, Marianne. *Columbus.* Evergreen Profile Book. New York: Grove Press, 1961.

Mills, Dorothy. *Renaissance and Reformation Times.* New York: G. P. Putnam's Sons, 1939.

Mitchell, Rosamond J. *The Spring Voyage; The Jerusalem Pilgrimage in 1458.* London: J. Murray, 1964.

Morison, Samuel Eliot. *Admiral of the Ocean Sea.* Boston: Atlantic-Little, Brown and Company, 1942.

———. *Christopher Columbus, Mariner.* Boston: Atlantic-Little, Brown and Company, 1955.

Outwaite, Leonard. *The Atlantic, History of an Ocean.* Toronto: Longman's, 1958.

Parry, J. H. *The Age of Reconnaissance.* London: Weidenfeld & Nicolson, 1963.

Power, Eileen. *Medieval People.* University Paperbacks. New York: Barnes & Noble, 1963.

Quinn, D. B. "The Argument for the English Discovery of America between 1480 and 1494." *Geographical Journal,* CXXVII, Part 3, 1961.

———. "John Day and Columbus." *The Geographic Journal,* Vol. 133, Part 2, June 1967.

Raisz, Erwin Josephus. *Mapping the World.* New York: Abelard-Schuman, 1956.

Routh, Charles Richard Nairne. (ed.). *They Saw It Happen in Europe; An Anthology of Eyewitnesses' Accounts of Events in European History, 1450-1600.* Oxford: B. Blackwell, 1965.

Ruddock, Alwyn A. "John Day of Bristol and the English Voyages Across the Atlantic Before 1497." *The Geographic Journal,* Vol. 132, Part 2, June 1966.

Sellman, Roger R. *The Elizabethan Seaman.* Methuen's Outlines. London: Methuen, 1957.

Walsh, Richard John. (ed.). *The Adventures of Marco Polo.* New York: John Day Company, 1948.

Wood, Herbert John. *Exploration and Discovery.* London: Hutchinson House, 1951.

Williamson, James A. *The Cabot Voyages and Bristol Discoveries Under Henry VII,* from The Hakluyt Society series, No. CXX, Second Series. Cambridge University Press, 1962.

The Author

Kay Hill was born in Halifax, Nova Scotia, and now lives in the historic village of Annapolis Royal, not far from Cape Breton Island where John Cabot, the fifteenth-century discoverer of North America, is believed to have made his landfall.

For authenticity in her story of Cabot, Miss Hill traveled for two summers in Europe, following the track of the intrepid Venetian from Genoa where he was born, to Venice where he spent his youth and early manhood, to the various ports of the Mediterranean which as a seaman and spice merchant he would have visited, then on to Spain and Portugal where his path would undoubtedly have crossed that of Columbus, and finally to Bristol, England, from which he set sail in 1497 to discover the northeastern coast of America.

Kay Hill's two earlier books for young people—GLOOSCAP AND HIS MAGIC and BADGER THE MISCHIEF MAKER—also came out of the Nova Scotia region she knows so well, for it was there that the legendary Indian hero, Glooscap, had his lodge on Blomidon. Miss Hill is also the author of many radio, television, and stage plays, produced and published in Canada, the United States, and England.